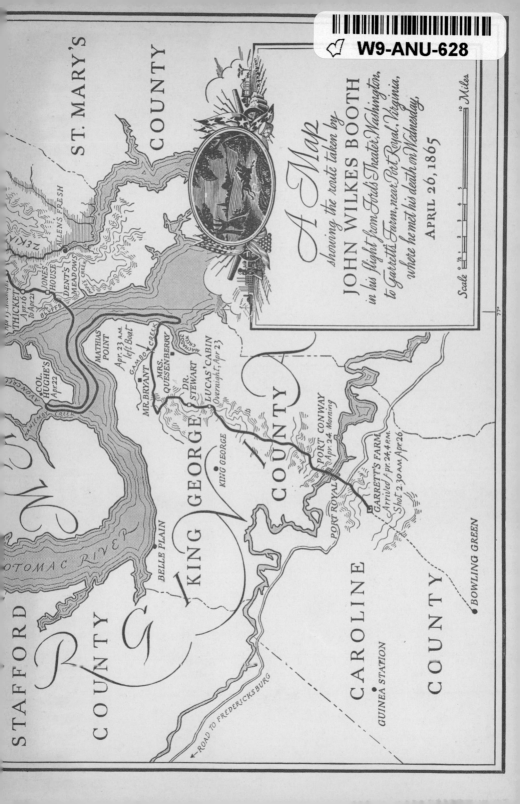

*A Map*

showing the route taken by

JOHN WILKES BOOTH

in his flight from Ford's Theatre, Washington, to Garrett's Farm, near Port Royal, Virginia, where he met his death on Wednesday,

APRIL 26, 1865

Scale 0 ½ 1 2 3 4 5    10 Miles

ST. MARY'S COUNTY

STAFFORD COUNTY

KING GEORGE COUNTY

CAROLINE COUNTY

POTOMAC RIVER

RAPPAHANNOCK RIVER

THICKET
Apr 16
To Apr 21

COL. HUGHE'S
Apr 22

JONES HOUSE

DENT'S MEADOWS

BLUFFS

POPES CREEK

ALLEN'S FRESH

MATHIAS POINT

Apr. 23 A.M. left Boat

GAMBO CREEK

MR. BRYANT

MRS. QUESENBERRY

DR. STEWART

MATTOX CREEK

LUCAS' CABIN
Overnight, Apr 23

KING GEORGE

PORT CONWAY
Apr. 24. Morning

PORT ROYAL

GARRETT'S FARM
Arrived, Apr. 24, 4 P.M.
Shot 2.30 A.M. Apr 26.

BELLE PLAIN

GUINEA STATION

BOWLING GREEN

ROAD TO FREDERICKSBURG

How many ages hence
Shall this our lofty scene be acted o'er
In states unborn and accents yet unknown!
—*Julius Caesar*, Act III, Scene I

JOHN WILKES BOOTH

# THE MAN
# WHO KILLED
# LINCOLN

*The story of* JOHN WILKES BOOTH
*and his part in the assassination*

PHILIP VAN DOREN STERN

THE LITERARY GUILD OF AMERICA, INC.

*New York* 1939

**CL**

*Manufactured in the United States of America*

# List of Characters

## THE CONSPIRATORS

JOHN WILKES BOOTH, actor; aged twenty-six.

LEWIS PAINE (*formerly* POWELL), ex-Confederate soldier; aged twenty.

DAVID HEROLD, former druggist's clerk; aged twenty-three.

GEORGE ATZERODT, German-born carriage maker and boatman from Port Tobacco, Maryland; aged thirty-three.

Mrs. MARY SURRATT, Washington boarding house keeper; aged forty-five.

JOHN HARRISON SURRATT, JR., her son; Confederate spy and dispatch-runner; aged twenty-one.

SAMUEL ARNOLD, clerk at Fortress Monroe; aged twenty-eight.

MICHAEL O'LAUGHLIN, Baltimore clerk; aged twenty-seven.

## WASHINGTON PEOPLE

LOUIS J. WEICHMANN, Government employee and boarder in Mrs. Surratt's house.

Captain WILLIAM WILLIAMS, of the Washington cavalry police.

JOHN DEERY, billiard champion and owner of a saloon over Grover's Theater.

PETER TALTAVUL, barkeeper of a saloon next to Ford's Theater.

Sergeant SILAS T. COBB, in charge of the guard at the Navy Yard (Anacostia) Bridge.

v

# List of Characters

## PEOPLE IN FORD'S THEATER

JOHN MATTHEWS, actor.

EDWARD SPANGLER, sceneshifter.

JAMES L. MADDOX, property man.

HARRY HAWK, actor, who is playing the part of ASA TREN-
CHARD in *Our American Cousin*.

LAURA KEENE, star of the company, playing the part of
FLORENCE TRENCHARD.

LEWIS CARLAND, costumer.

JAMES J. GIFFORD, stage carpenter.

JOHN E. BUCKINGHAM, doorkeeper.

## MARYLAND PEOPLE

JOHN M. LLOYD, innkeeper at Surrattsville.

Dr. SAMUEL A. MUDD, country doctor living near Bryantown.

Mrs. SARAH FRANCES MUDD, his wife.

OSWALD SWANN, colored, Booth's guide to Cox's house.

Colonel SAMUEL COX, plantation owner.

THOMAS A. JONES, Cox's foster-brother.

Colonel J. J. HUGHES, plantation owner.

## VIRGINIA PEOPLE

WILLIAM L. BRYANT, farmer.

Dr. RICHARD STEWART, wealthy householder at whose
home Booth seeks refuge.

WILLIAM LUCAS, colored, Dr. Stewart's former slave.

WILLIAM ROLLINS, owner of the ferry between Port Conway and Port Royal.

Mrs. GOLDMAN, innkeeper at Bowling Green.

# List of Characters

WILLIAM JETT
M. B. RUGGLES
Lt. A. R. BAINBRIDGE
} ex-Confederate soldiers from Mosby's command.

RICHARD H. GARRETT, farmer living near Port Royal.
WILLIAM GARRETT
ROBERT GARRETT
} his sons.
ANNIE GARRETT, his daughter.
Miss L. K. B. HOLLOWAY, schoolteacher boarding at the Garrett farm.

## *CAVALRYMEN*

Lt.-Colonel EVERTON J. CONGER
Lt. EDWARD P. DOHERTY
Lt. LUTHER B. BAKER
} officers in charge of a squadron of twenty-five cavalrymen in pursuit of Booth and Herold.

Sergeant BOSTON CORBETT

vii

# PART ONE

★

*TELEGRAM*

Appomattox Ct. H., Va.
April 9, 1865. 4:30 P.M.

HON. E. M. STANTON, *Secretary of War*, Washington:

General Lee surrendered the Army of Northern Virginia this afternoon on terms proposed by myself. . . .

—U. S. GRANT, *Lieut.-General*

# I

---

## Tuesday, April 11, 1865

---

FOR two days John Wilkes Booth had been wandering through the streets of Washington listening to the cheering crowds, looking on, heartsick and weary, at the sight of a Yankee mob gone mad with the news of victory. Word of Lee's surrender had reached Washington early on Monday morning, and the city had been in a frenzy of celebration ever since. The North had been piling up victory on victory. Petersburg and Richmond had fallen only a week before, and now this news of the surrender of the Army of Northern Virginia had come.

Booth stood far back on the sidewalk watching a parade of Government clerks who were marching down Pennsylvania Avenue carrying torchlights and illuminated signs of victory. Light from the moving torches flickered on his handsome sullen face as he stood under the shadow of the trees lining the wide street. His dark hair and mustache made him seem even paler than he actually was, so that the rosy light

3

lent no color to his features. He stood alone, a silent and brooding figure, unnoticed by the passing crowds. Only his eyes, half-closed and heavy-lidded, gave any indication of his reactions.

He hated the smug Yankees around him. He was sick of their incessant cheering, irritated by their enthusiasm. He was smiling contemptuously as he watched the parade, but his face twitched nervously in the red glare of the torches. He had gathered his long cloak around him in his favorite theatrical pose, for even in his misery he was still the actor.

Yet his unhappiness was real enough. His mind was numbed with fatigue and disaster. For two days he had been unable to sleep at all. Minute guns had been fired in an endless salvo of victory, and their thunder had beaten like hammer blows against his brain until he had found himself counting off the seconds in order to anticipate each explosion. And through all the confusion of sounds and images came the realization that his beloved South was being crushed in defeat. That thought was with him always, and there was no escaping it.

He had tried to get drunk, but no amount of liquor could make him forget what was happening. He felt compelled to walk through the city in order to see everything. What he saw filled him with helpless fury, but he had to see it. He had tortured himself now to the point where his whole being cried out for action. He wanted to fling a bomb into the midst of these cheering fools. He could feel the smooth round shape in his hand and the long free motion of his arm as he threw it. It sailed out over the heads of the crowd and landed in the street with a terrific explosion. . . .

Booth's mouth was set in a grim hard line as these thoughts of vengeance coursed through his mind. His hand clenched the edge of his cloak as he pulled it tightly around his shoulders. He had been feeding too long on his own rage—he had to have some outlet for it now.

And then, at this moment when he was at the very pitch of his fury, the humiliation of his position as a Confederate sympathizer was brought home to him. Out of the crowd's impersonal mass, shuttling, shifting and ever changing, two soldiers suddenly lurched forward, making straight for Booth in their drunken stupor.

He saw them head for him. His first impulse was to draw out the pistol he had in his pocket and fire it blindly into their silly leering faces. His hand, almost unconsciously, moved toward it, but he knew that the slightest gesture would incite the Yankee mob around him to a howl for blood. Yet he had to do something, express in some way his contempt for these blue-coated ruffians who were drunk with victory and cheap Washington whiskey. He immediately resolved that he would not budge an inch for

5

them, although he was unnecessarily blocking their way.

The two soldiers stopped and looked at Booth solemnly. One of them nudged the other.

"Pretty, ain't he?" he said in the slow deliberate voice of insult.

Booth flushed but he gazed stonily ahead, determined not to show his annoyance. He could have killed them with no more compunction than he would have had in shooting a couple of rats, but he knew that he was powerless, and that there was nothing he could do except try to hold his ground.

Several people, scenting trouble, paused to see what was happening. A tall man, who had been leaning against a doorway, made his way through the crowd and tried to catch Booth's attention. He was Booth's bodyguard, but the infuriated actor had forgotten his very existence.

The soldiers moved closer and began to comment unfavorably on the man who was holding up their progress. Booth remained absolutely still, his face rigidly expressionless. The crowd waited expectantly.

One of the soldiers, the shorter of the two, a man with an incredibly wizened face and a saber streak across his forehead, turned to the crowd and asked belligerently: "Why ain't he in the army if he's such a God-almighty person? I don't see no uniform on him." He walked around Booth, examining him elaborately for any trace of a uniform.

# Tuesday, April 11, 1865

"Maybe he's afraid of getting his pretty face spoilt," his comrade suggested.

Booth's eyes glittered ominously. His bodyguard pushed forward, trying to reach his side.

The little soldier thrust his face close to Booth's and pointed at the saber cut on his own forehead.

"How'd you like to have something like that?" he screamed suddenly. "That's what—"

Booth's giant bodyguard strode up to him and raised his arm with the slow steady motion of an automaton. "Shut up!" he bellowed. "You can't talk like that to a gentleman."

Someone in the crowd laughed derisively.

"By God, I'll fix your fancy gentleman—" The little soldier pulled at the bayonet dangling from his belt. The crowd hastily backed away in a wide circle.

Booth stood on the sidewalk, his face a mask of studied indifference, but he had reached inside his cloak to the butt of his pistol. His companion towered over the little soldier who had drawn his bayonet and was holding it straight out in front of him.

Suddenly, through the ranks of the retreating people, an officer in Federal uniform made his way. "What's the matter here?" he asked quietly.

The two soldiers sprang to attention. "He's a Johnny Reb, sir," the little one said eagerly, trying to hide his bayonet.

The officer walked over to Booth. "Well, sir, what have you to say for yourself?"

7

Booth looked at him coolly. "Nothing," he said finally. "I was standing here minding my own business until these two men came along and tried to push me out of the way. I haven't spoken a word to them."

"Is this true?" the officer asked. "Did he say anything to either of you?"

The two soldiers looked at each other unhappily. They were making a desperate effort to appear sober, but it was obvious to the officer that they were drunk.

"You'd better get back to your barracks," he said. Then he turned to Booth. "I'm sorry, sir. Some of our men are a bit out of hand with all this news of victory." He smiled genially. "I hope you'll overlook their actions. The circumstances are perhaps—extenuating."

"Certainly," Booth said frigidly. "I quite understand." He moved back into the shelter of a doorway. The officer, puzzled by his behavior, bowed formally and turned away. The two soldiers had already disappeared.

As soon as he was alone, Booth grinned slightly, elated by his small triumph over the Union Army. Then the tired heavy feeling that had weighed on him for hours settled down once more, and he knew that he had no right to indulge in even a moment of elation while his country was in her hour of agony.

People were hurrying past him, and the parade was far down the Avenue, almost out of sight. The whole city was turning out to go to the White House, where the President had promised to speak. A self-appointed deputation of citizens had gone there on the previous evening to ask him for a speech in honor of the occasion. But he, reluctant to speak extemporaneously at this critical hour when every word would be considered a declaration of policy, had addressed them briefly and requested them to return on this night so he could have an opportunity to prepare what he wanted to say.

Booth knew where the crowds were headed. He was keenly aware of the fact that this was the great moment of triumph in Lincoln's career, and his own wretchedness was increased by the knowledge that the man he hated above all others was to be showered with honor and glory. He hated Lincoln with a hatred that had passed beyond all reason; to him the victory of the North was Lincoln's personal victory, and the plight of the South was the result of Lincoln's malevolent persecution.

He stepped out of the doorway and looked indecisively up and down the Avenue. At one end was the dark pile of the Treasury Building and, beyond it, the White House. At the other end the newly completed dome of the Capitol gleamed softly against the darkening sky. There was an illuminated sign of victory on the long façade. He knew what the words were, even though he was too far away to read them. "This is the Lord's doing; it is marvelous in our eyes." He had been staring morosely at that sign for days.

9

# The Man Who Killed Lincoln

It had greeted him on his arrival in Washington and it had haunted him ever since. It had been erected to celebrate the fall of Richmond, but the rapid succession of victories had made it seem so appropriate to the citizens that they had not wanted to take it down.

There were signs of victory everywhere in the city —flags, banners and long strips of bunting flying in the breeze. The Yankees were convinced that the war was over. They were sure that the South was beaten and that no one was left to defend her. Four years of magnificent struggle could not be allowed to end like this. By God, he'd give them a lesson! He would show these Yankee hoodlums that a gentleman is never beaten—that he will fight gallantly against all odds, careless of danger and death. He would show them what the South was really like—the true South, the South they thought they had put down forever.

He, an actor bred in the tradition of great deeds and heroic gestures, would come to the aid of his country when everyone else had deserted her and her cause seemed lost. The curtain could not be rung down on this lame ending. Too much had already been sacrificed for that.

In the past he had been too dilatory, too easily put off by the hope that half measures could succeed. For months he had been working on a plan to capture Abraham Lincoln and take him to Richmond as a prize of war. Now he knew that his plan had been silly and ill-considered. If he had been more resolute there would be no Lincoln in the White House, no victory for these cheap little clerks to celebrate.

The day for a little coup had passed. Only determined and ruthless action could count. There was one thing left for him to do—and he must do it quickly....

He nodded to his tall companion to follow him. Then he turned toward the dark end of the Avenue and walked briskly in the direction of the White House. He wanted to see his enemy face to face.

People by the hundreds had pushed their way into the White House grounds, trampling down the spring flowers in their haste to get places near the building. Late-comers had to stand farther away under the trees that were scattered across the lawn. Against one of these trees Booth was leaning, grimly watching the house in which Lincoln dwelt.

In this building, he thought, in one of its historic rooms, surrounded by admiring friends and omnipresent guards, my enemy is waiting for his triumph. He has made a career of murder and used warfare to further his own importance. And these people have trooped here like school children to listen eagerly to whatever he has to say.

Booth snorted aloud with disgust, turning to look at his companion who was standing behind him, gazing with an impassive face at the enthusiastic crowd on the lawn. But this man paid no attention to Booth's gesture. He had lost the quality of wonder, and he was curious about nothing—four years of warfare had stamped out of him everything but primitive lusts. He was twenty years old and he had been educated only in killing. Booth had picked him up when he was starving and attached him to himself by giving him food and a master to follow. Lewis Paine was the name this incurious giant had adopted since deserting the Confederate Army, and he was Booth's bodyguard, his man of action who was expected to do whatever he was told.

Booth turned away, realizing that Paine was incapable of understanding his own reaction to the scene. The crowd was becoming restless and noisy. Suddenly a light appeared in one of the windows. The people nearest the building began to shout, and their cry spread across the lawn. A brass band struck up an ear-splitting tune. The window swung open, and a tall gaunt figure could be seen standing there.

The crowd had gone wild with cheering. The noise rose to a tremendous crescendo. The man in the window raised his hand, and the cheering and the music died away. The crowd waited, eager and attentive.

Why don't they fall down to worship him? Booth thought. He was looking up at the window, his eyes smoldering with fanatic rage. A light began to flicker uncertainly as someone stepped forward with a candle, so the President could see to read from a roll of papers he was carrying. He began to speak, and his voice, at first thin and indistinguishable, became louder as he progressed.

Booth listened carefully, paying more attention to the way Lincoln spoke than to what he said. He is a dull speaker, he decided quickly. His voice and manner lend no conviction. He has no cadence—no emphasis—no fervor. He speaks like a man who wants to get through his lines as soon as possible. In a theater he would be hissed off the stage.

"As a general rule," the tired voice went on, "I abstain from reading reports of attacks upon myself, wishing not to be provoked by that to which I cannot properly offer an answer. In spite of this precaution, however, it comes to my knowledge that I am much censured for some supposed agency in setting up and seeking to sustain the new State Government of Louisiana."

So he closes his ears to all criticism, Booth said to himself. No wonder he proceeds with everything as though he were ordained by God. The man must number his enemies by the millions, but he doesn't even want to listen to what they have to say.

The President was explaining in detail his views on the Louisiana problem. "The amount of constituency, so to speak, on which the new Louisiana Government rests, would be more satisfactory if it contained forty thousand, or thirty thousand, or even twenty thousand, instead of only about twelve thousand, as it does."

Booth grinned. Evidently Old Abe was not finding it easy to bend the people of that conquered State
to his will. But he was saying something else now,
something that made Booth's volatile temper rise instantly.

"It is also unsatisfactory to some that the elective
franchise is not given to the colored man. I would
myself prefer that it were now conferred on the very
intelligent, and on those who serve our cause as soldiers. . . ."

The muscles in Booth's face tightened. So what he
had heard rumored was true. Lincoln was not satis-
fied with freeing the slaves—he was actually consid-
ering giving them the right to vote. The right to vote
—niggers to have a say in the government of the
white South! Booth felt hot angry blood surge up
into his face and he could no longer listen to what
Lincoln was saying. He seized Paine's arm and
gripped it with hard fingers.

"Lewis," he muttered furiously, "did you hear
that?"

"What does he mean—'elective franchise'?"

Booth was incoherent with rage. He released
Paine's arm and reached inside his coat. Paine quickly
put out a restraining hand.

"John, are you crazy? Let's get out of here. You
can't do anything like that."

People were looking at them curiously.

"John, come on away from here. They're watching us, I tell you." He pulled at Booth's arm. Suddenly Booth turned and began elbowing his way out of the crowd. He strode angrily down the long curving path to the gate. Paine could hear him talking to himself under his breath.

Paine marched along behind him, and as soon as they were free of the crowd, he began to plead with Booth to quiet down. "John, for God's sake, watch out what you're saying," he urged. "You can't do anything here."

"Well, by God, I will do something!" Booth said angrily. "I'll put him through—that's the last speech he'll ever make. He'll never get a chance to give niggers the vote— Lewis, did you realize what he was saying? He's going to—"

"All right, but let's get out of here. There's too many soldiers around this place."

Booth continued his way toward the gate, his mind in a turmoil. Lincoln was going to let the niggers loose upon the land like a lot of unchained beasts. This was a wedge of black murder the man was trying to drive into the heart of the South!

By God, this must be stopped! He knew what niggers were like. He had been raised with them, seen them grow up into tall children who could never become men. They were savages only a few years removed from the jungle. They lived like animals crowded together in filthy kennels. They rutted like animals, casually in the fields without thought of

15

consequence. Horrible, horrible creatures, parodies of men, but unworthy of human consideration, for they were born to be beasts of burden, to serve forever the white race that was their natural master!

He remembered something he had seen as a boy in the deep woods near his father's place in Maryland —a big, buck Negro, whose black skin glistened with sweat while he held in his arms a young mulatto girl who was hysterical with desire. He had stood watching them, fascinated and revolted. Then they had caught sight of him, and he had run away from them, dashing madly through the underbrush with the heavy pounding of the black man's feet behind him. He had escaped the fierce onrushing tread to arrive breathless at the refuge of his father's home, but the fright and the indignity of the situation had never left him. He could never think of Negroes except with anger and disgust. Lincoln's very mention of giving such creatures the right to vote was an indication that the man was preparing to wreak a terrible vengeance on the South. One might as well speak seriously of letting horses or cattle have a responsible part in government.

He must act—and quickly now. There was no time to be lost.

Booth pushed his way into a saloon. Some men standing around the bar looked up in surprise at his impetuous entrance. He walked past them and went to a table in the rear. He flung his hat on a chair and kicked another chair toward the table. Paine slumped down carelessly, ignoring Booth's display of temper.

"Where's the waiter?" Booth asked irritably. "I need something to drink."

Paine called out loudly. A man in a white apron hurried over to their table.

"What will you have, Mr. Booth?" he asked politely.

"Brandy," Booth said. "Bring the bottle and leave it here."

He was used to being recognized. That was the advantage of being an actor. People see you and remember. So much the better. There was to be no secrecy in what he was going to do. He wanted the whole world to see him do it.

"I'll have corn whiskey in a big glass," Paine told the waiter. "And a cigar."

Booth drummed impatiently on the table with his fingers while he waited for the drinks. "Do you know what 'elective franchise for the colored man' means, Lewis?" he asked, looking up at his companion's expressionless face.

"Something for niggers, I reckon. What's he going to give 'em now?"

"The vote, Lewis. He wants to let them vote."

"Well, I'll be damned! I didn't know niggers could ever vote. Isn't there something in the Declara-

17

tion of Independence about being born free, white and equal?"

Booth grunted and kept drumming on the table. The waiter brought their drinks. Booth filled his glass, spilling some of the brandy in his nervous haste. He gulped the liquor down, and poured out another glassful.

"Let us drink," he said grandiloquently, "to the success of our plan."

"Sure," said Paine. "What is it now? There's been such a lot of plans I can't keep track of 'em all."

Booth was filling his glass for the third time. He paid no attention to Paine's question, for his mind was fastened again on Lincoln. That tall figure, which represented the supreme authority of the North, had become a symbol to him. In Lincoln's voice, with its flat whimsical monotony, he heard the North speaking. It was the voice of a trader; behind it was the avarice of men who dealt in shop wares, who thought only in terms of money. He had heard that the man had once actually tended a store somewhere in the wilderness. A fine sort of person he was to put into the White House to lead the destinies of a country that had once been ruled by gentlemen. The big hands, gnarled and powerful, were hands that had done manual labor. The sparse, shaggy body, on which clothes hung loosely and seemed always ill-fitted, was the body of a peasant, grotesque and brutalized by toil. Booth was sensitive to the physical aspects of people, and he held Lincoln's ugliness against him as though the man himself were responsible for it.

He felt too that Lincoln was a hypocrite; the North had been filled with stories of the President's kindliness and compassion, but Booth was convinced that Lincoln had fostered these tales of his magnanimity to further his own reputation. He saw the man plotting slyly every move he made, calculating carefully the effect it would have on public opinion. This astute politician was forever pardoning soldiers who had been derelict in their duty, while he casually sent tens of thousands of their fellows to death in battle.

In his hatred for the man he could trace dimly a pattern that seemed somehow to be repeated from his own past. Somewhere he had suffered at the hands of someone who resembled Lincoln. The image that was troubling him plagued him at night, disguised in the capricious forms of his dreams; it came close to him even in his waking moments, but he always fought shy of recognizing it. He was willing to admit to himself only that it was associated somehow with the man he hated.

For months he had been obsessed with the idea of striking a blow against Lincoln. At first he had been concerned only with the idea of capturing him. He had gone to Canada to consult with the heads of the Confederate group in Montreal that was organized to harass the North by sending out raiding parties across the border. His abduction plan had met with mild approval, but he had received no tangible assistance; so he had returned to recruit his own little band of conspirators. He and his men had actually made several attempts at abduction, but they had always been defeated by misfortune. Lincoln had simply not appeared at the places where they had lain in wait for him, and they had been forced to return empty-handed and furious with disappointment.

Abduction was impossible now. Richmond and all the territory south of Washington were in the hands of Federal troops. The death of this archenemy of his people was the only solution left. It seemed to him now that he had always known he would at last come to this decision—this culmination had been implicit even in the first beginnings of his plot. He was the man appointed by destiny as the slayer of his country's enemy, and there was no use trying to substitute anything else for the stark necessity of death.

He reached again for the brandy, and he studied the face of Lewis Paine as he raised his newly filled glass to his lips. Here was one man who knew all about killing. Paine's eyes, dull and unresponsive, were looking into his.

"Tell me, Lewis, how does it feel to kill a man?" Booth asked in a voice that he tried to make sound casual.

A slow smile started to spread across Paine's face.

# Tuesday, April 11, 1865

He looked around to make certain that no one was standing near them. Then he said: "So you've changed your mind about capturing a certain person, ch, John?"

"How does it feel to kill a man?" Booth repeated imperturbably. "You ought to know. You've killed enough of them."

Paine drew on his cigar and exhaled a great cloud of smoke. Then he leaned his arms on the table and bent close to Booth.

"It don't feel so good the first time you do it, John, but you get used to it soon enough. Ever kill sheep or hogs or anything like that?"

Booth made no answer. Paine went on, speaking in a quiet, passionless voice. "I felt pretty bad when I shot my first Yank. He was bending over to drink from a spring and he didn't see me at all. I plugged him right through the back of the head, and he fell into the water, making it all bloody." He stopped speaking in order to see the effect his story was having on Booth, but the trained features of the actor, who was now in complete control of himself, expressed nothing at all.

"It wasn't so bad after that," he continued. "You get used to it easily. They get to be just so much meat. I killed three of 'em at Gettysburg before they got me. Did it with a bayonet, too. That's worse than a bullet. You can feel the bones scrape against it. . . ."

He was smiling wryly, and his fingers were pressed flat against the edge of the table.

Booth poured out another glass of brandy. Paine's mouth twisted wider into a grin. He thrust his head close to Booth's. "There's going to be some killing now, ain't there, John?" He spoke in a whisper, although they were far away from the men at the bar. Booth looked at him sharply, and then nodded almost imperceptibly. Paine leaned back, clenching his hands into enormous fists. He seemed to be suddenly invigorated, and his usually somnolent eyes were wide open, glistening, studying Booth's face eagerly. "I thought there would be before we got through," he said with a curious note of triumph in his voice. "I thought there would be. In fact, I was pretty sure of it a long time ago. I never had much use for all these ideas about capturing him—"

"Why didn't you say so?"

Paine shrugged his shoulders and slumped down in his chair. His eyes were half-shut again and his voice became almost sullen. "This is your affair. You're running it." He picked up his cigar and clamped his teeth down on it.

Booth drank his brandy. The attitude of this placidly murderous giant puzzled him. It was impossible to think of Paine as the boy of twenty that he actually was. He was a man already superannuated in experience. Lincoln was to blame for his twisted mentality, Booth decided. Four years of nothing but

22

killing! And for a boy who might now be following the plow on his father's farm. There would be no place in the world for him when the war was over; his brothers had been slain in battle, his family was scattered and lost, and his life had been ruined even before he had reached his majority. It was fitting that this young veteran should be used in his plot against Lincoln, Booth thought. Only death could expiate the crime that the bloodthirsty war President had committed against hundreds of thousands of young men.

Paine roused himself out of his lethargy. He looked slyly at Booth. "What do I do?" he asked.

"I haven't had time to think much about it yet," Booth said uneasily. "Everything will have to be changed now...." He avoided Paine's eyes. "I want to clean out the whole damned nest of them if I can. The Cabinet . . . the Generals . . . everybody. . . . You'll have an important part to play. I know I can trust you and that you won't be afraid."

"Afraid? What is there to be afraid of?" Paine snorted. "All they can do is hang us if we get caught. And they have to catch us first. I'm not afraid of hanging—"

Hanging! Booth shuddered at the sound of the word. He had once seen a hanging, and the experience was still terribly vivid in his memory. At the time of the raid at Harper's Ferry he had volunteered for service in the Richmond Grays and he had been present at John Brown's execution. The sight of that tortured body turning and twitching at the end of a rope would never leave him. He had talked with the old man in his cell and he recalled how filled with fierce energy and life that aged body had been. John Brown was a man whose beliefs were in direct conflict with his own, but he had to respect him for his complete dedication to action. When they had hanged him he had felt what the helpless prisoner had to endure. To have your eyes hooded in darkness while the earth suddenly gave way under your feet . . . to be hauled up short in mid-air by a rope around your neck, choking, strangling . . . while your hands were tied powerless at your sides. . . .

Booth tried to force the frightful image from his mind. He would never let himself be hanged. He was too clever for that. Even if he were caught there would always be some other way out. Still, people did get hanged. . . .

He turned desperately to Paine. "Lewis, you've been through this sort of thing. You know what it is to kill and to risk death yourself. Tell me, if a man is hit in the head with a bullet he dies right away doesn't he? That Yankee soldier you shot—"

"Sure," Paine said easily, "you don't feel a thing. You're just blotted out. You never know what happens to you. It's not hard to die if you get hit clean."

Booth picked up his empty glass and began to turn it around in his fingers. "Hit clean." It was a beauti-

24

ful expression. He could always die that way himself
if worst came to worst. There must surely be a brief
moment before actual capture when a man could turn
his own pistol on himself. And he must kill Lincoln
with one certain shot. There was something godlike
in the delivery of such a death. The lightning strikes
and obliterates with the impersonal gesture of a man
treading out the life of an insect. "Hit clean." A bullet through the head at close range. No blood on his
hands, and no horrible struggle with a wounded
screaming creature whose cries would return to haunt
him forever.

"Hit clean." He knew what the term meant from
hunting. There was nothing to regret when a bird or
a rabbit was stopped with a single shot that drove the
life out of it instantaneously, turning the swift moving creature into a warm limp bundle of bloodstained
feathers or fur. But when the shot only crippled, and
you had to take the maimed little thing into your
hands. . . . "Hit clean." That was the way to do it.
This was not murder but assassination—a killing for
a cause, so that the deed transcended the ordinarily
ugly business of inflicting death. He must endow the
act he was going to commit with some great and magnificent gesture. He must make it evident to the world
that he was impelled not by any petty personal motive, but by righteousness, by God-inspired wrath.

And with Lincoln the whole Northern hierarchy
must be swept away. He would need all his men to

25

fling them against the various officers who held the power of the North in their hands. Grant, Seward, Johnson, Stanton—they all must go. He wished now that he had a regiment at his disposal instead of the pathetic handful of conspirators he had been able to win to his cause.

Of the men he had involved in his plot only Paine was outstanding in his absolute devotion and fearlessness. Only he possessed the reckless desperation that drives men on to do deeds that can be justified only by an inward consciousness of their rightness. Booth looked across the table at his companion. Paine's cigar had gone out. He struck a match to relight it. Booth watched his face as the flame lighted up his broad strong features. This is the one man worthy of the task that lies ahead of us, he thought. He, alone of all the others, can be counted upon to act surely and swiftly. It is strange that he and I should be bound together in this, for we have only one thing in common—the willingness to kill for an abstract cause and to die for it if necessary. And he is here because his own life has already been made bitter and useless, and death has ceased to have meaning for him. Yet there is reason even in that. The others have joined with me for adventure, or for the hope of getting money, or for no reason at all except that they have permitted themselves to be persuaded to support a cause in which they only half believe.

He examined in his mind the men who had worked

with him in the plot to abduct Lincoln. To one of them, at least, he was doing an injustice, he decided. John Surratt was a man in whom he had great confidence. He was very young—hardly more than a schoolboy, but he had been trained in the hazardous profession of espionage. He carried dispatches regularly from Richmond to Montreal for the Confederacy, and he knew all the tricks and subterfuges one must use in furthering a secret conspiracy. He was neither reckless nor desperate, but he was used to danger, and he was unquestionably devoted to the Southern cause. He, among all the conspirators, was the only one with whom Booth could discuss his plans intelligently.

Surratt, unfortunately, at the moment was in Montreal. He had left Richmond just before it had been taken by the Federal troops, and he had stopped in Washington for only one day before going on to Canada. Booth felt sure that he could induce him to return to Washington, but he was afraid that it would be difficult to get him to join a plot to kill. Surratt had been in the very center of the abduction plot. His widowed mother, who was now running a boarding house in the city, was an ardent Southerner, and she had willingly lent her home as the headquarters of the little group that had striven for months to capture Lincoln. They were both eager enough to see Lincoln taken as a prize of war, but Booth realized that Mrs. Surratt surely, and her son almost certainly, would draw back when they heard that simple abduction was to be transformed into political assassination. They were former slaveholders who would risk much to advance the cause of the South but they were also devoutly religious people. They would probably be unwilling to participate in anything that was so violently opposed to the tenets of their religion and to their own natural scruples.

Yet Booth knew that he needed John Surratt's assistance, for Surratt was the key to a situation which could be of inestimable value in arranging for their escape. Surratt had told him that he could enlist the services of certain unnamed men who were holding governmental positions but who were also secretly supporting the South. These men had promised their help during the abduction plot. They were going to arrange to have telegraph wires cut, the pursuit confused. . . . Let them do these things now. Then Booth and his party might have a chance to get away free. Surratt had always been reluctant to tell Booth much about these men, but there was no doubt that he had excellent connections in Government circles. He had proved this again and again in his career as a secret agent for the Confederacy.

Surratt must by all means be recalled to Washington. The other conspirators were almost worthless to Booth. Two of them had already practically deserted him, and two of them were only good-natured fools who liked to fancy themselves desperate characters.

The two who had deserted him were the first who had joined his conspiracy, Samuel Arnold and Michael O'Laughlin. They had been raised together, gone to school together, Arnold, O'Laughlin and Booth. They had fished and hunted together, drunk, caroused and slept with the same women. From boyhood these two had always looked up to Booth as their leader. But now they were growing up, growing away from him, wanting to follow their own ways, and they had become increasingly independent and even resentful sometimes of his leadership.

The defection of these two boyhood friends had weakened Booth's forces. Arnold had recently gotten a clerkship in one of the Government forts. He was a cautious fellow, probably better suited to be a clerk than a conspirator. O'Laughlin's desertion was a more serious loss, for he was always willing to take chances; he loved excitement and danger, and he was afraid of nothing. But O'Laughlin was poor and he was in constant need of money. Booth remembered with distaste how his patriotic fervor had varied with the state of his pocketbook.

These two were clever but faithless. The last two men in Booth's shakily organized little band were faithful enough, but they were subordinates who could be expected only to carry out orders and they could not even do that very well. One of them, David Herold, a young Washington boy, formerly a druggist's clerk, but now unemployed, was eager to do anything Booth asked, but he was shiftless and irresponsible. He could be depended upon to take instructions, but he was incapable of thought and deficient in courage as well as in intellect. The other, George Atzerodt, a German carriage maker from Southern Maryland, had been taken into the abduction plot for two reasons: he knew the Potomac River country and he owned a flatboat which could be used as a ferry to Virginia. He was the most useless of them all, for he was an arrant coward, a drunkard who could not stomach liquor, and he was a clown more suited to a low-comedy part than to the high tragic role Booth was trying to force upon him.

It was difficult, as Booth had long since found out, to get the right men for a dangerous and secret conspiracy. One had to use great care in approaching a new person. Every step in winning a man over had to be taken with elaborate precautions, and then, if the fellow balked at any point, there was always the risk of his revealing what he had learned. Even when a new man was willing to come along with him, there was a chance that after he had come so far, he would begin to make reservations, disagree about matters of policy, and endanger everyone in the conspiracy by threatening to withdraw from it. Booth was afraid that Atzerodt would give him trouble as soon as he found out that he was being involved in a plot to kill. And yet it was impossible at this stage of the game to let him go. He knew too much already.

# Tuesday, April 11, 1865

Atzerodt's character made him a highly uncertain risk. Booth explained this to Paine, who disliked the little German intensely. Paine sat and listened morosely, saying nothing until Booth had finished; then he stretched out his long arms and said, quite simply: "Why don't you let me get rid of him? He's no good anyway."

Booth examined Paine's grim face.

"Well," said Paine irritably, "what about it? This is a serious business. We can't afford to have anyone around who might talk. We'll swing for sure if we do."

"I can't permit anything like that," Booth said, looking down at his own hands. "George hasn't actually done anything wrong. We made a mistake in getting him into this, but we can make use of him somehow. God knows we need men badly enough. We—"

Paine spat on the floor and pulled his hat down over his forehead.

"Sometimes I can't make you out, John," he said. "If you're going into a thing like this you've got to go whole hog."

Booth was smiling.

"Surratt's another one," Paine said. "I can't figure him out either. Him and his mother and their praying. There's something queer about 'em both."

Booth explained patiently that Surratt was a

Southern patriot who had secret connections with men in the Government.

"He's in Canada now," Paine objected. "We've got to work fast."

"I can send word to him."

Paine drained the last few drops of whiskey from his glass. "Why don't you?" he asked practically.

"I will," Booth promised. "I'll telegraph to Montreal tonight."

# PART TWO

★

Lieut.-Gen'l Grant, President and Mrs. Lincoln have secured the State Box at Ford's Theatre TONIGHT, to witness Miss Laura Keene's *American Cousin*.

—ADVERTISEMENT
in *The Washington Evening Star*
April 14, 1865

## 2

---

*Friday, April 14*

---

O N TENTH STREET, only a few blocks from the
White House, a rehearsal was being held in
Ford's Theater. Word had been received that the
President and General Grant would attend the performance that night. The President was no novelty
to Washington theater audiences, but Grant could be
expected to draw a good crowd, since very few people had seen this victorious Union commander who
had become a world-famous figure at Appomattox.
A messenger had been sent to the newspaper offices to
insert advertisements announcing the gala occasion.

The stage was bare of scenery; daylight filtered in
through the high windows, and a few of the gas-
burning footlights had been turned on. The actors,
dressed in their street clothes, were rapidly running
through their parts. The play, Tom Taylor's im-
mensely successful comedy, *Our American Cousin*,
was so familiar to them all that it hardly seemed
necessary to go through its lines again, but rehearsals

35

were a matter of regular routine for Laura Keene's company, and this one had been called even before it was known that the President was coming.

The play in rehearsal bore little resemblance to the performance that would be given in public. The actors hurriedly mumbled their lines, raising their voices only when they came to the end of their speeches so as to give the cue. The empty house rustled and murmured with the echoes of their voices, and the comedy lines were received with stony silence by rows of vacant seats. Only the stage manager was paying any attention to what was going on, and he was chiefly interested in finishing the rehearsal so he could go out to get his lunch. Actors stood in little groups at the back of the stage, trying to converse in tones loud enough to overcome the noise made by a carpenter who was hammering vigorously at the framework of a large piece of scenery laid out on the floor.

At the rear of the orchestra, far back where the overhanging dress circle shrouded the lower floor in darkness, John Wilkes Booth was sitting. He had come to the theater to pick up mail addressed to him there. As he had stood at the box-office window, the ticket seller had told him that Lincoln would attend the evening's performance. The news had hit him like a sudden blow, freezing the smile with which he had greeted the man. Then he became the actor again. He opened his letters and deliberately read them through in the presence of the ticket seller, letting his face betray nothing of what was passing through his mind. One of the letters was from John Surratt in answer to his telegram, but even this never gave him pause, never stopped his exchange of light banter with the man at the window. Yet all the while he was saying to himself triumphantly: This is my chance! This is my chance, and fate has delivered my victim into my hands!

All the cords of the net were drawing together now. Surratt would be in Washington that very afternoon. His other men were ready. This was the day, and this theater was obviously the destined place. A more perfect setting could hardly be imagined, Booth thought. Here the deed could be done in the grand manner before an audience that would see him make history. Everything was working in his favor. He was more at home in Ford's than in any other house in the city. He had often acted there. He was on friendly terms with the stagehands as well as with the management, and he was acquainted with most of the actors. The idea of using a theater in his plot against Lincoln had been with him for a long time. He had once considered using this very house as a place from which to abduct the President, but he had not been able to solve the problem of removing a living person from the building. There was no such problem now.

He was shaping his plans for the evening. He wanted to make a careful inspection of the interior of the theater. It was already familiar to him, but he wanted to fix every foot of it in his memory so he could prearrange his movements precisely. He had to plan every step in advance, provide for every contingency that might arise.

The entrance door leading from the lobby was behind the place he was sitting. The stairs leading to the dress circle were to his left. He looked up, across the busy stage to the upper right-hand box. He had been informed that this was the one that would be given to the President. A removable partition divided it now into two sections, but this would be taken out before the evening's performance in order to make one large box.

This box opened directly on the stage and was about ten feet above it. Booth decided that it would be easy for him to jump down from there and make his exit through the wings to the rear of the theater. He had often made more spectacular leaps—in fact, he liked to introduce such novelties into his stage roles, and he had attracted attention in *Macbeth* by making his entry with a startling leap from a huge pile of scenic rocks.

These novelties of which he was so fond had not always met with the approval of the critics—particularly those who wrote in the metropolitan papers. They had called him the "gymnast actor." The term had rankled then, but he no longer cared. He was willing to give up acting forever if need be. He was in a position to control the destinies of actual nations now, and he was through with the fictitious kingdoms about which he had soliloquized on the stage.

It was no light gesture for him to give up his profession, for even though the metropolitan critics had been unkind, he had been successful enough in it to make an income of twenty thousand dollars a year. His reputation was not so great as his brother Edwin's, but he had had his share of acclaim, and he had thoroughly enjoyed the celebrity that comes with being a leading actor.

He knew that if he lived through this night at all it would mark the end of his career as an actor on the American stage. But what an exit he would have! There would be a distinguished group of people present to see him in this, his last and most sensational appearance. He must prepare a farewell speech that would have a telling effect on his audience. He would have only a moment on the stage, but in that moment he must immortalize himself. What should he say? Some bit from Shakespeare? There must be something in *Julius Caesar* that would fit the occasion. "Liberty! Freedom! Tyranny is dead!" That was a good line. Cinna had cried it when Brutus attacked Caesar. "Tyranny is dead!" It *was* a good line. He might be able to use it.

He rose from his seat and walked up the carpeted stairs that led to the dress circle. The whole stage was spread out before him. The stage manager had jumped up and was wrangling with one of the actors about some small business in his part. The carpenter was still pounding on the framework of the big flat. The blows of his hammer resounded hollowly through the empty house.

Booth looked across the half-circle of seats toward the President's stage box. The door that led into it was partly hidden in the shadows. It was a narrow little white door at the end of the passage that led around the back of the dress circle. He stood watching it, thinking how easy it should be to gain access to the box by passing behind all the people who would be seated here with their attention fastened upon the play.

He became oblivious of the noise on the stage. His mind leaped forward to the time when he would be able to stroll casually, slowly, without attracting any notice, toward the door that was beckoning to him now through the shadows. From where I am standing now, he thought, I shall be able to reach the box in less than a minute. He began to sidle toward it, counting the seconds as he moved cautiously along the back of the seats. No one on the stage paid any attention to him. He was at the door in forty-five seconds, moving always slowly, just as he would have to move on this night which was rushing toward him even as he counted the seconds away.

He sat down for a moment in one of the seats near the box. I must return to this place after the rehearsal

is over and examine the passageway that lies beyond
the door, he said to himself. His eyes swept around
the theater and he saw the house as it would be when
the audience had filled it. All this dark emptiness
would be gone, and the interior would be alive and
breathing when people were sitting in the now vacant
chairs. Even the sounds of the actors' voices would be
different, and all the haunting little echoes that were
murmuring through the house would disappear.

There will be a thousand of his friends sitting here
around him, he thought. And he will be in there, beyond the door, watching this silly comedy. The form
and the face of Lincoln rose in his mind, taking on
a vague semblance to some other person more familiar, but still evading final recognition. His hatred
mounted. I shall pass among all these people, his
friends, and go through that door to kill him. On his
own head he has called down this wrath. He who has
brought so much violence into this world shall himself perish by it!

He got up silently and went down the stairs to the
orchestra. The second scene of the third act was going
on. Some of the women standing at the rear of
the stage were laughing so loudly that they almost
drowned out the actors' lines. The hammering of the
carpenter kept ringing through the theater. Booth
rested his arms on the back of one of the seats and
watched the familiar rehearsal scene.

This was the part of the play in which the scheming English mother, Mrs. Montchessington, who had matrimonial ambitions for her daughter, finds out that the Yankee cousin is not the wealthy heir she thought he was. She was railing at him now. Mrs. Muzzy, who played the Montchessington part, had a voice that she could throw into the gallery, and she liked to use it even in rehearsals. "I am aware, Mr. Trenchard, that you are not used to the manners of good society," she boomed, "and that alone will excuse the impertinence of which you have been guilty." She swept off the stage haughtily, leaving Harry Hawk, who was playing the title role, there alone.

"Don't know the manners of good society, eh?" Hawk soliloquized. "Well, I guess I know enough to turn you inside out, old gal—you sockdologizing old man-trap!"

Booth was leaning forward now, watching the play with sudden interest. This is the very time to do it! he said to himself excitedly. Hawk is the only one on the stage. Muzzy is on the way to her dressing room. Keene is waiting to make her entrance. The wings are almost clear. This is the very moment for it! It couldn't be better if I had chosen the play myself.

Hawk was going on with his lines: "Wal, now, when I think what I've thrown away in hard cash—"

This scene should go on shortly after ten o'clock. Good. There would be plenty of time for preparation by that hour. Booth repeated the words Harry Hawk had just spoken. They were to be his own entrance cue. *Don't know the manners of good society, eh? Well, I guess I know enough to turn you inside out, old gal—you sockdologizing old man-trap!* Perfect! And appropriate, too, that the signal should be given in a nasal Yankee twang. Booth was delighted. The gods who arrange such things were having their little jest. This was a fine touch—a dainty fillip that added to the artistry of the performance. By God, they would be discussing this affair in the green rooms of the world's theaters for a generation to come! *Don't know the manners of good society, eh? Don't know the manners of good society . . . the manners of good society. . . .* He gave the words a nasal quality even in his imagination.

As he turned to leave the theater, he heard Laura Keene come on the stage to rehearse the lines she was never to speak that night.

It was nearly two-thirty. Booth was two hours nearer to his appointment with destiny. He had been making his plans for the night's work. He had already been to a livery stable to choose with great care the horse that was to carry him to Maryland and the South. He had been to his hotel to dress himself for riding, and he was ready now in boots and spurs as he walked toward Mrs. Surratt's house.

Long columns of soldiers in dusty blue uniforms were marching on the other side of the street. He stopped for a moment to watch them as they passed by, their guns glinting in the sunlight. There must be thousands of armed men like these in the city, he thought. The solid ranks moved past him laden with weapons. What chance had he against this army that covered all the land? The odds were hundreds of thousands to one against him.

He walked along slowly, trying to free his mind from fear by concentrating on the problems at hand. He was planning the moves for his pawns on the great chessboard of the city. He would use Atzerodt, who was the weakest of his men, against Vice-President Johnson, who was the least important of the people he intended to attack. He would place Paine in a more strategic position—utilize his fearlessness by sending him to the residence of William H. Seward, Secretary of State. Seward, at the moment, was lying in bed invalided as a result of a carriage accident in which he had broken his arm and fractured his jaw. Yet only a determined man could get to him, for his home was within pistol shot of the White House, and it was almost next door to the military headquarters of the city. Only a man like Paine could be depended upon to enter this house, force his way past the guards and servants, and by sheer strength and ferocity gain access to his victim's bedchamber. Davy Herold would go with Paine to hold his horse and guide him out of the city. Booth had reserved Surratt as his own aide— he would need someone at the theater to help him, for

Grant would be in the box with Lincoln, and Grant was a soldier who could be expected to put up a fight. O'Laughlin had come to the city and had visited Booth during the morning at his hotel, but the fellow had been drunk, whining as usual for money. Booth had been convinced then that he was unworthy even of being asked to rejoin his conspiracy.

He must be ruthless with everyone now. Too much was at stake to make any compromises or take any unnecessary risks. Only by being brilliantly hard and inflexible could he hope to succeed. Once he got out of the city and into the country beyond the Potomac, he could find Southern sympathizers who would assist him in his flight. He could go on to Mexico or Spain —countries that had no extradition treaties with the United States. Somewhere there would be a place for him. Somewhere he could take up his life again.

He hurried on toward the house on H Street. It was a remarkable establishment—this quiet little boarding house that Mrs. Surratt was running in the center of the Northern Government's capital city. From the outside it seemed to be only one of the hundreds of lower-middle-class lodging houses which had sprung up in Washington during the last few years, but it had sheltered some of the most important undercover agents of the Confederacy. And its mistress, who was eminently respectable and devoutly religious, in her fervor for the cause of the Confederacy had thrown herself into the furtherance of many plots and conspiracies the nature of which she often only partly understood.

Booth had found her house ideally suited to his purposes. It was a congenial home maintained by people whose loyalty to the South was unquestioned; it was a household trained in secrecy and discretion. Also its semi-public nature as a boarding house made it possible for him to bring all sorts of people there without arousing the suspicions of the neighbors.

Atzerodt had visited the place and was known to its occupants as a good-natured, if somewhat uncouth, German whom they called by his nickname "Port Tobacco." Paine had been introduced with great solemnity as a Baptist minister under the name of the "Reverend Mr. Wood." He had even dressed the part by wearing a clerical collar. The conspirators had been entertained socially by Mrs. Surratt and her daughter Anna. They had discussed their plans in her house and used it as a meeting place and a mailing address. When John Surratt had been in the city, they had consulted with him there about the route for the abduction party, and had agreed upon a former home of the family, about ten miles south of the city, as the first stopping place in their flight to the Confederate lines.

This country house, now leased by a tavern keeper named John Lloyd, was still to be the meeting place of the conspirators after their night's work was finished. Booth was carrying a package he wanted Mrs.

46

Surratt to take there for him, so he could pick it up on his way to the South.

A colored girl received him cordially at the door. He waited a few minutes in the dark little parlor until Mrs. Surratt came downstairs. She entered the room, surprised at his unexpected appearance in the middle of the day. But she greeted him warmly, eager as always to please this handsome young actor whose visits to her modest home were so flattering.

Booth bowed to her ceremoniously. Ordinarily he treated her with a combination of easy jesting and respect, but the errand he had come to ask her to perform today was one that was fraught with danger, and he was already beginning to feel that it was unfair to involve her in this plot at all. She sensed immediately the hesitancy in his manner. She seated herself on the high-backed sofa and turned expectantly to him with a gravely inquiring expression on her face.

Booth leaned his elbow on the marble mantelpiece and looked at her for a moment without speaking. The relationship between them was a very curious one. She was nearly twice his age, the mother of three grown children, and he regarded her with the deference that he always paid to people a generation older than himself. But she obviously looked up to him and admired him, and she would unquestionably do anything that he asked her to do, no matter how dangerous it might be. And yet she was certainly not what

47

one would call a brave woman—nor by any stretch of
the imagination would one call her reckless. Under
the circumstances perhaps it was better not to tell her
too much—then she would have to take no conscious
part in his plot.

He hesitated, at a loss for words before her evident
willingness. "You told me a few days ago that you
might be driving down to Surrattsville today," he said
finally. "I want to have this parcel left with John
Lloyd."

"I'll be glad to take it, Wilkes. Mr. Weichmann is
out hiring a buggy now." She stopped speaking and
looked up suddenly at his face. "Why are you looking so serious? You seem to have something on your
mind. What is it?"

He smiled reassuringly. "Nothing, really. I'm just
wondering how much I ought to tell you about this
little package."

"Tell me all about it, of course," she said
promptly. "What is it?" She reached her hand out
for the brown paper parcel.

He handed it to her. "It's a spyglass," he said.

She arched her eyebrows in surprise. "Why do you
make such a fuss over it then? It seems harmless
enough."

"I want to tell you two things about it. First of all,
don't tell our good friend Louis Weichmann that I
gave it to you. Secondly, impress upon Lloyd that it

is important, and that he shouldn't get drunk tonight
—for once."

"What is all this about, Wilkes? You're acting very
strangely. You—"

"You know I've never trusted Weichmann," he
said bluntly. "I never could understand why you let
him stay here. He's an employee of the War Department, and if he were ever to say anything about some
of the things he has seen in this house, he might get
all of us into trouble."

"But he's my son's friend. I can't believe that Louis
would ever betray us to the Government. After all,
he's a Southerner himself."

"Yes, I know, but—"

"Well?"

"There's something about him that I just don't
trust."

"But what has all this to do with a field glass? And
John Lloyd—" She stopped suddenly and looked at
him with startled eyes. "Wilkes," she said, "don't tell
me that—that this is the Lincoln business again? Oh,
you couldn't—not now—The war is all over. You
wouldn't have a chance."

He nodded grimly. "It's the Lincoln business, as
you call it, all right. And the war isn't over—but it
will be if someone doesn't come to the aid of the South
now."

Her hand caught at her throat, and she looked at
him silently, waiting for him to explain.

"Something must be done for the South, Mother, and this is my chance to do it. Perhaps I, as an individual, can do something the world will call illegal, but what I do will at least give my country another chance to fight for her just and honorable legal rights."

"But I'm afraid, Wilkes. Afraid for you."

"My life doesn't matter now. Too many lives have been sacrificed for one more to count. Besides, I have my plan so perfected that there is every chance of my getting away alive."

"Your plan failed before," she said gently.

"It won't fail this time."

"Why do you try it, Wilkes? You can't send him to Richmond now."

He smiled. "We have a better place than Richmond to send him to."

"I'm so glad my own boy isn't mixed up in this. Thank God, he's in Canada."

"Have you heard from him?" he asked casually.

"Yes—I got a letter from him only this morning."

"What did he say—if I may ask? Did he say anything about returning here?"

"No, he didn't. I'd just as soon he didn't come back now until the war is all over. It's dangerous for him here. I feel sure that the Government suspects him. Sometimes I think that this house is being watched."

Booth looked up uneasily. "What makes you say that?"

"Well, you know John wouldn't sleep here the last time he was in the city. He insisted on going to a hotel. Oh, I'm getting to hate this whole business of spying and secrecy and— I wish this horrible war would end so we could all lead normal lives again. I'm so afraid for John."

"Perhaps it will end soon now," Booth said reassuringly.

"Don't you think you'd better tell me more about your plans, though? Perhaps I can help you in some way."

"I think it would be better if you didn't know too much about what we're going to do. Then you can't be implicated. Just take that field glass to John Lloyd and you'll be doing your part. Tell him we'll be coming through about midnight."

"I wish you wouldn't do it, Wilkes. I do wish I could persuade you to give up the whole idea."

"This is the South's last chance," he said stubbornly. "Tell me, did you ever see the play *Julius Caesar?* Or read it?"

She shook her head. "No. Is it something you're going to play in, Wilkes?"

He smiled. "In a way, perhaps. Read it when you get the chance. The part of Brutus is very interesting. When you read it you'll understand why I am doing what I am doing."

She came over to him and put her hand on his arm. "You'll be in great danger," she said. "You are head-

51

strong, Wilkes. I hope that what you are doing is right. For the South's sake I must wish you success, but I am terribly afraid. Thank God, John isn't here. . . ."

"Thank you for your good wishes," he said gravely. "I shall need them. Be sure not to mention this to Weichmann."

She smiled unhappily. "God speed you. . . ."

"I may not see you for a long time, but I'll write to you—as soon as I can."

He bowed and went quickly out of the room. As he entered the hallway, he saw Louis Weichmann standing at the front door with his hand still on the knob.

He could not rid himself of his suspicions of Weichmann. The fellow was supposed to be John Surratt's closest friend, but Weichmann's pasty white face and furtive ways had made Booth dislike him from the start. He felt sure that Weichmann had been standing in the hallway trying to listen. He could hardly have understood the significance of their carefully guarded words, though. And it was unthinkable that he would do anything that would endanger Mrs. Surratt. She had always treated him as if he had been her own son.

It was only a short distance from H Street to the Herndon House, where Booth asked at the desk for a Mr. James Sturdey—the name Surratt had agreed in his letter to use in registering. He went up the stairs to a room on one of the upper floors and knocked at the door. It opened slowly. Surratt, tall, lanky and pale-faced, stood there blinking at him. He was partly undressed, his hair was mussed and his eyes were bloodshot.

"I thought I'd try to get some sleep," he said. "I've been traveling on railroad trains day and night to get here on time. What's it all about?"

"I've just come from your mother's house," Booth said. "It's just as well you didn't tell her you'd be in town."

Surratt stared at him sleepily. "I didn't have a chance to tell her. I left Montreal in such a hurry that— What's happening? Your telegram didn't say much. It couldn't, of course."

"We've given up the idea of capture."

"Yes?"

"Yes."

"So what's the plan now? You certainly didn't send for me unless you had something important in mind. What is it?"

"We're going to do the job right this time."

"What do you mean?"

Booth explained his reasons for transforming the long-drawn-out abduction plot into a plan to kill. Surratt listened to him, sitting on the edge of the bed and watching him unhappily, but saying nothing.

"I'm going to shoot him myself," Booth went on, speaking the words as though he had learned them by heart. "And I don't consider myself a murderer for doing so. This isn't murder—it's an act of war. If I were to kill a man on the battlefield no one would think anything about it. This whole nation is a battlefield now...."

Surratt was picking at his fingernails. He kept his head lowered and made no comment.

"General Grant is going to be with him," Booth went on. "I want you to go with me to take care of Grant. I can't handle both of them alone."

Surratt remained silent.

"Well?" Booth asked irritably.

"What do you want me to say?"

"Say 'yes' first of all. You don't seem to be very enthusiastic."

"I can't be enthusiastic about killing someone."

"You've killed plenty of men before."

Surratt looked up sharply. "What do you mean?"

"The dispatches you have carried— Don't you think men have died as a result of the information you brought to our army? That didn't bother your conscience, did it? There's no reason why it should, of course. This is war, John. Men have been dying by the thousands every day for four years now."

"But damn it, I didn't kill them with my own hands!"

"What's the difference?" Booth said disdainfully. "Their blood is on your soul—if there be such a thing."

# Friday, April 14

Surratt got up and began to walk up and down the room. Booth took his place on the bed and followed him with his eyes. The sun beat down on the windows, and the air was hot and close. There is an odor of death about this place, Booth thought. This room has a thick, heavy air about it, as if a corpse were lying here awaiting burial. He clasped his face in his hands, and felt the warm moisture of perspiration on his skin. He shook his head vigorously to throw off this sudden malaise.

"Well, John, what do you say?" he asked again.

Surratt stopped and looked into his eyes. "I don't know what to say. I never considered anything like this."

"Are you afraid?"

Surratt smiled feebly. "It's not that. You know the kind of work I've been doing. It can't be said that I'm a coward." He sat down on the bed beside Booth and ran his hands through his hair. His fingers seemed very white against the sandy-colored strands.

"This is the only move we can make now," Booth said patiently. "We can't abduct Lincoln. There's no place to take him."

"No, I suppose not. But I don't like the idea. You know, Wilkes, in Montreal they think the war is as good as over. Lee's surrender—"

"The war is over unless we do this. The Southern armies—what's left of them—will fight if they see a chance to win. What we do will throw the North

55

into confusion. The South can take advantage of the crisis and enter the field again. There is no choice for us, John. We must act!"

Surratt looked down at his bare feet, twisting his toes uneasily.

"You've got to help me," Booth pleaded. "I can't trust any of the others as I can trust you. They have their parts to play and so have you. You can be of more assistance to me right now than any other human being in this world. You have connections in this city. You know who the friends of the Confederacy are. You know men who can fix the telegraph wires—"

"I can do a lot of things," Surratt said. "But to do them I must go out, see people, walk openly through the streets. I may be recognized. You know I'm a marked man here. Detectives have been looking for me. They may find me—especially in the places I shall have to go. I didn't want anyone to know I was in Washington today."

"You'll have to risk it. It may mean the difference between our getting away alive and being intercepted and shot. Everything depends on you. Millions of people in the South . . . the army. . . . You know, John, this one blow struck swiftly now may do more good than a fresh army of a hundred thousand men. John, you've got to do it. You've got to!"

Surratt leaned over, picked up a boot and stuck his foot in it slowly.

"All right," he said, "tell me what your plans for the night are."

Booth seized his arm eagerly. "You'll never regret this, John, no matter what happens. I promise you that." He outlined his plans hurriedly and explained the arrangements he had made for their escape to the South.

"Between ten and ten-thirty, then," Surratt said finally. "Suppose the telegraph lines go out of order at ten-thirty. How would that be?"

"Perfect."

"I'll be back here by five—I hope," Surratt grunted, pulling on his other boot. "You'd better get in touch with me then, so I can let you know how I make out."

Booth stood up. "Thanks, John," he said, holding out his hand. Surratt took it and they shook hands warmly, looking into each other's eyes.

Surratt opened the door, and Booth went out into the long dark hall. There is an odor of death in that room, he kept thinking. Suddenly he shivered.

It was after three o'clock when he reached Pennsylvania Avenue. An open carriage was coming from the direction of the White House. In it, smiling and bowing, were the President and his wife.

Booth had been drinking. The sharp stimulation of alcohol raised his fear-worried mind to a pitch of exaltation that caused him to forget all thought of possible failure. He could drink an enormous quantity of liquor without showing any outward signs of being drunk. Alcohol simply speeded up his reactions, made his brain race quickly with a torrent of eager thoughts that chased each other across the foreground of his consciousness. And from this outpouring came new schemes, new ideas for action. He needed liquor now to stir up his mind and bolster his courage.

He had discovered its value early in life. His first few awkward performances on the stage, made when he was only sixteen years old, had been miserable failures. He had been afraid of the audience seated out in the darkness beyond the footlights. He had forgotten his lines and been laughed at. He had felt that he was a disgrace to his family. The ability to act was something they had taken for granted, and it was expected that a Booth would be born with it.

Then he had learned how alcohol could help him. He had gotten drunk, and he had played his first successful part under the influence of liquor. It was queer how brandy could make another man of him. It changed him into a reckless, nerveless creature like Paine, afraid of nothing, willing to try anything, no matter how impossible it seemed.

He was engaged in marshaling the plans for his subplots, trying to fit into the general pattern of this coming night of terror the subsidiary actions that would help to paralyze the North by depriving it of a number of its leaders at once.

# Friday, April 14

He had moved Atzerodt into the Kirkwood House so he could keep a watch on Vice-President Johnson who was staying there. Booth was eager to strike at Johnson. He regarded Johnson as an archtraitor—a man who had been a Southerner by birth and who had sold out his birthright for the opportunity of becoming Military Governor of Tennessee. He had been richly rewarded by the Northerners for his treachery. They had made him Vice-President during the recent election. It was unthinkable that this man could ever be permitted to succeed to the Presidency. He was a common tailor—a poor white really, and an opportunist to boot. If Atzerodt could be made to do his part, Johnson would be dead before the day was over.

Booth went to the hotel, but there was no sign of Atzerodt there. He entered the bar, and, as he stood there drinking, an idea occurred to him. He might be able to do something that would damage Johnson's chances for becoming President, something that would provide insurance against the possibility of Atzerodt's failure.

He would send his card up to Johnson, asking for an interview. Whether Johnson saw him or not did not matter—it would become known that the slayer of the President had sought to visit the Vice-President on the very day of the assassination. Johnson would be placed in such an embarrassing position that he might never be permitted to assume the title of President. His past record was none too good. He had been outrageously drunk during the inauguration ceremonies. He was a Southerner looked upon with distrust by the Northern politicians, and he had enemies everywhere.

Booth called for a blank card, and grinned maliciously as he wrote on it: "Don't wish to disturb you. Are you at home? J. Wilkes Booth."

The card was returned in a few moments with word that Mr. Johnson was not in. Booth gave the card to the desk clerk with instructions to put it in Johnson's letter-box. He also left a note under Atzerodt's door, telling him to be at Paine's room in the Herndon House at eight o'clock without fail.

Then he sauntered out on the Avenue and walked toward Pumphrey's livery stable. While his horse was being saddled, he sat down on a feed box and leaned tiredly against a bale of hay. The stable reminded him of the big barn on his father's farm in Belair.

I shall never see my home again, he thought. I shall never see another springtime in Maryland. By tomorrow I shall either be dead or in exile. The stable-boy called to him that his mare was ready. He swung himself into the saddle and had the boy adjust the stirrups carefully. The odor of brandy and sweated leather and manure mixed confusedly in his brain. He felt depressed and lonely. The effect of the liquor was wearing off quickly. His fears were coming back to gnaw at him again.

His horse jogged out of the side street into the wide

openness of Pennsylvania Avenue. He rode along slowly, his mind filled with foreboding. His life had been a pleasant one; money had always come easily to him; he had achieved a certain amount of prominence; he was admired by women everywhere; he had a home and a devoted mother. There was every reason to believe he could go on from one small success to another, adding luster to the Booth family name.

He had nothing to gain from what he was about to do and everything to lose. And he was afraid. A nameless and unreasonable fear gripped him and made his stomach feel queasy. Before the night was over he might be dead—shot down by some armed person in the audience or captured in full flight through the streets of Washington by some wandering patrol that might be near the theater at the wrong moment. It was not death itself that he feared, but the impact of violence on his person. The thought of a bullet striking him full in the face, or a saber-thrust, searing and slashing through bone and blood-spurting flesh, made him feel sick. And worst of all, the very root of his fear was nothing tangible, had nothing to do with exile or pain or death. He was most afraid of the unknowable—of what might happen when he exposed himself to a new set of circumstances, which, once started in action, would go on remorselessly to an end that he could not hope to foresee.

He was acutely aware of the effect that his deed would have on the lives of those who were nearest to him. It would ruin the careers of his brothers and sisters. He was only slightly concerned about them, though. They would never have to undergo even a faint portion of his danger, or share more than a fraction of the calumny that would be poured out on him.

The only person he really cared about was his mother. She would never be able to understand how her son, who was still only a little boy to her, could take into his hands this problem of altering destiny by violence. She would never be able to stand up under the terrific flood of denunciation the North would let loose upon him. She would hear her beloved son called a murderer and a traitor, and she would never even be able to comprehend the motives that had compelled him to act.

One other person's life, though, was bound up with his. He had stupidly, incautiously, allowed himself to drift into a love affair with the daughter of Senator Hale of New Hampshire. Almost against his will, it seemed now, he had become involved in an engagement to marry her. The engagement had never been announced publicly, but word of it had reached his family, and it was known in certain circles in Washington society that Bessie Hale was going to marry the actor, John Wilkes Booth. Her family had bitterly opposed the match. Her father was contemptuous of all actors, and he had forbidden Booth to come to his house.

This opposition, more than anything else, had been

# Friday, April 14

responsible for Booth's proposal of marriage. The girl actually meant very little to him. He was certainly not in love with her, but her family had looked down upon him and his profession, and he had retaliated by winning her away from their influence.

He had never had any compunction about making use of her. He had persuaded her to get him a ticket of admission to the speaker's stand on Inauguration Day, and he had stood close to Lincoln when he took the oath of office for the second time. He had gone to the Capitol with no definite plan in mind, vaguely hoping for some opportunity to attack the man he hated. The opportunity had never come. Lincoln had been too well guarded during the entire ceremony.

If Booth had struck then, Bessie Hale's life would have been ruined by the direct connection she would unknowingly have had with the conspiracy. Now, at least, she would be free of any charge except that of having been acquainted with the chief conspirator. Since their engagement was not generally known, her father's influence would doubtless be great enough to quash any legal investigation of his daughter's relationship with the President's assassin. The Senator had recently been appointed Minister to Spain, and he would doubtless soon be leaving the country anyway.

Booth had never taken the girl seriously, never considered for a moment the fact that she might be sincerely in love with him. He had been in and out of

63

love so many times, and so casually, that he took it for granted that everyone else was as little affected by love as he. Women had always thrown themselves at him. He received a great many letters from girls who had seen him on the stage and who wrote to tell him of their passionate devotion. He took their declarations at their face value and he believed that if women could give their love so lightly it must surely mean very little to them. He could understand maternal love, which was selfless and superior to any physical attraction, but sexual love, to him, was something that could be had easily, bought cheaply if necessary, and could soon be forgotten. If he was willing to sacrifice his mother to this cause, he certainly need not regret the effect his actions would have on Bessie Hale's life. She would get over it and forget him and marry some other young man with prospects more in line with her family's ambitions.

He could permit nothing to stop him now. He was ready to renounce all emotional ties, ready to cut himself off forever from everyone who meant anything to him. He knew that he could be ruthless in doing this. His fears for himself were more difficult to dispose of. Yet he felt compelled to go through with his plan, if only because he had dedicated himself to its fulfillment. And the others were expecting him to carry it out. He could not back out now even if he wanted to. For months he had been obsessed with the idea of his plot against Lincoln, but it had been only an idea—something that had existed in his own mind, to be dwelt upon or put away as he wished. Now the forces of external circumstances were compelling him to act. In a few hours Lincoln would arrive at the theater. All the parts of his plot structure were falling into place—and his own part was among them. The conspiracy was no longer only an exciting game, a thing of secret discussions and elaborate planning. It was his master now—something beyond his control —and it was pushing him forward inexorably. Surratt was already setting the stage for the night's work, and Paine, like a caged tiger, was waiting silently in his hotel room. . . .

He must justify himself in the eyes of the world, though. Everyone must be made to understand that he was acting not for himself, but for the South. He would write his reasons down so they could be published afterwards. He was not a murderer but a liberator. *This shall make our purpose necessary and not envious; which so appearing to the common eyes, we shall be call'd purgers, not murderers.* O Brutus! You knew the name of action and heard the call that makes men kill, so that other men may henceforth be free!

He turned his ambling horse toward Grover's Theater. He could write in the manager's office there. Dwight Hess would not be in the house at this time of the day, and he could have the place to himself. The saloon of John Deery, the billiard champion, was over the main entrance to the theater. He decided to stop there for more brandy.

The smoke-filled room was silent except for the click of the ivory balls. A small crowd was clustered around one table where a player was making a long run. Booth greeted Deery, who was watching the game, and then he stepped to the bar.

He drank quickly and stood turning the empty glass in his fingers, staring moodily at it. He was trying to think of what to write. Phrases from a letter he had written several months before kept recurring to him. This letter, carefully sealed, was still in the possession of his sister Asia, but he felt that another one must be written now to explain his new purpose, for the first letter had been concerned only with his motives in the abduction plot. He had said then: "I have ever held the South were right. The very nomination of Abraham Lincoln, four years ago, spoke very plainly of war, war upon Southern rights and institutions. His election proved it. . . . The country was formed for the white, not for the black man." O God, the insolence of men who have once been slaves and then are freed! They would prey upon the country like a black pestilence. The condition of the Negroes might have been slowly bettered in some way, but it was insane to set them all free at once. Men had to learn to take the heady wine of freedom, or it would drive them mad. The South had to continue its struggle for the rights of its white citizens. He had

66

written: "The South can make no choice. It is either extermination or slavery for *themselves* (worse than death) to draw from. I know my choice. . . . My love (as things stand today) is for the South alone. Nor do I deem it a dishonor in attempting to make for her a prisoner of this man to whom she owes so much misery." He had signed himself: "A Confederate doing duty on his own responsibility."

What a pity his abduction plan had not succeeded! The South might now be victorious and in a position to dictate its own peace terms. He would be famous, forever a hero to the people he had saved. . . . But now there was nothing left but killing—a last desperate gesture, and one that was fraught with terrible risk and danger to himself.

He drank several glasses of brandy gloomily, looking at the image of his own face in the big mirror behind the bar. It looked to him like the face of a stranger, someone he had never seen before.

He opened his hand and straightened out the fingers, moving the supple joints as if to make certain that the hand was actually his. On the wrist the initials J.W.B. were tattooed. This hand, this flesh, at the command of the cunning directing brain—all this being, alive and responsive—was he, he, the only thing in all the mad welter of this world that he could be sure had existence at all. Lincoln was simply a concept, an evil force that his too fertile mind had created. Now he must do away with this careless spawning of his own brain, for it represented a power that had always troubled him—a power of authority that was opposed to his, a power of final dominance that challenged his right to godlike supremacy. The words of Prospero came to his mind: *Our revels now are ended. These our actors, as I foretold you, were all spirits and are melted into air, into thin air. . . . And, like this insubstantial pageant faded, leave not a rack behind.*

More brandy now! The pleasant fumes of alcohol in his nostrils—the sharp strong taste of the liquor in his throat. . . . The men around the billiard table were applauding the end of a long run. They would be talking tomorrow of how they had seen John Wilkes Booth drinking on this fatal day at Deery's bar. He drank again and tried to think of the letter he had to write. He must go down into the dark interior of the theater and put on paper the lines for this, the last part he was ever to play on the American stage.

Deery was standing beside him now.

"You're not looking well, Mr. Booth," he said. "You've been very nervous and jumpy these last few days. I'll bet your billiard game is off too, isn't it?"

"I haven't had much time for billiards these days. Too many things have been happening."

"Aye, these are bad times for billiards," Deery agreed. "There's too much excitement in the air. Men would rather go out and holler and get drunk than settle down to a serious game. I've been making

68

more from my bar than I have from my tables. Well, it's a great victory. A great victory, sir. And now perhaps the country will be quieter, and men will have a chance to—" He turned abruptly to one of the table boys. "Jerry, don't let those two drunks have a table. They'll be tearing the cloth and they didn't get drunk here anyway. Sorry, Mr. Booth. You have no idea of the trouble I've been having. You can't get good billiard cloth any more. The mills have been so busy making stuff for uniforms that they won't bother with it, I guess."

Booth poured out another glass of brandy. He was sick of victories. Always victories, Northern victories. He must write his letter. He had to think of what he would say.

"Thank God they haven't shut down on the liquor supply," Deery went on. "The imported liquors are hard to get and high as all Harry to pay for, but they're still making lots of good cheap whiskey. They have to, to keep the army going, I suppose. I never saw so much whiskey drunk in this town before."

Booth backed away from the bar. He must go and write his letter. He had heard enough of Deery's petty business problems. He said good-by to him abruptly. Then he went down the stairs into the street and entered the cool shadows of the theater. As he had hoped, the manager's office was empty.

He took pen and paper, and sat down to write. The words he wanted eluded him, although their substance was clear in his mind. How could he justify himself in the hostile eyes of the Northerners or even make the people of the South understand what he was going to do? All sorts of irrelevant subjects kept recurring to him. Deery's broad earnest face and his voice, endlessly talking, came back to him against a background of clicking billiard balls. The odor of brandy clung to his nostrils, and his throat called for more of the bright sharp liquor. He had still to think of what he would say in that brief moment on the stage tonight. Tyranny. Something about tyranny. His father's stern face looked down upon him from a framed portrait hanging in the entrance hall of the house in Belair. A candle was burning under it, sending up from the frame a long streak of black shadow that met the ceiling. He turned the pen over in his fingers. The old man had made fun of his childish voice declaiming Shakespeare, and he heard again the deep rich tones of his father speaking the lines he had tried to memorize. He could feel his mother's bosom, soft under the heavy taffeta. She, only she, could understand what he— Enough of this. He must write.

The words suddenly crowded into his mind. He took the pen and wrote swiftly. He explained how he had devoted all his efforts for a long time to effect the abduction plot; how he had had to change his plans quickly now in order to give the South another chance. He went on to say that he expected censure for his act, but some day, when wartime anger had cooled, posterity would surely justify his deed. And then, without consulting the others, he signed the letter boldly: "Men who love their country better than gold or life. J. W. Booth—Paine—Atzerodt—Herold." Out of consideration for Surratt's mother he omitted the name of her son.

He felt relieved now that the letter was written. There would be some tangible record of his purpose left behind him. He folded the paper, sealed it and placed it in his pocket. He must get some more brandy now.

As he rode slowly along Pennsylvania Avenue he saw a man he knew, John Matthews, an actor whom he had once tried to persuade to join his band of conspirators. He greeted him and swung down from his horse.

Matthews was employed at Ford's Theater, where he played secondary roles. He was eager to better himself, so he questioned Booth about his theatrical plans, hoping for a chance to appear with him in a more important part.

"I've lost all interest in the theater now," Booth said. "I've found a more lucrative profession. You should have come in with me when I asked you."

"You mean that oil speculation you told me about?"

Booth carefully refrained from giving a direct answer. He simply smiled and said nothing.

"You have to have money to go into that sort of

thing," Matthews said earnestly. "It's a risky business too, and I don't think it's going to last. Frankly, I believe you can do better as an actor, Wilkes, although, of course, it's none of my affair. You could be one of the greatest leaders of our profession if you would only work at it."

"I'm doing well enough," Booth said curtly.

"In the oil business?"

"Well—not exactly in the oil business." Booth looked down and slapped the dust off his boots. Matthews was studying him curiously. They stood in silence for a few moments under the budding branches of the trees that lined the sidewalk. The flagstones were covered with newly fallen catkins. Booth pushed a little pile of them together with his foot.

"Perhaps you would do a favor for me," Booth said finally. "I have a letter here—a letter of the utmost importance that I want to have delivered to the office of *The National Intelligencer* tomorrow morning. I'll be out of town then and I don't like to trust these wartime mails. Will you see that it gets there? I wouldn't ask you if it weren't a matter of great importance."

"Of course, of course, Wilkes. I'll get it there without fail. Let me have it."

Booth handed him the letter. I am trusting this man with my life, he thought. If he should lose this letter, or open it before the deed is done, we shall all be hanged.

He grasped Matthews' shoulder. "I can't tell you how much this letter means to me. Will you pardon me if I caution you to guard it against loss and make certain that it reaches its destination tomorrow morning—not before then or later?"

Matthews smiled. "Certainly, Wilkes. It's a simple enough thing to do. Why are you so concerned about it?"

Booth's horse pulled suddenly at the reins. Men were marching down the street dressed in the tattered gray uniforms of the Confederate Army. A file of soldiers in blue walked on either side of them as guards.

"Who are these men?" Booth demanded of Matthews, as if he were accusing him for their presence. "Who are they and why are they here?"

Matthews looked at the marchers, puzzled for a second, then he said slowly: "They're officers from Lee's army, I guess. They're probably being taken to the Old Capitol Prison."

Booth seized the bridle of his horse sharply. "Good God! Matthews, I have no country left." Lee's officers here in Washington! It was unthinkable—there would be no leaders to call the men to arms when his summons went forth. He mounted his horse and sat heavily in the saddle, watching the prisoners filing past. They shuffled along the rutted street, broken, defeated men with heads bent low, seeking to avoid the stares of people on the sidewalks. The late after-

noon sun streamed down the wide Avenue. The slant-
ing rays stained their unshaven faces to a sickly jaun-
diced color.

And then among them he saw one face, dirty,
emaciated and partly masked in bandages. The eyes
looked for an instant into his. The man hesitated and
then marched on, never turning around. At first the
face seemed only terribly familiar, but slowly, out
of the features grown older, sharpened by time and
emaciation, came the memory of a young boy's face,
and Booth realized that he had seen someone from
Belair who had played with him in the fields around
his father's home. He could not remember the boy's
name, although he could see him standing against a
background of autumn leaves in the sunshine. The
fresh odor of the woods came back to him. Jerry—
that was it—Jerry! He tightened his grip on the reins
of his horse, dug his spurs quickly into her sides and
rode off after the marching column without even noticing Matthews' surprised face.

Dim now and fragmentary, the scenes of his youth
rose through his mind. In the growing darkness the
lights of his father's house burning, and he outside,
late for supper and afraid to go in. Jerry's voice in
the twilight... "A licking ain't so bad—it can't hurt
forever ..." "He'll never dare touch me—it's not
that. . . ." Jerry had been through the war as a
Confederate officer since then—and now he was
wounded!

# Friday, April 14

His horse had slowed its pace and was moving along the Avenue at a walk. Booth suddenly realized that he had no desire to speak to this boy who had become a stranger to him. He let his horse have its head and he rode on, thinking about the war and the effect it had had on the lives of people he had known.

For four years he had seen his friends drawn into it on both sides of the struggle, and many of them had bid the world a mute farewell in the form of a name in small type on a casualty list. He had promised his mother that he would never enlist, never serve with arms the cause he supported secretly. Actually it had not been difficult to keep that promise. Much as he loved the South, the idea of fighting in the ranks had never appealed to him. He was not afraid of hardship or danger or death, but he dreaded the thought of having his body mutilated by shell or shrapnel. The legless and armless men who were now flooding the country as strange new products of war were loathsome to him, incomplete and horrible creatures that were surely better dead. And army life with its stern discipline was a mode of existence he could never tolerate. He could not imagine himself being made subordinate to some stupid officer who could command his existence utterly. He could never permit himself to be flung upon the battlefield to sacrifice his life in taking a hillock or a trench that meant so little actually in the major conduct of the war. He was willing enough to meet death in the enterprise in which he was now engaged, for it was *his* enterprise. He was its originator and its moving force, and the goal it would accomplish was of a greatness commensurate with his own.

He had already done much to help the South. In his passage from city to city as an actor, a person no one would bother to suspect, he had often carried messages and secret information across the border. He had smuggled badly needed quinine through to the blockaded States. He had done everything in his power to assist his country and he had often exposed himself to arrest, imprisonment and death by his activities.

He had come to have a contempt for the stupidity of Northern officials. They had never even suspected him, never made a serious effort to search him. He had passed through their defenses easily. He was clever and they were stupid. He would always be able to get away through their clumsy fingers. They would never take John Wilkes Booth.

And yet he knew that blockade-runners did get caught, and that spies were hanged without mercy or delay. The risks he had run had often brought the notion of his own death close to him, and he had brooded over it with long self-searching. But it was something he could not seriously entertain—it seemed too utterly impossible.

He felt that somehow he had always existed—certainly he could remember no origin, no beginning.

76

# Friday, April 14

The memory of his life ran back into his childhood years until it became gray and indistinct, but it never stopped abruptly anywhere, so that at one point he could say: "Then I began to exist and before that I did not." The world he saw through his eyes, heard with his ears, smelled through his nostrils, tasted with his tongue, felt with his fingers, and became most aware of when the sudden sharp stab of physical pain ran through injured flesh, was a world that had actual existence only in his own mind. External things, even people, became tangible and real only when they touched his own existence. *What do these dream-shadows matter that walk the world in my waking sleep?* But that this world should have an end seemed absurd, for it had never had a beginning, and that he himself could stop was obviously nonsense. *What would there be left?*

On the stage he had taken the cup of poison to his lips night after night, and night after night he had died, only to rise again. He had often thought: What if the poison tonight is real, and I were to feel it spreading through my veins with the cold brittleness of death invading my body? But the cup, of course, had held only water, placed there for him by the faithful property man, and he had always got up from the stage floor to realize that he was still alive and that the future extended limitlessly before him.

And yet how easy it was to die! Life passed with an easy casualness through the flesh that housed it. Every beach in the world was littered with the debris of death, and every forest was rooted in the decayed bones of its ancestors. All the earth was a great burial ground piled higher and higher every year with the castoff bodies which life had used up. Only in himself could he feel the pulse of life beating; only through his own eyes could he look out upon a world that was perhaps nothing more than the creation of his own mind.

Around him the street traffic surged, and his horse, unguided, ambled idly along the Avenue. The buildings of the city, mean little brick houses and even meaner little houses of wood, stretched far away with an occasional Government office looming above them. Why should any part of this city exist, except that part which my eyes see now? he thought. Were I to enter another street, a new series of buildings would spring into existence because my mind would bring it into being. He looked around at the sun-flooded street. It appeared to him suddenly to be like a stage set, insubstantial, painted on canvas to give the illusion of reality. He closed his eyes and shook his head. As his eyes opened, the scene was still before him, unchanged, but still unconvincing.

Then along the Avenue he noticed a carriage coming toward him with a soldier riding behind it. On the box, sitting with the driver, was a man with a bearded face. Booth stared at him. He had never seen him before, but the face was entirely familiar. He

78

realized suddenly that he was looking at General Grant. There were two women inside the carriage, and luggage was piled on the back.

He followed them until a traffic block gave him an opportunity to speak to the mounted guard.

"Isn't that General Grant?" he asked casually.

The guard grunted and looked at him suspiciously.

"I thought he was going to be at Ford's Theater tonight with the President," Booth persisted. "A lot of people are going to be disappointed."

"That's just too bad," the guard said, "but he's going to the railroad depot to get a train for Philadelphia; so they'll just have to be disappointed."

The street was clear again. The coachman on the box with Grant clucked to his horses. The carriage moved on, and the guard followed it, grinning sardonically at Booth.

So Grant wasn't going to be at the theater! Well, that would make it just so much easier for him to deal with Lincoln. He would have to get in touch with Surratt quickly, in order to tell him to follow Grant on the train. It was after five o'clock. Surratt should be back at his hotel by this time. He turned his horse toward the Herndon House and spurred her into a gallop.

Surratt had not yet returned. Booth waited for him impatiently in the hall on the floor where his room was located. Finally he saw Surratt's thin figure coming up the stairs. He hurried him into his room and, as soon as the door was closed, he told him about Grant.

"We can't let him get away," he said excitedly. "He's the best General the North has."

Surratt was startled. "I didn't expect anything like this," he said, avoiding Booth's eyes.

"Neither did I, but we have to adapt our plans to the circumstances. That's the first rule of warfare. Come on, hurry up, or you'll miss the train. It must be the one that leaves at six o'clock—at least I think so. That's the only one he can get now. Were you able to arrange everything?"

Surratt nodded as he dragged his carpet bag from under the bed. "You'll have plenty of help, all right. Our cause has good friends here."

"Don't you think it's about time you tell me who they are?" Booth asked. "I'm risking my life in this venture. I surely have a right to know."

"I'd like to tell you, Wilkes, but I can't. I've sworn not to tell anyone—anyone at all. Not even you. You can depend on these men though. They mean business, and they want Lincoln out of the way just as much as you do."

"But, good God, I'm chancing more than they are! I might at least be permitted to know with whom I am working. They know about me. Certainly they must trust me. Even if I were captured alive—which I never will be—I would never tell—"

# Friday, April 14

Surratt crammed his clothing into the bag. "You wouldn't ask me to violate an oath, would you, Wilkes? I told you I had to swear—"

"I don't ask you for their names. You know that. I'm only trying to find out what sort of people they are." An uneasy thought crossed his mind. "Are they Richmond people? Are they—"

"Wilkes, I can't tell you anything about them," Surratt said desperately. "I'm sorry, but I just can't. You'll have to trust me. You know that I wouldn't— Well, you've got to trust me. I assure you that everything is all right. You'll get more assistance than you ever dreamed of. We'll all have a good chance of getting away scot free."

"I hope you're right," Booth said gloomily. "I'll have to do the job in the theater alone now. I had hoped to have you with me—"

"Why don't you let Atzerodt help you?"

"I told you that I need him to take care of Andy Johnson."

"Maybe you'd better take him with you, Wilkes, and let Johnson go. He's not important. George could hold your horse if you don't trust him to help you inside the theater."

Booth shook his head stubbornly. "I can handle Lincoln alone if I have to. I'll get one of the stagehands to hold my horse."

"You don't really think that George Atzerodt is going to attack Johnson single-handed, do you?"

"That's a chance I have to take. I'd have Davy Herold do it, but he has to guide Lewis out of the city. Lewis won't let Atzerodt help him. I have to make the best use I can of my men now. There's no time to try to get anyone else."

"You'd do better to turn Atzerodt loose and forget about Johnson," Surratt said, pushing his luggage toward the door. "Atzerodt is the sort who might spoil all our plans."

Booth was impatient. "Let me worry about him. Are you ready now? You'll have to move fast to catch that train."

"All ready, Wilkes. I'll get it all right. I'm used to catching trains at the last minute."

"You have a revolver, of course?"

"Of course."

"Good-by, then, and good luck. The South will always remember what we are going to do for her tonight. We need no other reward."

"Good-by. If all goes well I'll see you in Spain some day—I hope."

They shook hands solemnly.

"Hurry now," Booth told him, clasping his shoulder. "Don't miss that train—and don't miss!"

In the narrow alley in back of Ford's Theater, Booth could always be sure of a welcome from the stagehands who were flattered by the attentions of a well-known actor. Several of them were sitting around the stage door, smoking quietly and talking. Some Negroes who lived in the little shacks among the stables were leaning against the north wall, interestedly watching the white men at play. This alley was a democratic place, far removed from the elegance of the front of the theater. It was shabby and dirty and plain, but Booth liked it because the men who worked there admired him.

He rode toward the group at the stage door and waved a greeting to them.

"That's a nice horse you have there, Mr. Booth," Ed Spangler said. He had worked as a carpenter when Booth's father was building his new house at Belair, and although he had known Booth ever since childhood, he insisted on calling him "Mister" now that he was a famous actor.

"What do you know about horses, Ed?" one of the men said tauntingly. "I thought you were a fisherman."

"A crab fisherman, too," said Maddox, who was the property man. "Real fishing is too hard work for him. All a crab fisher has to do is sit and wait."

"Well, now, Ed ought to be right smart at doing that. He's got the sort of bottom that's just made for sitting."

"You bet he's good at it," Maddox jeered. "Why, he even steals drop ropes off the set so he can steal crabs off the deepest bottoms in the river. He's a bottom-scratcher, all right."

# The Man Who Killed Lincoln

"What do you do with all them crabs, Ed?"

Spangler glowered at the men's laughter. He hated to be made fun of in front of Booth, who was sitting idly in the saddle, smiling good-naturedly.

"He took a rope away from here the other day that was long enough to reach down to Hell and snag the Devil out," Maddox went on. "He had it wound around his middle under his shirt, so no one could see what he had."

"You're a damned liar," Spangler snapped, "and I don't have to—"

This was getting serious, Booth decided. Spangler had taken the rope for him. It was lying now in the attic of the tavern at Surrattsville, where it had been placed with other articles that were to have been used in the abduction plot.

"Easy," he said, coming forward as peacemaker. "Don't pay any attention to what they say, Ed. They're only trying to make fun of you."

There was a moment of silence. Spangler stood up, and in a quiet voice said:

"Do you want me to put your horse away in the stable, Mr. Booth?"

"Thanks, Ed," Booth said lightly. "First I want to show you gentlemen how nicely she runs—just like a little cat." He made the mare rear up on her hind legs. She got off to a fast start and galloped down the full length of the alley, wheeled and came back again. She

84

stood in front of the men, dancing lightly and flinging her head high.

"She's r'arin' to go, all right," Maddox said admiringly. "Where'd you get her? She's real smart."

"Pumphrey's," Booth said. "She's a new horse there."

"She's a dandy." Maddox went over to her and tried to pat her nose. The mare backed away from him, tossing her head. Spangler snickered.

"Shall I put her away now?" he asked, taking the bridle in his hand.

Booth swung to the ground. "All right, Ed, put her in the stable, but leave the saddle and bridle on. I'll need her again soon. Hurry back and have a drink with me and the boys."

After Spangler had stabled the horse, they all went into a restaurant next door to the theater. Booth ordered whiskey for the group, and, as he stood drinking at the bar with the stagehands, he asked Spangler if the President's box had been made ready for the evening's performance. He was told that it had.

As soon as the men went off to get their early suppers, Booth slipped back to the alley, passed through the unguarded stage door and crossed the darkened stage. Then he jumped down into the pit, ran up the stairs to the dress circle and entered the passageway to the state box. The front of the box had been draped with flags; the usual stiff seats had been taken out and replaced with a sofa and several upholstered chairs.

# The Man Who Killed Lincoln

At the rear—nearest the entrance—a large rocking chair had been placed—evidently for the President.

Luck had been with him all day, he thought. This chair made it possible for him to know exactly where Lincoln would sit. The chair was in an ideal position now—no need to move it. He stepped back into the passageway and examined the inner door that led into the box. Then he took a gimlet out of his pocket and bored a hole through a panel. He closed the door and peered through the hole. It was too small for him to see through it clearly. He opened his pocket knife and made it larger. Now he could see the dim outlines of the back of the armchair.

He went back through the narrow passageway to the outer door and struck a match. At some previous time the door had been forced open. The lock was broken; the screw hinges were loosened. There was no way to fasten the door from the inside. He lit a cigar and stood for a few moments in the passageway quietly puffing at it. A wooden stick three or four feet long could be braced against the wall to block the door, he decided. He made his way down to the stage again and searched through the scattered piles of scenery. Finally he found a broken music-stand support that would serve his purpose. He returned to the box with it and tried it against the door. It slipped off the smooth wall as soon as pressure was brought against it. He would have to make a hole in the plaster to keep the butt from slipping.

## Friday, April 14

He felt around in his pockets and brought out a little leather-covered notebook. In a pocket in the back of it were several photographs of women. He took one—a picture of the actress Effie Germon—grinning as he did so, and held it against the wall under the spot where he had to make the hole. He dug into the soft plaster with his knife and caught the chips with the picture. He drew hard on his cigar, so that a tiny circle of red light illuminated the wall as he worked. He dumped the plaster into his coat pocket and put the picture away in his notebook. Now the wooden bar held perfectly, closing the door firmly against any intrusion. He hid the stick behind the door and walked out into the dress circle.

Someone was crossing the stage. He hastily sat down on one of the seats, covering the lighted cigar with his hat. He surely could not be seen from the stage in the darkness. Whoever it was went away quickly, and then Booth sauntered downstairs and out into the open air. The afternoon was almost gone.

He took his horse from the stable and rode out of the alley. He stopped for a moment at the Herndon House on the next block to leave a message there for Lewis Paine, telling him that he would visit him at eight o'clock. Then he rode back to his hotel for dinner and a few minutes' rest.

# PART THREE

★

---
---

## FORD'S THEATRE
*Tenth Street, above E*

---

Friday Evening, April 14th, 1865

---

*This Evening
the Performance will be honored
by the presence of*

PRESIDENT LINCOLN

---
---

BENEFIT AND LAST NIGHT OF

*Miss* LAURA KEENE

in

Tom Taylor's Celebrated Eccentric Comedy,
as originally produced in America by Miss Keene,
and performed by her upwards of
one thousand nights,

entitled

OUR AMERICAN COUSIN

---

# 3

---

*Friday, April 14. Evening*

---

BOOTH opened his trunk and took out of it a single-barreled Deringer pistol. He pulled back the hammer and snapped the trigger to make certain that it was in perfect working order. Then he loaded the barrel carefully and placed a percussion cap under the hammer. His fingers closed around the tiny wooden stock, and the weapon, which was only six inches long, lay in his hand completely concealed. He would have only one shot, one chance. If the gun misfired he would be forced to use his knife, but his mind shrank from the thought of having to plunge its blade into the back of the unsuspecting man who would be sitting in the box. The pistol was so much more remote, so much more impersonal in its action, and, above all, if he succeeded with it, he would not have to touch the body of the man he was going to kill.

He took out a false beard and some material he could use for disguising himself. He had already

91

scornfully rejected the idea of entering the theater in disguise, since he wanted to be identified as the slayer of his country's enemy, but he saw no reason why he should not employ such a device if he needed it during his flight afterwards.

He lay down on the bed. The dark little room was close and stuffy. The furniture and carpet had a smell of ancient dust about them that even the fresh air of springtime coming through the open window could not dispel. He could hear the street sounds that always seem to be unduly loud at night, and, as he looked at the ceiling, he could see vague shadows move across it.

What I am going to do now, he thought, will break my life sharply into halves that can never be joined together again. From now on I shall have to be another person, a fugitive who can never return to this land.

The image of his father's house recurred to him. All the years of his childhood had been associated with that house, and with the broad level land around it. Through the rooms where he had played as a boy he could see his mother's figure moving. He saw her silhouetted against the diamond-paned windows when she came to wake him in the morning sunlight of a summer day. He could see her among the flowers in the garden, standing, too, under the big sycamore tree on the lawn. Day turned into night, the seasons changed, rain came pounding down on the tin roof of the house, sweeping the leaves along with it. Snow

92

covered all the world with a whiteness that made the ceiling of his room glow with light. In this spectral half-light he saw her again, standing beside his bed with a shawl over her shoulders; and when she had gone he could hear her footsteps, slow and uncertain, moving along the bare resonant halls.

The big brick house in which Booth had spent the years of his adolescence was dearer to him than any other place on earth. He liked it because it was associated with his mother. His father had built it, but he had not lived to see it finished. He had dwelt only in the old house, a small log structure still standing on the lawn near the new building. Junius Brutus Booth's presence lingered in that low-ceilinged cottage, and his son tried to avoid the place as much as he could.

Until Booth was almost fourteen years old, his life had been dominated by the unpredictable actions of the celebrated but eccentric actor who had been his father. The little cottage would suddenly be filled with a cantankerous old man who stormed about, criticized everything, and then, just as suddenly, was gone again on one of his acting tours.

It was only after his father had died that Booth realized how much he had hated and feared him. His death had been a tremendous relief, removing the ever-present threat of his return to a household that, so far as Booth was concerned, managed to get along very well without him.

# The Man Who Killed Lincoln

Certainly the old gentleman had been a very difficult person to have around. Even when sober, he was sullen and moody. When drunk, he was completely irrational and perverse. At all times he was unpredictable. He could not tolerate physical cruelty of any kind; he never laid a hand on one of his children, yet he made their lives miserable by his taunts and jeers. He could be charming, malicious or indifferent, and it was impossible to tell just what state of mind he would be in next. He was as whimsical as a Shakespearean clown, and he possessed a mordant humor that sometimes impelled him to do things bordering on the ridiculous.

Vivid in Booth's memory was an incident of his childhood: His father had become tremendously attached to a little pony which had grown old in his service. When the pony was dying, he had the servants bring a mattress out to the stable so the little animal could lie on a soft bed. As soon as the pony had died, he made his wife attend a ceremonial funeral service, dressing her up in a white sheet and forcing her to sit on the carcass. The children watched in frightened wonder as their father walked solemnly around the dead animal with a gun in one hand and a Bible in the other. The first was to ward off any human interference; the other was to invoke heavenly aid for the soul of the defunct beast. It was a part of Junius Brutus Booth's personal creed that all living creatures had immortal souls, and he often made a nuisance of himself with his evangelical efforts in behalf of the animal kingdom. He read the services in his deep impressive voice, and wept genuine tears of sorrow for his beloved pony.

Stories of his father's eccentricities had come back to Booth during the years after his death. And he learned something else about him, something that he would mention to no one, dreading to hear it confirmed. He had been told that his father had had a previous wife, some common person with whom he had made a youthful misalliance in England. And, according to backstage gossip, Junius Brutus had never been divorced from her, so that he was not legally married to his second wife.

If this story was true, then he, John Wilkes Booth, was of illegitimate birth, and, worse still, his adored mother had been tricked into a false marriage. Booth was careless enough about his own relations with women not to take much stock in the sanctity of wedlock, but when it came to his mother he was fiercely resentful of anything that might injure her good name. He hated his father for this crime against his mother. And he could attribute to him the years of misery during which he had never been free from the fear that someone would call him bastard to his face.

Nor was illegitimacy the only inheritance for which Booth had his father to thank. The family had always looked upon Junius Brutus' quirks of mind as aberrations of genius, but Booth realized that his

95

father had not been entirely sane. He had searched his own mind for evidences of any taint, and he had finally convinced himself that there were none. But he knew that the possibility was always there, and he was afraid. What he was now about to do, of course, was not the irresponsible act of a madman. His mind was too vividly clear, he knew. He could marshal the reasons for his contemplated deed with inexorable logic. It was true that he had been dwelling for months on the idea of striking a blow against Lincoln until the idea had become such a part of his existence that it lived with him even during his sleep. But this was due simply to his great devotion to a cause—a cause, furthermore, that was of such tremendous importance that it transcended every interest he had ever had. His hatred of Lincoln had become the dominant motive of his life. He was ready to sacrifice anything —anything—to kill the man. He admitted to himself that the whole abduction plot had been a blind. Once Lincoln had fallen into his hands he would surely have done away with him. The very thought of the man's face, of his hideous and repulsive body, made him want to stamp him out like a spider. . . .

And then through his memory, misted over with the half-recollections of sleep, rose some of the disjointed and irrelevant images of the symbolic Lincoln that haunted his dreams. The man had always appeared to him, not in his normal Washington surroundings, but in Belair, in the little cottage in which

# Friday, April 14. Evening

Booth had been raised as a child. He had seen him lurking in the dark twisted rooms, ready to spring out at him from the shadows around the chimney corner. He had seen his figure stalking across the fields like a giant, searching for him under trees and bushes, and reaching his enormous hand through the windows to pluck him out of his own bed. He remembered him asking his mother where she had hidden her son . . . the creature had seized her violently . . . her screams still rang in his ears . . . and he heard the Lincoln-demon's voice booming. . . . Strange, he thought suddenly, Lincoln has a high-pitched voice, not deep at all—and then, quickly, he forced himself to stop thinking of his dreams.

The hotel room was warm and close, and the walls seemed to shut him in from the city. He thought of his mother again. She was in New York, in Edwin's house. She would surely be safe there. He had to go out now—outside on the streets. He felt lonely and afraid, like a small boy who realizes that he is going away from home for the first time to be among people who are hostile and strange. The city beyond his windows was dark and enormous. It stretched to the horizon on every side, and it was filled with soldiers and diplomats, officials and clerks, every one of whom would take up the cry against him. The army, now at the height of its wartime power, was already holding the nearer cities of the South where he might once have taken refuge.

97

# The Man Who Killed Lincoln

He took the little deringer in his hand. The feel of it gave him strength. The simple pressure of his finger on the trigger would send thunder crashing into the world to obliterate the monster Lincoln. This one small weapon might have a greater effect than all the huge mortars, howitzers and cannon that had been fired during the last four years. His single shot would start their mighty voices roaring again. . . . He would snatch victory at this last moment. . . . He heard the people of the South acclaiming him. . . . No actor in all the world's history had ever had such an ovation.

And yet he might fail. He might be stopped before he reached Lincoln's side. Someone in the box might strike up his hand. And how could he be certain that the pistol would fire? He began to walk up and down the room with the deringer in his hand, his finger held loosely over the trigger.

The fate of a nation depends on the functioning of this bit of steel and wood, on the fallibility of this tiny percussion cap, he thought. He examined the little weapon carefully. Single-shot pistols were sometimes uncertain in their action and wartime percussion caps had often been known to fail. He would surely not have time to pull out another pistol if the first one misfired.

He went to the window and looked out at the street with these disturbing thoughts running through his mind. Here within the confines of this skull, he said to himself, looking out on the world through these

98

eyes, is the being that is John Wilkes Booth. From the center of this being, within a few hours now, destiny will go forth at my bidding to change the fate of nations and alter the history of mankind. In one brief instant I shall strike down the colossus that bestrides this world and shatter his image into nothingness. His name and mine will forever be associated.

He could see himself standing in the box, holding the pistol to Lincoln's head. The report of the shot would freeze the play into sudden silence, and then his moment would come. Tyranny. Tyranny. What could he say about tyranny? "Liberty! Freedom! Tyranny is dead! Run hence, proclaim, cry it about the streets." How had they phrased this in Latin when Brutus struck great Caesar down? *Libertas. Tyr— tyrannis.* . . . He knew no Latin. *Tyrannis.* . . . And then it came to him suddenly: *Sic semper tyrannis!* "Thus always to tyrants." That was the motto of Virginia, the capital State of the Confederacy. *Sic semper tyrannis!* It was the very phrase he needed. He mouthed it over, rolling the r's under his tongue.

The bells of the city began to strike eight o'clock. The metallic clangor of their tongues rolled through the dark streets. He slipped the pistol into his pocket and armed himself with several heavy revolvers and a knife.

The curtain at Ford's Theater had already been raised.

# The Man Who Killed Lincoln

The Herndon House was on Ninth Street, only a block away from Ford's Theater. Booth went upstairs without being announced and knocked on the door of Paine's room. There was a shuffling sound inside, and Paine, disheveled and morose as always, opened the door.

"Are the others here yet?" Booth asked. "It's after eight o'clock."

Paine shook his head. Booth entered the dark room. There was a heavy odor of tobacco and corn whiskey in it. He sat down and hit the sides of his chair impatiently while Paine lighted the gas.

"Why are they always late?" Booth asked petulantly. "Don't they realize—"

"You're late yourself, John," Paine said mildly.

Booth went over to the window and looked down at the street. Paine stretched himself out on the bed and yawned. He possessed, to an astounding degree, the ability to lie still and wait with immobile patience until it was necessary for him to spring into action. His training as a soldier had taught him that, and as a boy in the Southern forests he had learned the ways of the hunter. And yet, for all his self-imposed restraint, he had a temper that drove him to unwarranted deeds of violence. Booth had picked him up during a period when he was down and out in Baltimore as a result of one of these terrible outbursts. He had taken offense at some remark made by a Negro servant girl in the house where he was boarding. He

# Friday, April 14. Evening

had seized the girl by the throat. He would surely have killed her if he had not been pulled away by the other boarders who broke into his room when they heard the girl scream. In his short life this youth had seen so much violence and suffering that pain and death had come to be trivial things to him. He was capable of great devotion—he was unquestionably strongly attached to his new leader—but he could never understand that other people could feel pain, since he himself was so indifferent to it.

He was looking at Booth with doglike eyes, studying every motion he made. His master's attention was fixed on something outside the window now, so he simply made himself comfortable until Booth was ready to talk to him again.

Booth was watching a scene that was taking place in a building on the other side of the street. In a window, under the half-lowered shade, he could see a woman undressing. Her thighs were bare, and he noticed, as she leaned over to pick up some article of clothing, that she was young and not unattractive. She sat down for a moment on the bed, but its heavy solid footboard concealed her. He waited impatiently until she got up, but then she immediately moved across the room out of sight.

"Lincoln is going to be at Ford's Theater tonight," Booth said without turning around. "Are you ready for action, Lewis?"

Paine grunted.

# The Man Who Killed Lincoln

"In a few hours our work will be done. You'll be famous, Lewis. Every woman in the South will be in love with you. Our names will never be forgotten after tonight."

"Is that all you're worrying about?" Paine said. "Well, anyway, I'll be glad to get out of here. I'm awful tired of this hotel room. I've counted every God-damned flower on the wallpaper a dozen times over. I'll be glad to see some fighting now. When you fight you can forget about yourself."

"Don't tell me you're developing a case of nerves," Booth said with an amused smile.

"Nerves, hell! It's not the waiting I mind—it's the thinking. I never had to think in the army—I just had to sit around until we were ready to fight. And there was always somebody to talk to, at least. This business is different. I don't know what's going to happen. You don't tell me much. I don't get a chance to talk to the others. I don't know what I'm going to have to do. It's better to know. You can sort of chew it over beforehand...."

Booth was still looking out the window. The woman's legs had come in view again. He watched her silently, paying hardly any attention to what Paine was saying. Suddenly she came to the window and pulled the shade all the way down. Booth turned and spoke to Paine.

"I'll tell you all there is to tell," he said irritably. "I figure that the stage will be ready for me about

# Friday, April 14. Evening

ten-fifteen or ten-twenty. I have gone over the play to get the time set as closely as possible. I saw it in rehearsal this morning and I have the exact moment picked. I'm going to spoil Laura Keene's entrance. She'll be waiting in the wings to come on next."

"You never forget that you're a play actor, do you, John? Well, what about me? What do I do?"

Someone knocked on the door. Paine got up and asked quietly who it was. They recognized the rough guttural accents of Atzerodt. Paine opened the door, and the little German shambled into the room, twisting his hat in his hands.

Booth regarded him with distaste. He was a sorry-looking figure, small, rabbit-like in the way his eyes darted furtively around the room, and there was about him a perpetual cringing attitude. As usual, he was dirty, and his clothes looked as if they had been slept in for weeks. Hair grew out of his face and head in a wild profusion that intensified his natural feral appearance.

"I couldn't find Davy Herold," he said apologetically. "He said he'd be at Leary's oyster bar, but he wasn't there."

"We'll have to get started without him then," Booth said. "Time is getting short."

"Time for what?" Atzerodt asked innocently.

"Time for killing, you fool!" Paine said viciously. "What do you suppose you're here for?"

Atzerodt shrank into himself. He sat down on a

103

chair in a corner and looked at the floor. Paine motioned impatiently to Booth.

"Go on, John," he said. "I told you this German rat would curl up his tail when the time came for action."

Atzerodt kept looking at the floor.

"George will be all right," Booth said encouragingly. "I'm depending on him to play a very important part in what we are going to do."

"Get on with it, John. Don't waste time on him."

Paine sat down on the bed and leaned against the wall. He kept studying Atzerodt's face, watching every fleeting change of expression that passed across the little man's mobile features as he listened to what Booth was saying. Atzerodt's misery was obvious, but he said nothing. He sat very still, avoiding Paine's cool stare. His head was hunched down below his shoulders, and he kept turning his ragged old hat nervously in his hands.

Booth finished his explanation. "Now as to your parts," he said, standing up and looking over Atzerodt's head at Paine. "Lewis, you are to take care of Seward. He shouldn't give you much trouble."

"How am I going to find his house?"

"Maybe I could show him?" Atzerodt suggested eagerly. "I could hold his horse, too."

"You could not!" Paine snapped. "I don't want you anywheres near me. I'll get Davy Herold to show me the way."

## Friday, April 14. Evening

"I have work cut out for you, George," Booth said. "You've been keeping a close watch on Andy Johnson as I told you to, haven't you? You know where his room is now?"

"I guess so."

"Well, do you or don't you?"

"I know."

"Very well, then. At exactly quarter after ten you go to that room and demand to see Johnson. Force your way in if you have to." Paine struggled to choke down his laughter. Booth quieted him with a peremptory gesture. "Have your knife in hand. Use it! It will make less noise than a pistol."

Atzerodt's hands were shaking visibly.

"Well?" Booth asked sharply.

"I—I can't do it, Mr. Booth. I never was much good at that sort of thing. I bargained to let you use my boat—"

"You filthy little rat!" Paine jumped off the bed and started toward Atzerodt.

"Leave him alone, Lewis," Booth said in a quiet voice. "I have something to tell him that may change his mind."

Atzerodt shrank back in his chair, whimpering.

"Listen to me, George," Booth said. "You're in this as much as we are. I've written a letter to *The National Intelligencer*, telling them what we are going to do, and your name is signed to it as well as ours. They'll have that letter in the morning. Furthermore, I put a card in Andy Johnson's letter-box that will implicate all of us. You've got to act with us or you'll hang by yourself."

Atzerodt stared up at Booth dumbly. Paine reached out a menacing hand.

"Stop it, Lewis," Booth said. "George is going to help us; aren't you, George?"

Atzerodt nodded feebly. There was a knock at the door. Atzerodt looked up hopefully, but it was only Davy Herold. He came into the room with his small eyes opening wide at the sight of Paine standing threateningly over Atzerodt's seated figure. Booth barked at Herold angrily for being late. He smiled good-naturedly and tried to explain that he had not received the message until the last minute. He sat down meekly on the bed. He looked like a schoolboy as he sat there staring around the room, a silly air of expectancy on his face.

"Do I have to go over all this again?" Booth said. "Lewis, you tell David about our plans, and explain what he is to do. He knows where Seward lives. I want to talk to George for a few minutes."

He took Atzerodt aside and tried to persuade him that he had no choice but to help them. The man was so frightened that he agreed to everything Booth said, but it was obvious, even to Booth, that he would probably be useless to them. Finally, Paine finished with Herold. The two men stood looking silently at Booth and Atzerodt. Booth walked over to them.

106

# Friday, April 14. Evening

"We have very little time left now," he said. "I want you two to be at Seward's house at precisely ten-fifteen. David will hold the horses and stand guard outside. The house is on Lafayette Square near Augur's headquarters, so you'll need a lookout. That's where you come in, David. Lewis, I don't need to give many instructions to an old soldier like you. I would suggest that you represent yourself as a messenger from the family's doctor. David can pick up some sort of medicine from a drug store and find out the name of Seward's doctor for you. Once you get inside, it's your business to discover in which room the gentleman is lying. The rest is up to you. Is everything clear?"

Paine grunted assent.

"I want you to time your actions carefully with mine," Booth continued. "That's why it's important that you enter the house at exactly quarter after ten. The actual work shouldn't take you more than five minutes, if everything goes well. Then David will lead the way through the city to the Navy Yard Bridge and guide you to Surrattsville."

He glanced at Atzerodt who was still sitting in his chair, clutching at his hat. "George has agreed to help us. He's going to the Kirkwood House, and he will enter Johnson's room at the same time we all strike. That will be three of these damned Yankee officials out of the way—Lincoln, Seward and Johnson. John Surratt is on the train with Grant. If he is successful, we'll get Grant too. Surratt has persuaded certain people here in Washington to help us. The telegraph wires will go out of commission at ten-thirty. It will be impossible for the Government to telegraph ahead to intercept us. We have every chance of getting away safely."

He smiled and held out his hand to Paine. "Good luck, Lewis. I know I can count on you." Paine's enormous hand gripped his in a firm grasp. He shook hands with Herold and patted him affectionately on the shoulder.

"I'll go downstairs first with George," he said. "You two can follow a few minutes later. We shall all meet at the tavern—about midnight, I suppose. Then south to Port Tobacco. We should be in Virginia by morning."

Booth's horse clattered down the narrow alley that led to the open space in back of the theater. Negro women, sitting on the steps of their shanties, ceased talking as they heard the horse approach. It was completely dark except for the light of a single lamp over the stage entrance at the far end of the alley. No one was in sight near the theater. Booth dismounted and led his horse to the doorway. He stepped inside, holding the reins over his arm. A man was standing in the passageway near the door.

"Tell Ned Spangler to come out here for a minute, will you?" Booth asked quietly.

## Friday, April 14. Evening

The man recognized him and sauntered off in search of Spangler. Booth examined the mare's saddle-girth. He made sure that the deringer was in his pocket and he loosened his bowie knife in its sheath. Then he looked up at the narrow slit of sky where the stars were shining between scattered clouds. Rain would be fatal. It would turn the clay roads of Southern Maryland into a morass of sticky impassable mud. There were so many things beyond his control, he thought, so many things that could defeat him. Courage, even reckless courage, was not enough. The little gods of chance that can cause a pistol to misfire, or a blundering guard to get in the way, must withhold their spitefulness now, or he would fail and be lost.

The Negro women began to talk again. He could hear the soft murmur of their voices coming from the darkness beyond the circle of light around the stage door. He patted the smooth flank of his horse, and she turned her head inquiringly to look at him.

Now the moment is fast approaching, he said to himself, forming the words on his lips as though he were speaking to another person. When I come out of this doorway I shall have finished forever with the role of the admired young actor, John Wilkes Booth, and I shall have thrust upon me a new part wherein I play the fugitive with a snarling, shouting crowd at my heels. The hatred of twenty million Northerners will follow me always, and wherever I go men will look at me and whisper: "He is the man who killed Lincoln."

The narrow alley, with its odor of stables and shanties, seemed to him to be a ludicrously inappropriate waiting place for an actor who was about to take the leading role in a drama of world-shaking importance. The occasion called for a more impressive background. He remembered Shakespeare's description of what had taken place in Rome on the eve of Caesar's death.

He closed his eyes, shutting out the commonplace scene before him. As the magic words coursed through his mind, the fiery warriors fighting in the clouds and the ghosts shrieking and squealing in the Roman streets, became as real to him as they had been to Calphurnia. There should be some portent, some omen in this placid Washington sky, he thought. What I am going to do is no less than what Brutus did.

He opened his eyes suddenly, half-expecting to see something unusual. But only the brick wall of the theater was in front of him, pierced by the dark rectangle of the stage doorway. He stared at the opening, and as he looked fixedly into its blackness, the thought occurred to him that he had lived through this moment before. Somewhere he had waited like this, waited to kill. The face and figure of a man rose up out of his memory, and he felt that he would now at last be able to find out who it was. Then Spangler came out of the doorway, cursing angrily, and the image he had been trying to recall was rudely shattered.

"Damn it! I can't be ordered out here like this, Mr. Booth," the man was saying. "I've got to be on the stage. They'll be changing sets in a few minutes. I can't stand here holding a horse."

"Then get somebody who can," Booth told him peremptorily. "I have business here that can't wait. But be sure the horse is held here for me."

He thrust the reins into Spangler's unwilling hands and asked him if the President had arrived. The man nodded sullenly. Booth swung around and entered the theater.

"May I cross the stage now?" he whispered to someone standing inside.

"No. The dairy scene has just gone on, and the stage is open all the way back. You can't get across. Go down underneath."

He stood for a few minutes in the wings, looking out at the brilliantly lighted stage. The actors moved about busily, eager to catch a laugh from the audience seated out in the black void beyond the footlights. Tall piles of scenery were stacked around him, and he could smell the familiar odor of paint, hot gaslight and freshly cut lumber.

The sight of the play being enacted before him gave him new courage. What he had to do seemed very simple now. He had only to walk on to play his

111

part as he had done a thousand times before. He had killed dozens of men with sword and pistol—on the stage. He had made all sorts of desperate gestures—on the stage. What he was about to do now could not be so very different. He had only to wait for his cue: "Don't know the manners of good society, eh?" And there was plenty of time, plenty of time before he would be called upon to act. He would have a chance to reinforce himself with brandy as he always did before undertaking the performance of a new and difficult part.

He went down the stairs to the understage passage and walked through, groping in the darkness. He could hear the shuffling of feet on the boards overhead, and the players' voices came to him as disembodied sounds, permeating the blackness with the strange senseless quality of words chattered in delirium. Words like these were too dangerously close to the echoes of sounds that sometimes rose up from the depths of his own mind, terrifying him with their insistent urging, their dark summoning. . . . He was glad when he got beyond their reach into the open street in front of the theater.

The sidewalk was brightly illuminated. Two soldiers were sitting on the wooden carriage platform under a flaring gas lantern. The downward rays of the lamp threw their features into strong relief, making their eyes seem like black holes, and drawing heavy lines of shadow across their mouths. They stopped talking and stared at Booth.

Immediately he sensed danger. Perhaps these men were special guards detailed to the theater. The War Department might have learned something. . . . The image of Weichmann, waiting furtively in the hallway of Mrs. Surratt's house, came back to him. Could these soldiers have been sent here to watch the theater? And then he realized why they were looking at him. Why, of course! He was John Wilkes Booth, the famous actor. What could be more natural than for these yokels to gape at a celebrity? He turned away, stroking his mustache impressively. He had forgotten his own fame.

He looked at the clock in the lobby. It was still early. He stood and watched the scene on the sidewalk. Some curiosity-seekers, attracted by the advertised presence of the President as the guest of honor, were gazing at the playbills posted in front of the house. "Benefit and last night of Miss Laura Keene, the distinguished Manageress, Authoress and Actress . . . in Tom Taylor's celebrated eccentric comedy, as originally produced in America by Miss Keene, and performed by her upwards of one thousand nights, entitled *Our American Cousin.*" And there were announcements of a benefit for Miss Jennie Gourlay in *The Octoroon,* to be held on Saturday, April 15, and notices of a forthcoming engagement of Edwin Adams—for twelve nights only.

# The Man Who Killed Lincoln

Poor devils! Booth thought. They would surely never play their scheduled performances. He smiled grimly. The thunderbolt imprisoned in his pocket would shatter not only the lives of the great; little people, too, would have their petty plans twisted and thwarted by its mighty detonation.

He was like a god now with the power of life and death in his hands. Like a great sword, the swift force of his will would descend upon the world, cleaving through the flesh of these lesser mortals. Down, down, down, the bright blade falling, all resistance swept away before it. What did these scurrying insects matter? They were spawned upon the earth only to die. What were a few days more of their trivial existences worth? Away with them! Only he triumphant, bending a nation to his will, driving on the defeated to a new victory by the force of his example.

He paced up and down on the sidewalk. By God, at this moment he should be on the stage! Never had he felt the vast surge of energy so tremendous within him. He could move an audience to tears, to shouts, to wild salvos of applause. It was a pity that he had to wait until after ten o'clock. He wished that he could leap upon the stage now, to stand defiant before the footlights, bringing the flaming spirit of war and vengeance to these Yankees who were sitting in the theater, smug with the thought that victory was already theirs. But they would never forget this coming moment, never forget this single figure who would fling the cry "Unconquered!" in their faces while they sat helpless in the very heart of their own Northern citadel.

And then beside him, someone walking, someone speaking to him. He stopped abruptly. It was Lewis Carland, the costumer of the theater, a soft little man with the low whining voice of one who is destined to life's perpetual defeats. He was puffing on a cigar that seemed enormous in his small silly mouth. Booth felt that he would like to pick the fellow up and break him between his hands like a pulpy log of rotted wood.

Carland backed away, taking the cigar from his mouth. His face, in the white glare of the street light, looked like some monstrous-eyed fish with its mouth gaping open.

"What's the matter, Mr. Booth?" he said, still moving away. "Is something wrong?"

Booth smiled, and in the soft voice of conciliation said: "Wrong? Why, no, of course not, Mr. Carland. You simply surprised me while I was going over my new part."

Carland laughed nervously. "Oh, you actors—always trying to live your parts. I know how you are. I'd have gone in for acting seriously myself if I had only had the figure for it. It was a pleasure to play with you in *The Apostate*. You were magnificent."

He had been pressed into service in one of the minor

115

roles of this play when Booth had acted here for a single performance during the previous month. It was evident that he would never forget the experience.

Booth kept walking. Carland tagged along at his heels.

"What sort of part are you going to play, Mr. Booth? I'll bet it's a tragic part, isn't it? Tragedy suits you best, you know. Comedy parts are all right for men like Harry Hawk, but they never really get you anywhere—" He waved his short little arm in a circle. "You were really superb as Pescara." He stopped, drew back his foot and thrust out his hand as though he had a sword in it. "Ha! ha! a Moor— one of that race we have trodden down from empire's height and crushed—a damned Morisco! . . . Rise, Spaniards, rise! Rush on these slaves and revel in their blood!" People were staring at him, but he was oblivious of the attention he was attracting.

"I see that you have a just appreciation of the tragic role," Booth said gravely.

Carland laid his hand on Booth's arm. Booth gently pulled his own arm away and stepped back from the round perspiring face. Carland's eyes fell.

"Tell me what sort of role you're preparing for now, Mr. Booth," he said. "I'll design a costume for it that will do you justice."

"I'm awfully sorry, but I can't say anything about it yet. I've promised not to discuss it with anyone."

## Friday, April 14. Evening

"I understand. You shouldn't either. There's a lot of nasty jealousy in our profession. It doesn't pay to tell everyone of your plans, but you know I can be discreet. . . ."

"I'm sorry. I really can't tell you. You startled me into mentioning the fact that I was preparing a new part, or I wouldn't have said anything about it at all. Please don't tell anyone. . . ."

"Of course, of course." Carland sighed heavily. "Well, anyway," he said finally, "we expect great things of you, Mr. Booth. You have a magnificent tradition to carry on. I remember your father, although I was only a boy when I saw him. A wonderful man. You are living in a more fortunate era. The theater is going to have a period of prosperity now that the war is over. People will want entertainment, art, fine things. . . . You'll see. Even the poor bleeding South will rebuild her temples to our art."

Booth had always suspected that Carland was a Southern sympathizer, but he had refrained from discussing political matters with him because he felt that the man was a fool, unworthy of trust. He began to walk again. Carland followed him.

Carland threw out another feeler. "You will surely return to the stage in Richmond and New Orleans, won't you? Those cities will be glad to welcome you again. . . ."

Booth motioned vaguely. Damn the fellow! Would he never stop talking? Why did he have to listen to the endless babbling of this dapper little tailor?

Gifford, the stage carpenter, walked toward them, solid, substantial, puffing energetically at his pipe as he came. His stubby-bearded face broke into a momentary smile of greeting.

"Talking about the war, I'll wager."

Carland nodded curtly. Gifford took his pipe from his mouth and spat into the gutter.

"Well, there isn't much else worth talking about these days, is there? I suppose Mr. Carland here has been describing the finer strategic points of the recent campaign in Virginia," he said to Booth as he knocked the ashes out of his pipe. "He's the one to do it, too. The man is a born general—he certainly should be in the field. I never could understand how a man like him could stay out of the army."

Carland shifted about uneasily. Gifford, evidently enjoying himself, went on speaking. "Of course, I never could quite figure out just which side General Carland would fight on, but that really doesn't matter much, does it? I'm sure either side would be glad to have him. It's a shame—such a waste of talent." He rubbed some tobacco briskly between his hands in order to fill his pipe which he seldom allowed to cool.

Carland looked up at Booth as if seeking his support. Booth's face was stonily unresponsive. Carland turned to Gifford. "The science of military tactics

# Friday, April 14. Evening

has nothing to do with fighting in the field," he began. Gifford guffawed. "Besides we weren't talking about the war," he went on feebly. "We were discussing the South—her chances for recovery, and—and things like that."

"Aye, it's time to stop talking of war now, I suppose," Gifford said, cramming the tobacco into his pipe. "Recovery, reconstruction, rebuilding, reconciliation—all 'R's' too, aren't they?—anyway, they're the order of the day now. Well, it's going to be a hard time ahead of us, a precious hard time. I shouldn't like to have the job of the man who's sitting in the state box of this theater right now. There's too much bitterness about, and a hard cruel bitterness it is that will go on for generations. This country can never be the same again. The old easy days are gone forever."

"But there's great prosperity ahead, too," Carland said hotly. "We'll have to build up the country again—"

"We'll build it up all right. Nothing will stop this country from growing; but mark my words, the days to come are going to be hard ones, with hard, selfish men in control. I've watched what's been happening. I've seen how some men have made fortunes from this war. They're going to keep right on making fortunes, and God help anyone who gets in their way!"

He lighted his pipe, drew on it and blew out a cloud of smoke that hung in the windless air. Booth shrugged his shoulders. This philosophical carpenter had amused him in the past, but he only irritated him now.

He looked at the lobby clock that was marking away the minutes to ten o'clock. They would be talking about him tomorrow, these philosophical carpenters and strategy-minded tailors. His name would be on the lips of every cracker-barrel commentator in the country. They would all have a new factor to contend with in their discussions of the problems of war and peace.

He turned away from the two men to look down the street toward Pennsylvania Avenue. Someone in uniform was approaching, beckoning to him as he came. Booth stepped quickly away from Gifford and Carland and put his hand in the pocket where he had placed his pistol. The man in uniform entered the circle of lamplight, calling out a hearty greeting to Booth. It was Captain Williams of the Washington police force, a man whom Booth knew very well.

"What's the matter, Wilkes?" he said, surprised by the startled expression on Booth's face. "You look as if you expected me to arrest you. And I must say that you seem to be prepared to make a desperate stand."

Booth laughed nervously and held out his hand to his friend.

"I thought you might want to step in somewhere for a drink with me," Williams said. "I have a wonderful little story to tell you about a certain lady who is playing right now in a theater not a million miles away from here."

Booth smiled at him, and clasped his shoulder with a show of good nature. "It breaks my heart to turn down an invitation like that, Captain, but Keene will be on the stage in a minute and I promised to look in on her performance tonight."

Williams lingered a moment, trying to persuade Booth to come with him. Finally, he went on his way, and Booth's tensed muscles relaxed. What terrible coincidence had caused this man to cross his tracks at this crucial instant? And was it a coincidence? He looked again at the two soldiers sitting on the carriage platform. They were no longer paying any attention to him, he noticed with relief.

Gifford and Carland were still talking together, but Booth gave up even the pretense of listening to them. Damn all these people who kept getting in his way! It had been a close shave with that fellow Williams. . . . He looked up at the lobby clock. The minute hand had crept forward to five minutes to ten. Paine and Herold should be riding through the streets toward Lafayette Square now. . . .

Carland and Gifford clung to him, arguing between themselves. When he moved, they moved with him as though he were a necessary audience to what they were saying. *Why do these two fools talk about the war as if it were all over?* Atzerodt's frightened face recurred to him. What was the fellow doing now? He should never have trusted him. Perhaps Paine was right. One must be ruthless in matters where great issues are concerned.

Carland suddenly announced that he had to go backstage to inspect Laura Keene's costume before she went on. Gifford still hovered about, talking now about the imminence of Johnston's surrender to Sherman. It surely must be ten o'clock, Booth thought. He tried to disengage himself from the carpenter's clutches.

"I'm going inside to see Keene's performance," he said. "Will you excuse me?"

Gifford protested that she would not be on the stage for another fifteen minutes. In desperation, Booth mumbled something about not wanting to miss her entrance and hurried toward the lobby. One minute to ten.

Buckingham, the theater's tall lanky doorkeeper, was standing with his back to the lobby. His arm barred the entrance way. Booth touched his hand lightly. Buckingham turned around, scowling.

"I guess you don't need a ticket from me, do you?" Booth asked pleasantly. The doorkeeper's long homely face cracked into a wide grin.

"No, sir, I should say not. Fact is you couldn't buy a ticket here if you wanted to. Courtesy of the house, sir." He bowed sweepingly. "Go right on in." He was proud of his acquaintance with this young star who was so democratic in his relationships with the theater's people.

He lowered his arm and stepped back, still grinning good-naturedly. Booth entered the theater. The house was well filled with an audience in which blue army uniforms predominated. The stage lights filtered back into the auditorium with a soft glow that emphasized the white shoulders of women and brought out the metallic gleam of epaulets and army insignia on the men.

The dairy set, which was used for the first scene of the third act, was on the stage, but the scene still had some time to run. Booth walked to the rear row of seats and stood behind it. The state box was brightly lighted by one of the two big chandeliers that hung over the stage, but it was difficult to see inside the box. Flags and lace curtains concealed the opening. He could just make out the forms of an army officer and a young girl in evening dress, and he could see a rather stout woman who was probably Mrs. Lincoln. Lincoln himself was hidden from the audience by the front wall of the box. Evidently the rocking chair had not been moved.

Booth walked over to look into the boxes on the other side of the stage. They were all empty. This was so unusual that it frightened him for a moment. Could there be some purpose in not selling any of the seats in the other boxes? Then he realized that this had probably been done for the protection of the

President, and the idea gave him a certain grim pleasure. It was a fortunate thing, after all, since no one could look directly across the stage into the rear part of the state box where Lincoln was seated.

Booth walked across the theater again and went up the dress-circle stairs. As he reached the top, his eyes immediately sought the little white door leading into Lincoln's box. He expected to find a guard seated at the entrance. A chair was standing there beside the door, half-hidden in the darkness, but it was empty and no one was near it. The guard had evidently wandered off in search of a better seat from which to watch the performance. All the little gods of chance were with him now, he felt, and they had even given him this unforeseen opportunity of entering the box without being challenged.

He went down the stairs, exulting. Surely destiny was on his side! Second by second the clocks of the world were eating away the life of the man he was going to kill. Paine and Herold were moving at this minute toward the Seward residence, and somewhere in the dimly lighted corridors of the Kirkwood House, Atzerodt was lying in wait for Johnson. Even Surratt, miles away from him now and speeding northward, was safely on the train with Grant.

As Booth re-entered the lobby, Buckingham was waiting eagerly to present a group of his friends to him. Booth glanced at the clock while the introductions were being made. Three minutes after ten. Not much longer to wait now. He bowed mechanically to the men as they were presented. Buckingham offered him a chew of tobacco, which he accepted. He bit into the sweet-smelling brown cake.

"When are you going to play a Shakespearean role again, Mr. Booth?" asked one of the men who were crowding around him in an admiring circle. He spoke with a pompous air through a great black beard that lent dignity to everything he said.

"Very soon, I hope," Booth replied, smiling politely at the huge beard. "Very soon indeed."

"That is very good news," the beard enunciated slowly. "I saw you play with your brothers in New York last November in *Julius Caesar*. A great performance, sir, a great performance, even though it was marred by the despicable attempts of the rebels to fire the city." The words came out importantly, discouraging the other men from trying to speak at all. Booth ignored his reference to the rebel plot and bowed in acknowledgment of the compliment. "You should bring a cast like that to our fair city," the man continued, speaking with solemnity. "You would be richly rewarded, I assure you."

Booth thanked him. It was four minutes after ten.

Buckingham was grinning happily at his friends. In less than ten minutes the fatal second scene of the third act would be on. Booth decided that he needed a drink.

One of the men offered him a cigar, a thin evil-looking stogie. He declined it gracefully, excused himself and sauntered out to the street, where he promptly got rid of the chewing tobacco. He could hear the boom of the black-beard's voice follow him as he went. Gifford was still waiting on the sidewalk, but, fortunately, he had turned away to look toward the Lincoln carriage, which was standing at the curb near F Street. Booth managed to slip past him unnoticed, to seek shelter in Peter Taltavul's barroom.

The far end of the long bar was still covered with glasses left by the theatergoers during the last intermission. Taltavul was leisurely putting the glassware on a tray. He walked forward and greeted Booth cordially.

"What'll it be this evening?" he asked, wiping the surface of the bar in front of Booth with a beer-stained rag.

"Same as usual, Peter. The brandy bottle and a glass of water."

"Quite an honor having the President next door," Taltavul commented cheerfully. "I wish he'd come oftener. It's good for business. There's a fine crowd there tonight." He pushed a bottle of brandy toward Booth and filled a glass with water.

Booth indicated that he was glad the President's visit was good for business.

"Well, to tell the truth, I can't complain about business anyway," Taltavul said, wringing out the wet rag. He leaned on the bar and thrust his grizzled face toward Booth. "Business has been very good. Yes, sir, very good. This celebration, you know...." He winked solemnly. "A lot of liquor went down the nation's gullet when Richmond fell."

Booth finished two glasses of brandy and then stepped back to see the clock at the front of the bar. Seven minutes after. They would be changing scenes in a few minutes now. Just time for another drink. He filled his glass again. This was the last drink he would ever be able to take in the city of Washington. He lifted the glass in a silent toast to the Confederacy. So many people were counting on him ... so much human happiness depended on his success ... the South ... the old South—God bless her!

Taltavul was still talking about the celebration. Booth realized that he was asking him a question.

"Sorry, Peter," he said. "I didn't hear you. What did you say?"

"Thinking about the ladies again, eh, Mr. Booth?" Taltavul chuckled. "Well, I can't blame you. I do myself sometimes. I was just asking you, did you think they would hold a big parade—you know, bring all the soldiers here to march down the Avenue, maybe?"

"Undoubtedly ... undoubtedly." Booth took up the water glass and drank from it, staring at the barkeeper over its rim. Victory, victory, victory—all these filthy little shopkeepers were thinking of nothing but victory and their own profits.

# The Man Who Killed Lincoln

"God, wouldn't that be magnificent?" Taltavul said gleefully. "All them soldier boys brought here to Washington, and every one of 'em thirsty."

Booth put some money down on the wet bar. Taltavul started to make change, but his customer had already left the saloon, humming a tune as he went.

The air outside was cool and fresh. Most of the loiterers had gone, but Gifford was still waiting. He seemed surprised to see Booth come out of Taltavul's saloon, but he immediately collared him and tried to engage him in conversation again. Booth felt that it was impossible even to attempt to be polite to the man now—he had to get rid of him quickly. The play inside was moving on, line by line, to the moment when his cue, "Don't know the manners of good society, eh?" would be spoken. He had to be in the theater before then, and he could allow nothing to stop him.

Gifford was standing in the lobby entrance, blocking his way. Booth interrupted his flow of meaningless words and asked him abruptly: "Can you see the time on the lobby clock?"

Gifford turned to look, and Booth took advantage of his movement to slip past him.

"Ten minutes after ten," Gifford announced in a loud voice. "What's your hurry?" he asked in surprise. "Miss Keene won't be on for at least five minutes yet."

Booth felt Gifford's hand touch his arm. This restraining gesture drove him to such fury that the thought of knocking the man down occurred to him. Then he controlled himself, and in a normal voice said: "I want to find a comfortable seat somewhere —if there is one." He paused, using up some of his time which had now become precious. "You can understand that, can't you?" he said, smiling ingratiatingly. "I don't often have the privilege of seeing a play from the front of the house, you know."

Gifford grinned sympathetically and released his arm. Booth went through the lobby, bowing as he walked past Buckingham and his friends. Still some few minutes yet. The second scene of the third act was about to begin. The big flat with the large doorway had already been dropped. He stood watching the actors make their entrances upon the stage. The whole performance at that moment seemed so utterly nonsensical that he wondered, for the first time in his life, what it was that brought the public to see a play. What sort of pleasure could people possibly get from looking at other human beings go through the empty gestures of living, when life itself was so much richer, so much more exciting than any counterfeit a dramatist could conceive? The actors' lines sounded as if they had been learned by rote, and to him they seemed especially artificial because he knew every word and he could foretell every gesture. A child could see through this pretense—these characters had not even the semblance of life.

129

# The Man Who Killed Lincoln

He watched the actors wearily, waiting for his moment to come. The play moved on with deadly slowness. I am tired of the life of the theater, he thought. I have had enough of being Macbeth, Hamlet, Brutus, Pescara, and all the others who strut the stage for an hour, mouthing another man's words. I have become death's emissary in order to rid myself of the many ghosts I have caused to walk the earth again, speaking through my voice, living in my body. Away with them! They are as insubstantial as everything else in this world that I have dreamed. I lent them reality for a moment, as I lend it now to these people here around me. . . .

On the stage, Mrs. Montchessington began to advise her daughter, Augusta, to set her cap for the wealthy Yankee, Asa Trenchard. I have seen all this happen before, Booth thought. I know what these people said during the first act, what they are going to say now, what they would say in the next scene, if I were to let it go on. Have I lived through my own part too, and is all this that I am now doing only a repetitious and meaningless action that goes on forever, over and over again? He knew then he must go up the stairs to the dress circle. He turned to the left of the orchestra pit, and with slow deliberate steps began the ascent. He could see the image of the lobby clock before him as he went, and it seemed to him that his own feet were keeping time with the monotonous beat of its heavy pendulum. As he stepped on

130

to the dress-circle floor he saw Harry Hawk appear on the stage to play Asa Trenchard's part.

"Ah, Mr. Trenchard, we were just talking of your archery powers," Mrs. Montchessington said in a voice that seemed to be even louder and more raucous than usual.

He could hear Asa Trenchard answer in the drawling Yankee tones that reminded him of Lincoln's homely accents. "Wal, I guess shooting with bows and arrows is just about like most things in life. All you've got to do is keep the sun out of your eyes, look straight—pull strong—calculate the distance, and you're sure to hit the mark in most things as well as shooting."

Well spoken, Harry! Good advice even if you don't realize what your words suggest at this moment, Booth thought. He leaned against the back wall of the theater and looked around the house. The guard's chair at the entrance to the President's box was still vacant.

The play dragged on, its unreal comedy lines drawing unreal laughter from the audience. Like puppets pulled with strings the actors moved and gesticulated before the absurdly painted flat with its two huge vases and its writhing, tangled mass of drapery. Booth waited motionless, patient—although consumed with a vast impatience—his eyes intent upon the President's box. He saw Lincoln's hand reach out and place itself on the box-rail. His own hands were hot with sweat, and he kept digging his fingers into his palms.

Now the moment was very near. Mrs. Montchessington was learning that Asa Trenchard was not the millionaire she had imagined him to be. "No heir to the fortune, Mr. Trenchard?"

"Oh, no."

Augusta cried out: "What, no fortune?"

"Nary red," Trenchard told her cheerfully, "it all comes to their barking up the wrong tree about the old man's property."

These were the lines that came just before his cue. In a few seconds Harry Hawk would be alone upon the stage. Booth unhurriedly began his progress across the back of the dress circle. His feet made no sound on the carpeted floor, and he glided along the wall, hands outstretched, feeling his way in the semi-darkness. His black-clad, high-booted figure moved stealthily toward the door that led to the President's box. Asa Trenchard's sallies filled the house with laughter as he went. (A droll fellow, this Yankee, he'll put the English snobs in their places before he's through.) Down the steps now, the white door beckoning. Booth's face was rigid as his jaw muscles clenched, and his eyes stared into the darkness ahead of him. Step by step, nearer and nearer—the door was close to him now. He seized the knob and pushed his knee against the panel.

A man seated near the box entrance suddenly rose

and approached him. Booth's hand reached under his coat for his knife. Then he realized what he was doing, and he turned, ready to placate this inquisitive stranger. He drew out his cardcase and showed the man one of Senator Hale's calling cards. The man backed away, apologizing.

Now the way is clear. Trenchard's remarks sweep the house with laughter again. The door swings open and Booth is inside the passageway at last. He closes the door behind him and stands there with his hand on the knob, his heart pounding, and his breath coming in short spasmodic gasps. There is no light inside the narrow passage, and he is alone in utter darkness. He feels for the wooden bar he had left in the corner behind the door, and his fingers close around its smooth square sides—only a moment's work to slip it in place, closing the only entrance to the box against all intruders. Quickly, quickly now. There is no time to be lost. That fellow outside the door has made him lose precious seconds. The voices on the stage, muffled and far away, have been speaking, and he listens to them carefully for his first cue.

"Augusta, dear, to your room."

"Yes, Ma. The nasty beast!"

"I am aware, Mr. Trenchard, that you are not used to the manners of good society—"

The words send a sudden quiver through him. He knows that he will hear them again, and then he will have to act. Mechanically he moves toward the second door. The hole he had cut in the panel gleams in the darkness—a single malignant eye, unblinking and steady, drawing him toward it. He peers into the box—the high back of the armchair is in front of him, and he can see a dark head rising above it. Mrs. Lincoln is leaning toward her husband, speaking to him. Beyond them the lights from the stage shine through the lace curtains that hang like a mist in the background.

It is time for the two women to leave the stage now, and Booth listens for Asa Trenchard's words that will tell him when they are gone.

Now the final summons is about to be spoken!

The Yankee voice gives him the words: *"Don't know the manners of good society, eh?"*

There can be no hesitation. This is the moment! His final cue has been spoken, and he must make his entrance. His pistol is ready in his hand. His breath rushes into his lungs—can they hear the terrible sound of it? His left hand turns the doorknob—the door opens, letting in the light—his feet move silently on the carpet. . . . The people in the box are all watching the stage. They do not notice him. He steps forward, raising his hand with the deringer in it. He holds it close to that hated head. There must be no chance of missing. Now! Now! Asa Trenchard's voice still drawls on: "Well, I guess I know enough to turn you inside out, you sockdologizing old mantrap—"

# Friday, April 14. Evening

And then the report, sharp and loud—the pistol
almost seemed to go off by itself, kicking his hand
upward. *"Sic semper tyrannis!"* he cries. He has
done it! He has done it! He has killed Lincoln! The
man in the chair never moves. He sits there, his head
sagging forward, white smoke billowing around him.
Mrs. Lincoln's face, upturned and startled, looks
into Booth's for an instant. The officer at the other
end of the box is standing up, and Booth sees him
coming toward him. He drops his empty pistol and
draws his knife. The officer lunges at him. Booth
slashes quickly with the dagger. He feels the blade
tear through cloth and flesh. The man clutches for
an instant at his own arm, but he makes another attempt to seize Booth, snatching at his coat-tails as he
turns toward the edge of the box. The knife jabs back
again and Booth is free. Over the box-rail now to the
stage, the light burning in his eyes, and a tearing
sound as he jumps—one of his spurs has caught in
the flag draping the box, and he is thrown off balance. He lands on the stage heavily, all his weight on
his left foot. It crumples under him, and he sprawls
on the floor, half unconscious from the terrible stab
of pain.

He gets up and almost falls again. Harry Hawk
has stopped speaking and is looking at him wonder-
ingly. Booth is up now, and he begins to run across
the stage, forcing himself to bear the pain that is
crippling him. The lines he had intended to speak at

this supreme moment are forgotten; he struggles desperately to reach the protection of the wings. The audience, puzzled by what has happened, and thinking that perhaps it is all part of the play, watches him in silence.

And then there comes a scream from the President's box. A man sitting in the front row of the orchestra scrambles up on the stage and runs after Booth. Laura Keene comes out from the wings. Booth rushes past her, nearly colliding with a young actor who is just behind her. The audience begins to shout. Mrs. Lincoln is still screaming.

Booth runs with uncertain steps into the long passage that leads to the stage door. Someone tries to bar his way. He strikes with his knife, and the man scuttles out of his path. He is at the stage door now, tugging frantically at its handle. He hears the heavy tread of a running man behind him. The door opens with a rush of cool night air, and the quiet darkness of the theater alley lies before him.

A boy is lying on a bench near the stage door idly holding the mare's reins. He tries to get up, but Booth pushes him violently away and strikes at him with the handle of his knife. The horse shies. Booth seizes the reins, and the frightened animal stands still long enough to permit him to get his foot into the stirrup. As he springs up to mount the horse, the weight of his body on his injured foot sends another paralyzing wave of pain through him. He manages to scramble into the saddle, clutching in agony at the pommel. The horse starts off with a clatter of hoofs, tossing its head at this sudden strange treatment. The man who has followed him out of the theater tries to grasp the reins, but the horse is too quick for him. Booth kicks her side with his right foot and heads her down the alley, out into the broad expanse of F Street, which lies muddy and deserted in the darkness.

At ten minutes after ten, Paine and Herold rode into Lafayette Square and stopped their horses in front of the Seward house. Every window but one in its imposing brick façade was dark. Herold remained in the saddle, but Paine dismounted, tied his horse to a tree and stood for a moment looking around at the deserted square. No one was in sight, but it was possible that someone might be standing in the park, hidden by the trees. It hardly mattered though—the place was dangerous enough already. It was within sight of the White House, where there were armed guards, and it was less than a hundred feet from General Augur's headquarters. But Paine was not to be stopped by any consideration of personal danger. He was looking forward to this encounter with a fierce joy. It was like going into battle again. He felt strong now—every muscle was taut, ready for action. He made sure of his weapons, and then took out the package of medicine he had brought. He asked Herold for the name of the doctor he was to mention, al-

# The Man Who Killed Lincoln

though Herold had told it to him a dozen times already. He repeated the name to himself as he walked with a lithe eager step to the door of the house.

He rang the bell. There was only a dim light burning inside the doorway. The occupants of the house had evidently gone to bed early. He had to wait a long while before a young Negro came to the door. As soon as Paine saw the door open, he pushed his way inside, telling the boy that he had been sent by Dr. Verdi with some medicine which he must deliver to Mr. Seward in person.

The boy looked at him suspiciously. Paine's manners were hardly those of a doctor's messenger. "I'm sorry, sir, but I can't let you go upstairs," he said with firm politeness. "I have strict orders not to let anyone go up there. If you will give me the medicine and the directions for taking it, I'll see that—"

"Look here, nigger boy," Paine said, raising his voice in immediate anger, "you're talking to a white man, and I'm not taking orders from you. I was told to give this medicine to your master, and, by God, I'm going to give it to him!" He strode forward, snarling: "Get out of my way!"

"But honestly, sir, I can't let you—"

"Get out of my way, nigger! I'm going up." He walked to the foot of the stairs, the boy following him and pleading with him not to go.

Paine's boots sounded heavily on the stairs. The boy begged him to make less noise. Paine paid no attention to him but continued on his way implacably, his footsteps ringing through the silent house.

Before he reached the top of the stairs, Seward's son Frederick had come out on the landing. He asked in an angry whisper why they were making such a disturbance. Paine explained to him that he had medicine to deliver, and they stood for some minutes wrangling about it, before young Seward agreed to look into his father's room to see whether he was awake. This was exactly what Paine wanted, since he had no way of knowing in which room his victim could be found.

"You can't possibly go in," the son said, closing the door softly behind him. "He's asleep and the medicine will have to wait. Give it to me."

Paine shook his head stubbornly. "I was told to give it to him."

"Well, you can't go in. I'm in charge here. You either leave your message and your medicine with me or you don't leave it at all. I must say that you are a very strange messenger for Dr. Verdi to have employed. I intend to speak to him about your behavior."

Grumbling, Paine turned as if dissuaded, and started down the stairs. Then, with a catlike spring he whirled around, drawing his pistol from his pocket. He pointed it at the young man's heart and pulled the trigger. It clicked dully with a metallic snap. Paine struck out wildly with the heavy weapon, hitting Seward on the head. Seward fell to the floor, and Paine continued striking at him as he collapsed under the rain of blows. The Negro bolted down the stairs shrieking out "Murder!" as he ran. He tore open the front door and disappeared outside.

Paine stepped over young Seward's body. He had broken his pistol. He threw it away from him and took out his knife. He saw the door of the sick man's bedroom open slightly as someone peered out to see what was the matter. He sprang toward it like an animal, growling as he leaped. The door crashed open as he landed against it, and he slashed out with his knife at the person inside.

He picked himself up from the floor. The man he had knifed was retreating with blood streaming down his face. Only a single gas jet turned down low was burning in the room, but there was light enough for Paine to see the figure of a man with his neck swathed in bandages half sitting up in bed. With one stride, Paine was across the room. He flung himself on the bed, striking downward with his knife. The blade struck something hard. He slashed again at the throat of the terrified man on the bed, but someone jerked his arm. The blow went wild and laid open his victim's cheek.

Another man had come into the room. Paine fought desperately, slashing at the two men who were trying to pull him off the bed. Seward managed to roll over and fall to the floor out of their way. Paine struck out again and again with his knife until he had cut his way loose from the men. He gave one of them a final blow, striking at his head, and then he tore open the door of the room and dashed into the hallway. A young girl was standing there, screaming.

A man was coming up the stairs. Paine struck him full in the chest with his knife. He felt the blade sink deep. The man clutched at his wound and fell on the stairs, groaning. Paine rushed down, and some obscure instinct caused him to cry out, "I'm mad! I'm mad!" as he went.

The door in the hallway below was open. He ran out of it into the street, his face and hands spotted with other men's blood. His horse was still where he had left it, but Davy Herold had disappeared. Soldiers from Augur's headquarters were running toward the house.

He dropped his knife and scrambled into the saddle. The colored boy who had met him at the door followed behind him, calling to the soldiers to capture him. Paine rode slowly, so blinded by homicidal fury that he was oblivious of his danger. And then, at the north end of the square, he came to himself and put the spurs to his horse. The startled animal broke into a gallop that carried his rider away from the shambles he had left behind him.

White smoke was drifting out over the stage. Mrs. Lincoln's terrible cry had roused the audience from its dazed stillness. The people realized that something had happened, but they were not yet quite sure just what it was. They began to stand up, at first singly, then in little groups. Finally, they were all on their feet, asking anxious questions, trying to find out the meaning of the strange incident that had just taken place. Men began to run up the aisles toward the stage; some of them climbed up on it. Laura Keene, followed by a young actor in the costume of a lieutenant of the British Navy, walked to the front of the stage and tried to quiet the house. No one paid any attention to her. Everybody was looking at the state box. Those who were on the stage could see the President's figure sitting motionless in his rocking chair as his distracted wife bent over him. His head had sagged forward at an ominous angle.

Men were struggling with the door Booth had blocked from the inside. Major Rathbone, the officer in the box who had tried to stop the President's assassin, was pulling at the bar of wood which held the door shut. He was weak from loss of blood from his injured arm, and he had trouble removing the bar because the mob outside kept pushing against it. Finally he got it loose. Several men hurried past him, and one of them leaned out of the box, calling for a doctor. Mrs. Lincoln was muttering incoherently. They led her to the sofa at the far end of the box and persuaded her to sit down there. An army surgeon in uniform was lifted up from the stage; he climbed over the box rail and called to the men to stand back, so the stricken President could get air. Then he ordered the door to the passageway closed, and began to search for the wound. There was no blood to indicate where it was. Finally, one of the men pointed to a small dark hole on the left side of the head, just behind the ear. The surgeon examined it carefully.

"We'll have to get him out of here quickly," he said. "Take hold of the chair and carry him down just as he is."

Two of the men picked up the chair.

"I'll have his carriage brought up," someone suggested.

The doctor shook his head. "He can't possibly be moved any distance from here. I'm afraid the wound is fatal." He followed the men carrying the chair across the dress circle to the stairs that led to the lobby below. People were crowding around to see the President's homely familiar face as he was carried past them. He was thrown to one side of his chair like a sack of old clothing. His head was still bent forward, and he showed no sign of life.

There was a moment's delay at the stairs. The men were having trouble getting the chair down. Several hands lifted the unconscious President out of it and carried him down to the orchestra. The chair stood for a moment rocking gently back and forth on the carpet. People gathered around it, curious to see if there were any bloodstains. Then an usher picked it up and fought his way back to the box with it.

From the orchestra pit came the confused sound of many voices. Someone was cursing the assassin. "Burn the theater!" he yelled. "They must have helped him here. They let him get away. Oh, the dirty bastards—"

"Who was it? Who did it? Does anybody know?"

Booth's name was whispered half-fearfully by a few people who had recognized him. It seemed impossible that it could really be he—a brilliant young actor whom everybody knew. . . .

People began to look at each other with suspicion. This might be some gigantic rebel plot to seize the capital. It was possible that there were other rebels still in the theater. The audience might very well be filled with them.

"Burn the theater! Burn the theater! The whole lot of 'em is in on this. They let him get away!" a voice from the gallery kept calling. Other voices took up the cry, and then someone began to call the name of Booth.

The men carrying their awkward burden of dead weight had reached the exit door. A crowd was pressing forward under the gaslights in front of the theater. The cry of "Booth!" became louder.

Men were trying to back the President's carriage toward the entrance. The word "Booth" was being shouted in a vengeful chorus that could be heard outside the theater.

"Take him over there," the surgeon said desperately, pointing to a house on the other side of the street where a light was burning in the doorway. A man in shirt sleeves was standing on the high stoop. The long sagging body was carried across the street. The surgeon had rushed on ahead and was explaining to the man on the stoop that it was the President who was being brought to his house.

Up the stairs and through the long narrow hallway they carried him. A frightened boy on leave from the army had the little room at the end of the hall. He was roused out of bed and sent upstairs in his nightshirt with his uniform thrust into his arms. The huge ungainly figure of the President was too long for the bed, so it was placed on it diagonally, and pillows were put under the wounded head. The surgeon began to remove the clothing.

"Hot water! Hot water in bottles and plenty of it!" he pleaded. A man went down into the kitchen to stir up the fire into a roaring blast that boiled whole washtubs full of water.

The street was filled with cavalrymen. Soldiers went into the theater to clear the house. The long roll was heard as drums were beaten across the city, and the sound of hoofbeats echoed in the dark streets around the theater. The crowd was being forced back. Soldiers were everywhere and more kept arriving. Bugles passed the alarm from post to post.

In the bedroom at the end of the hallway the fantastic turmoil that was shaking the city seemed like an

145

echo of distant thunder. The sound of heavy breathing and whispering voices filled the room. Surgeons laid bottles of hot water against the cold bare flesh of the dying man. The carriages of state officials began to arrive. One after another, the grave-faced men crowded into the tiny room, tiptoeing past the open door of the front parlor where Mrs. Lincoln sat with her son Robert, who had been summoned from the White House.

The long vigil through the night began. The wounded man on the bed remained unconscious, his mind shattered by the heavy bullet which had plowed through his brain and lodged behind the right eye. Blood oozed from the little round hole in the skull occasionally, and the surgeons prepared to probe for the bullet. There were hardly any signs of life except for labored breathing and, once in a while, a spasmodic weaving of the long bare arms. The dying man sank deeper and deeper into the dark reaches of unconsciousness.

Atzerodt had been drinking. He had been drinking to make himself forget about what he had to do, and he had been drinking to make himself remember that he must do it. At quarter after ten he had to enter the room of Andrew Johnson, Vice-President of the United States of America, and stab him to the heart.

He had been drinking but he was not drunk enough. The liquor had only made him feel sorry for himself, and he was in a tearful, almost maudlin mood. He knew that this was no part for him to play. He had been used to associating with violence, but he had never actually committed it. He had been a friend and admirer of the rough-and-tumble boys in the Port Tobacco saloons, and in Washington he had naturally drifted to the billiard parlors and oyster bars that were the centers of vice and crime in that wartime city. But he had been only a good-natured foil to the habitués of those places. He was always eager to please them and joke with them, but as soon as violence flared up he was the first to hide under a table or creep behind the bar. Now for the first time in his life he was on his own as a full-fledged assassin with a pistol and a knife on his person. Johnson was a sturdy fellow, a backwoods Southerner himself, who might very well put up a desperate struggle. And besides, there might be someone else in the room —an army officer, or a guard of some kind.

It was distinctly unfair to expect him to do this sort of work. Capturing the President and whisking him away to the South to be held for ransom was something that his small-town training in horseplay could appreciate. The capture was to be a sort of super-prank—a barroom trick carried out on a grand scale. But killing was something different; especially when you had to do it alone, and with a knife, of all weapons.

He felt aggrieved. Booth was trying to take ad-

vantage of him. He had been dazzled by the man's
fiery and reckless ways. He admired him and he was
afraid of him, but he was even more afraid of Paine,
and he remembered the sullen ex-soldier's threat.
He had followed out their instructions to the point
of taking his horse out of the livery stable, and he was
riding now at an uneager pace toward the Kirkwood
House. It was nearly ten o'clock, and he had only a
few minutes more to bolster up his courage.

Perhaps some more liquor would fix him up. He
decided to go into the bar first. It was the only part
of the hotel that seemed friendly. It was in the basement, and it was much less grand than the big rooms
upstairs. There was always a jolly crowd down there
with whom he could feel at home.

He tied his horse to the rack and went into the
closely packed room that smelled familiarly of liquor
and smoke and tobacco juice. He ordered whiskey
and stood at the bar drinking it mournfully. No one
paid any attention to him, but then no one in these
high-class hotel bars ever did. For once, though, he
was not sorry to stand alone watching others have
their fun. God damn it, this was a fool errand he had
been sent on! Why should Johnson let him into his
room? He was certainly not going to open his door to
a stranger. After all, he was the Vice-President, and
even though he had once been common folks he had
a big job now.

Atzerodt looked at the clock over the bar. Five

after ten. He would have to leave at twelve after. He knew where Johnson's room was. It was on the second floor near the stairs—easy enough to get to, too easy, in fact, for people were passing up and down near it all the time. He poured out a second glass of whiskey. The stuff seemed to have no effect on him. Conversation flowed around him in a noisy babbling stream. Everyone was still talking about victory, and some soldiers were being treated to drinks by the crowd. One of them, a big fellow like Lewis Paine, was very drunk, and his voice kept rising argumentatively above the normal sound of conversation. Suddenly he began to pound on the bar. Then he turned around to address the crowd.

"We licked the dirty rebels fair and square," he said in a tone that harbored a disposition to quarrel. "We licked 'em fair and square. We drove 'em right out of their home town, Richmond, by Christ! We've got 'em on the run now. Are we going to let 'em get away? Gentlemen, I ask you—" he pounded on the bar for attention—"are we going to let 'em get away now?"

There was a murmur of approval from the crowd. Atzerodt remained discreetly silent, but his very unobtrusiveness drew attention. The soldier sidled along the bar toward him and put his glass down near him. Several of his comrades followed, eager for trouble.

"I didn't hear you say nothing, stranger. I didn't hear you say what we ought to do about those God-damned rebs." He thrust his face close to Atzerodt's. "Well, ain't you got nothing to say?"

Atzerodt gulped down his whiskey and tried to look friendly.

The soldier reached out and put his hand on Atzerodt's shoulder. It rested there lightly, but as he began to talk, his grip tightened.

"Well, stranger, are we going to let those dirty bastards get away?"

Atzerodt writhed nervously. "Yes, sir," he said meekly. "I think we ought to——"

"Ought to what?" the soldier howled, raising a mighty fist. "Ought to let 'em get away? Well, by Jesus, if ever I saw a——"

"Oh, no, sir, I don't mean that. What I mean is we ought to——to go after 'em and——"

"——and hang 'em to a sour apple tree," the soldier finished for him. "Yes, sir, that's what we ought to do. Hang 'em to a sour apple tree with Jeff Davis at the top and the others strung out on the branches all the way down." He clapped Atzerodt on the shoulder with a blow that almost felled him. "Yes, sir, this gentleman has the right idea. Hang 'em to a sour apple tree. Come on, boys, let's sing it. All together now——" He turned toward his comrades. Atzerodt ducked and ran. He scurried out of the bar and untied his horse frantically. It was quarter after ten, he knew. The clock was the last thing he had seen in the barroom.

# Friday, April 14. Evening

It was now too late for him to go up to Johnson's room. Booth had told him to enter the room exactly at ten-fifteen. He could not possibly time his actions with the others. It was certainly too late for him to try to do anything. That soldier had spoiled it all. He mounted his horse and rode quickly away from the hotel. Perhaps it was just as well. He felt no resentment toward the soldier.

He headed his horse toward Ford's Theater. He wanted to see what was happening there. Tenth Street was deserted as he rode up it. When he got near the building, he saw someone run out of the front door and speak excitedly to two soldiers on the sidewalk. Then men began pouring out of the theater, and the street was suddenly filled with a shouting mob.

Atzerodt halted his horse. He tugged at the reins and pulled the animal's head around. Booth must have done it all right, he thought. He lashed his horse and started off in the other direction, but at the corner he turned and rode around the block to the side alley entrance on F Street. A group of men were standing there, looking down the street. One of them called out something as Atzerodt came in sight. He turned and bolted again. His knife dropped out of his pocket as his horse ran past the Patent Office. He heard it fall on the street, but he did not dare stop to reclaim it. The men were shouting after him, and he had to get away from them quickly. He turned a cor-

151

ner and kept riding through the maze of streets north
of the theater.

The city was beginning to wake up now. People
were sticking their heads out of windows. Men came
out of houses, and some of them began to run toward
the center of the excitement. Atzerodt finally determined to go back toward the theater. What was happening there had a horrible fascination for him.

He got as far as the corner of Tenth and F Streets
—within a few hundred feet of the theater. From his
vantage point on the back of his horse he could see
over the heads of the fast-gathering crowd, and what
he saw froze him into horror. He had only a brief look
at the face of a man in the center of the milling, howling mob under a street light, but that one glance was
enough to make him stop his horse abruptly. The man
was a stranger to him, someone he had never even seen
before, but he realized the predicament this hapless
person was in. He had done nothing at all, apparently,
but the shouts of the mob made it evident that these
infuriated men had seized him simply because they
believed he was a rebel. They were trying to string
him up to a lamppost. Atzerodt saw himself in the
man's place, and he knew that if the mob realized that
he had been in this thing with Booth, they would tear
him to pieces on the spot. Policemen were trying to
fight their way through the crowd, but Atzerodt did
not wait to see what happened. He turned his horse
around and got away as fast as he could.

# Friday, April 14. Evening

He rode back to the livery stable and turned in his horse. He was afraid to go back to the room he had taken at the Kirkwood House—he was afraid even to go to his former quarters in the Pennsylvania Hotel. He wandered around the streets helplessly for a while and then he took a horsecar bound for the Navy Yard. He had friends in that section who might let him sleep in their house. He was disappointed, though, for they refused to let him in, and he had to return to the center of the city to spend the night in a general lodging room. At five in the morning he crept out of the place to leave Washington on foot.

Over the city the moon was riding high in the heavens. Across its face wind-torn wisps of clouds scudded, growing thicker with the hour. The sentry at the Navy Yard Bridge nodded sleepily. He heard the hoofs of a horse on the dark road leading from the city. He sprang up, bayoneted rifle in hand, and challenged the rider.

The horse was a little bay mare, and she had evidently been ridden hard. She stopped, with her sides heaving, as the man on her back reined her in. Her rider's left foot hung loosely out of the stirrup, but the sentry could not see this, since he was on the other side of the bridge.

Sergeant Cobb, who was in charge of the post, came out of the sentry-box. The sentry lowered his rifle and stepped back.

153

"Who are you, sir?" asked Cobb.

"My name is Booth," the man on the horse answered. "I'm going to my home in Charles County."

"What town?"

"I don't live in a town," Booth answered. "My house is in the country—near Beantown."

"No one is allowed to pass here after nine o'clock," Cobb told him. The sentry lifted his gun again.

The horse danced restlessly, compelling her rider to pull hard on the reins.

"I never heard of any such ruling," Booth said. "I've been detained in the city and I thought I'd have the moon to ride home by."

Cobb looked up at the sky. The moon had disappeared behind a cloud. The sentry whispered something to him. He hesitated and then walked over to the gate at the bridgehead.

"I guess it's all right," he said slowly. "You can pass through."

He swung the wide gate open. The horse sprang forward and clattered across the wooden planking of the bridge.

The two men looked after it for a moment. It was hardly out of sight on the other shore when they heard another horse coming down the road.

"We're doing a good business tonight," Cobb said, grinning as he shut the gate. The sentry stepped forward with his rifle.

# Friday, April 14. Evening

The second rider drew up his horse.

"Well," said Cobb, "what do you want? Who are you?"

The rider looked frightened. He was a young boy, and Sergeant Cobb was always suspicious of young boys who were out at night for no good purpose. The Sergeant grasped the horse's bridle.

"Come over here by the sentry lamp and let me get a good look at you," he said. He stared up at the horseman's face. Narrow little shifty eyes avoided his inspection.

"What's your name?" he asked harshly.

"Smith," the boy faltered. "Smith."

"Well, now that's an original name," said Cobb. "Your first name wouldn't be John, would it?"

The boy nodded. Then he said suddenly: "No, it isn't. It's Thomas."

"Ah, yes, Thomas. Well, Thomas, where are you bound for?"

"The White Plains. I live there."

"And how do you happen to be out so late?"

"God damn it!" the boy burst out suddenly. "Are you going to let me through or not? I've been— Well, are you going to let me pass?"

Cobb nudged the sentry. "Shall we let him through?"

The sentry spit reflectively on the planks of the bridge.

"He might get in trouble being out in the city so

155

late at his age. Washington's a pretty tough place. Maybe he better get home to mamma."

Cobb swung open the gate and the horse dashed through.

"Good Jesus, here comes another one!" said the sentry, turning around.

Cobb shut the gate quickly.

The third rider sprang to the ground, ignoring the bayonet leveled at him.

"Did a man go past here on a light roan horse?" he asked excitedly. "A roan with a black tail and mane. Double-reined bridle—English saddle—"

"And a boy named Smith on it?" Cobb asked.

"No, that's not the name. His name is David Herold. But did you see the horse?"

"It just passed through this minute. What's the matter? Stolen horse?"

"Looks that way. It's a livery horse from my stable. I saw the young rascal riding down this way on it. He has no right to take a hired horse out of the city at this hour."

"It does look queer, all right. But he said he lived at the White Plains, so we let him go through."

"He's stealing my horse, I tell you!"

"That's too bad, mister."

"Well, can I go after him?"

"Sure you can, mister, but you can't come back in."

"No?"

"No. Not until morning. We don't care much who

goes out of the city, but we can't let nobody in. Nobody at all. We don't take any chances with Johnny Rebs. There's too many of 'em down in Southern Maryland anyway."

The disappointed liveryman sighed. "I'll never see that horse again," he said, climbing heavily into the saddle. He looked across the river into the darkness. "I hope that young bastard gets his neck stretched. He's got it coming to him."

"Maybe he will, mister," Cobb said pleasantly. "Maybe he will."

The fools, Booth thought, to let me cross so easily. The hollow ringing sound of the mare's hoofs on the bridge planks stopped abruptly. He was on solid ground again. A few hundred feet past scattered stores and houses, and then a sharp left turn to the road up Good Hope Hill. He was out of Washington now, thank God, and he was on his way to the South.

A team of horses hitched to a wagon was coming down the hill. Booth kicked the mare's side with his right foot in order to send her quickly past it. He saw the questioning, upturned face of a man looking at him as he hurried by. Then the mare slackened her pace as the hill became steeper, and Booth found himself jogging along at a more comfortable rate under the wide cloud-shrouded sky.

He sank down in the saddle and let the horse walk

up the hill. His body felt heavy and tired, but his mind was filled with the one great thought that sang through his consciousness. He had killed Lincoln! There could be no doubt of it. Even during the excitement of his struggle with the officer in the box he had had a chance to notice that Lincoln had never moved after the shot struck him. His bullet must have blown that scheming brain to shreds, obliterating with one clean stroke all the man's dark plots against the South. He had killed him, his enemy, his people's enemy!

During his furious ride across the city he had been exultantly aware of this one fact: Lincoln is dead! The great god Lincoln is dead! *Tyranny is dead! Run hence, proclaim, cry it about the streets. Liberty, freedom and enfranchisement!* He, John Wilkes Booth, had thrown into confusion the plans of twenty million Northerners rejoicing at the prospect of victory.

He felt that he could laugh or cry or shout aloud the great news to the night winds. He, alone, now wandering obscurely through the deserted countryside, already a fugitive and a hunted man, had taken the course of history into his hands and twisted it violently into a new channel. By God, the world would remember this night! He had done more for his country than Jefferson Davis and Robert E. Lee. Every footprint that his horse was making would be recorded in the hearts of his countrymen forever. Some day they would mark with golden horseshoes the path he was taking now.

And the South lay ahead of him somewhere beyond the dark horizon of the hills ahead. Safety, comfort and rest awaited him there. Far beyond it was Mexico, where the laws of the Northern Government could not reach him. Mexico, then Spain perhaps. . . . He might even see Bessie Hale again, he thought suddenly. She would be with her father, living in regal style in the ambassadorial headquarters in Madrid. All that he had to do now was to get away from the power of the accursed city from which he had already escaped. Life still could be sweet, rich, exciting. There were thousands of well-born people in Europe who had supported the cause of the Confederacy. He would certainly find a welcome among them.

Damn the Yankee flag that had thrown him off his balance when he leaped from the box! If it weren't for that he would be able to ride like a streak, surely outdistancing all his pursuers. The shock and pain of his fall had driven out of his mind all the fine words he had wanted to say to that audience which had sat and stared at him in stupefied amazement. What a pity that he had missed that chance. . . . A tapping sound, a far-off steady tapping sound, roused him from his reverie.

He stopped the mare and listened. Peeper frogs from a near-by swamp were shrilling a chorus that he had not even noticed before, but through their thin piping he could hear the sound of hoofbeats on the road behind him. Someone was following him. There was only one horse, he decided. It might be Lewis Paine coming to join him—or Davy Herold or Atzerodt. It also might be a Federal soldier. He turned his horse aside into the shelter of some trees and waited.

The horseman approached. Booth could hear the sounds of steel horseshoes on stones. His own mare stirred restlessly. He drew his heavy Colt revolver from its holster. There was some light on the road from the moon behind the clouds. He peered anxiously to see the rider, but the light was too dim for him to make out who it was.

He waited until the horse and its rider passed the place where he was hiding, then he raised his revolver and called out, asking who was there. He heard Davy Herold's voice answer him quaveringly. He sheathed his revolver and spurred his horse out into the road.

"Well, David," he said quietly. "What happened? Where's Lewis?"

The boy cursed in a low soft voice. "You scared hell out of me. I thought someone had—"

"I'm sorry, but I couldn't take any chances in the dark. Tell me—where is Lewis? Did he do it?"

"He did it all right, I guess," Herold said sullenly. "He must have killed him. I couldn't wait to see. Somebody came out of the house yelling 'Murder,' and a woman began shrieking upstairs. Then some

# Friday, April 14. Evening

soldiers started running up from Augur's headquarters. I had to get away quick. I didn't see him come out. I left his horse there for him, though."

"But he doesn't know his way out of the city."

"I can't help it. They'd have had me in another minute. Something must have gone wrong. Maybe they got him. I don't know. I just couldn't stay there any longer."

"Well," said Booth finally, "I did what I set out to do anyway. I've killed Lincoln. I'm sure of that. I shot him in the back of the head. He never moved."

Herold shifted around in his saddle. "That's the most important thing, isn't it? The others don't count so much. Lincoln is the one that matters." He looked up at the gathering clouds. "Hadn't we better get out of here? There may be soldiers close behind us."

They were nearly at the top of the hill. Herold plunged his spurs into his horse's sides. Booth groaned with pain as his mare, in a sudden start to follow Herold's horse, threw his foot against the stirrup. Herold circled back and looked at him anxiously.

"What's the matter? Are you hurt?"

"I wrenched my ankle when I jumped down on the stage. I'll be able to ride all right, though. Go ahead. I'll follow you. We have to make time now." He urged the mare forward. He clutched the saddle with his left hand and hung on grimly. The road, white with clay and gravel, slipped by. Herold's horse was far in the lead, and the mare kept racing madly to keep up with it. Every step she made was torture to Booth, but he had to bear it. He was riding for his life.

It was after midnight when they arrived at Surrattsville. Booth was in agony. His foot, which had been jolted by the mare's uneven pace, burned with unceasing pain. He stopped his horse on the lawn in front of the tavern. Herold had dismounted and was pounding on the door.

After a few minutes John Lloyd came out, sleepy-eyed and smelling of his own whiskey. Herold immediately hurried him inside the house to get the articles that had been left with him.

Booth sat on his horse, sweat soaking into his clothing. He tried to forget the pain. This was an important stop, and there were things to be done. He saw a lamp being lighted inside the tavern. He called impatiently to Herold.

"David, for God's sake, bring me something to drink. This damned foot is driving me crazy."

The boy came out holding up a bottle. "There's no brandy here," he said apologetically. "Only whiskey. Lloyd is getting our stuff."

Booth seized the bottle eagerly and drank.

Lloyd brought out two carbines, some cartridges and the paper parcel which Mrs. Surratt had delivered to him that afternoon. He stripped the cloth

# Friday, April 14. Evening

cover off one of the guns and looked at the carbine admiringly.

"New kind of gun, ain't it?"

"It's yours," Booth said. "We're only taking one. I wouldn't let anybody see it, though. It's a Government carbine, and it might get you into trouble." He motioned to Herold to take the other gun, saying that he could not possibly carry anything himself, since he was having difficulty staying in the saddle at all.

Booth handed the whiskey bottle to Herold.

"Is there a doctor near here?" Booth asked Lloyd. "I've hurt my foot and I must get to a doctor."

"Well, there's a sort of doctor, but he's pretty old and not so good any more," Lloyd said. "Leastways folks don't go to him much."

"Never mind. We'll get our own doctor." Booth leaned down and spoke to Herold. "We'd better go on, I think. It's obvious that Lewis will never be able to find his way here alone, even if he got away from Seward's house safely. And as for George Atzerodt—"

Herold quickly tied a strip of cloth to one of the carbines and slung it over his shoulder. "That's all right with me. Let's go."

"Perhaps I'd better have another drink," Booth said. He finished the bottle, and then he sent it crashing into the bushes. The crude liquor had a quicker effect on him than brandy had ever had. It hit his pain-weakened nervous system with a jolt.

# The Man Who Killed Lincoln

"Pay our host, Davy," he said huskily. "Give him some money for his very good services. An adequate amount, neither niggardly nor extravagant...." He swayed slightly in the saddle.

Herold handed the innkeeper two dollars.

"Good night to you, sir," Booth said, waving his arm vaguely at Lloyd, "and many thanks for what you have done. It will be remembered, and you will be amply rewarded for it some day. Amply rewarded, I assure you. Amply rewarded..."

Booth stared around vacantly at the darkness.

"Amply rewarded... Meanwhile you may be glad to know that we have assassinated the President of the United States and, I think, several members of his Cabinet. You have played some small part in aiding us and you will be well compensated.... Come, Davy, the night hath a thousand eyes and we must away. Farewell, gallant innkeeper. Remember us in thy orisons."

And now his brain was jumbled with words as his horse clattered off after Herold's. Tags of Shakespeare and lines from the various plays in which he had taken part rushed into his mind to make a pattern of grandiloquent syllables, devoid of sense or meaning. But the words! The glorious words—rich, round, great-sounding—came without effort to him, and he flung them helter-skelter to the wind. The miles slipped by, forgotten in their painful traverse,

# Friday, April 14. Evening

as he poured out speeches from his actor's stock in trade.

John Matthews was frightened, more frightened than he had ever been before. He had slipped away from the theater to meet some acquaintances in a saloon a few blocks away. He did not have to appear on the stage during the first few scenes of the third act, so he had taken this opportunity to leave the house for a short while. He had put a cloak over his costume and had walked out with his hat and stick to meet his friends. He spent nearly a quarter of an hour in the quiet little saloon, and then someone stuck his head through the doorway, screaming that the President had been assassinated.

Matthews knew, of course, that Lincoln was in Ford's Theater, and if he had been killed, he must have been killed there. He rushed out into the street with his friends, but the fellow who had yelled through the doorway had already disappeared, and the sounds of drums and bugles were already echoing through the city. Out of the darkness came the furious hoofbeats of a cavalry patrol. The horses bore down on the anxious little group, driving Matthews and his friends to seek refuge in doorways and alley entrances. The troops were headed toward the theater—everyone in the city seemed to be going there. Matthews was separated from his friends by the frantic dash of the cavalrymen, so he hurried on alone.

# The Man Who Killed Lincoln

The city suddenly seemed to have gone mad. Stranger was talking to stranger in wild disjointed phrases, and everyone seemed to take it for granted that the rebels were making a surprise attack on the city.

The crowd thickened rapidly as he approached Tenth Street. There were so many people in the streets around the theater that it became almost impossible for him to get any closer. He tried to force his way through the wildly shouting mob, but the people were in a reckless mood, and his insistent pushing nearly got him into trouble several times. Finally, the pressure of human bodies became so great that he could make no further progress, and he was caught in the swaying mass of angry men about a block away from the theater itself.

He heard the word "rebels" used in a hundred different imprecatory phrases, and then he heard someone say "Booth." At first the word made no impression on him. The name was spoken again, this time by a man quite near him. There was no mistaking what he was saying: "Some bastard by the name of Booth done it. Sure, Booth. John Wilkes Booth, an actor in the theater. . . . Why, they say he jumped right on the stage. They must have helped him there or he could never have got away. We ought to burn the damn place down and shoot all the actors. . . ."

Oh, my God, he thought, Wilkes Booth. They are suspecting him and I have his letter in my pocket now. He turned and tried to get out of the crowd. It was somewhat easier to get away from the theater than it had been to advance toward it, but he emerged from the thickest part of the crowd with torn and disheveled clothing, and the cane he had been carrying had somehow been wrenched away from him. But he had succeeded in keeping a firm grip on the pocket that held Booth's letter. He could still feel the crisp paper under his hand.

He hurried along the street toward his hotel. People were still coming toward the theater. He was the only one headed away from it, and his set face and rapid walk caused him to attract unfavorable attention from some of the people he passed. Once he was actually stopped by an inquisitive soldier, but he managed to make a satisfactory, if somewhat incoherent, explanation to the man. Finally, he entered the deserted lobby of his hotel and called for the key to his room. The desk clerk innocently asked him what was happening outside. He was able only to stammer out that he didn't know, and he walked quickly—but not too quickly—to the stairs and went up to his room.

He closed and locked the door and lighted the gas jet. He looked around the little room as if he suspected that someone was hiding there, and then he sat down on the bed and took out the letter. "To the Editors of *The National Intelligencer*. Confidential and Important," the inscription read. He hesitated only a moment. Then he tore the letter open and read it with mounting horror. There could be no doubt. His friend Wilkes Booth had assassinated the President. He remembered certain conversations he had had with Booth. So this was the "business" Booth had gone into! The man must be insane! He knew the reputation Booth's father had had for his curious and wayward behavior, and he tried to remember instances when Booth himself had acted in any way that could be considered abnormal. He paced up and down the little room. It suddenly occurred to him that if this letter were found on him he would surely be lynched by the angry mob he had seen. He cursed Booth for implicating him. One thing to do now and quickly. He snatched up the letter and thrust it into the open gas flame. The paper curled up and blackened as the blaze seized it, but he held it in his hand until it began to burn his fingers. Then he stamped the charred, fragile cinders under his foot and ground them into the carpet.

The roll of drums still throbbed in the night air, and men's excited voices could be heard in the street. He turned out the light and crawled onto the bed, trying to quiet the fears that were thronging into his mind. . . . Oh, my God! John Wilkes Booth! he groaned. And I was seen talking to him only this afternoon!

The hour after the dawn had come, and the streets were gray under a sky that threatened rain. Cavalrymen were stationed in front of the little red brick house opposite Ford's Theater.

In the hall bedroom at the rear of the house, the leaders of the nation had gathered around the quiet figure that lay there unconscious, breathing in deep labored gasps. The gas was still burning, but daylight was creeping slowly into the room. There were more than twenty people there, standing motionless, cramped together, watching and listening always to the breathing that was now growing fainter.

Secretary of War Stanton was conducting an examination of witnesses in the next room. His voice could be heard through the thin wall as he badgered the frightened theater people who were being called upon to give an account of themselves.

Surgeon General Barnes held a whispered consultation with one of his associates. The laymen watched their faces eagerly as if they thought that these two men held the power of life and death in their hands. The verdict was evidently unfavorable—Barnes was sending for Mrs. Lincoln.

A moment later she was led in from the front parlor, where she had been kept waiting all night long. She stood on the threshold a moment, sobbing and looking dazedly around her. Then she rushed into the

room and sank down on the floor at the edge of the
bed. Her sobs grew louder. She clasped her husband's
head to her. His eyelids were stained with great dark
splotches, and there was blood on the towel spread
over the pillowcase. The breathing suddenly became
more labored; for a moment it seemed to stop alto-
gether. The surgeons tried to pull her away. She
thrust them aside and sprang back, screaming. Then
she collapsed on the floor.

Stanton, glowering, dashed into the room. "Take
that woman away and don't let her in here again!"
he thundered.

The surgeons gathered around the dying man,
soaking up the fresh flow of blood. The breathing became more regular, but it was more difficult to hear
now. Stanton stood in the corner, watching silently.

Barnes looked up and whispered something to him.
Soon now. Soon. The men around the bed stirred uneasily in the growing light. Soon now. Not much
longer to wait. The breathing fluttered and died away
and then came back again. A clock somewhere in the
house ticked on relentlessly, and from far away in the
city the long shrill notes of a bugle sounded.

The light in the little room grew stronger. Someone silently turned down the gas jet. The men standing around the bed could hardly hear any breathing
at all. Barnes bent over the great shaggy head and
raised his hand for absolute quiet.

"He is still breathing," he whispered. He took his

watch out of his pocket and looked at it. Seventwenty. He placed his finger on the dying man's pulse and counted gravely. He seemed puzzled, and bent over to listen to the breathing again. The second hand on the watch moved stolidly around in its course. It was seven-twenty-two. Barnes straightened up and looked around at the circle of curious faces. Then, without a word, he crossed the long bare arms on the quiet chest.

Stanton picked up his hat and put it on his head. Quickly recollecting himself, he took it off, and turned to the Reverend Mr. Gurley, the President's clergyman, and suggested that he lead them in prayer.

The minister's low rich voice filled the tiny room. As soon as the prayer was finished, one of the men leaned over and closed the dead man's eyes which were staring up at the ceiling. The others started to file out the door. Stanton began to pull down the shades, shutting out the daylight and the gray sky.

"Now he belongs to the ages," he said heavily, and followed them out of the room.

Carriages were beginning to drive away. The soldiers, standing by their horses, watched curiously. There was a murmur from the crowd which had been held back some distance from the house. The word of death had reached them. Mrs. Lincoln came down the stairs, muttering to herself as she passed through the door: "Oh, that dreadful house! That dreadful house!"

Her carriage rolled away toward the White House. The soldiers relaxed into easier positions and then looked suddenly upward. The rain had begun to fall. It splashed down on the street in big drops, and then it fell steadily, washing away the dark stains on the steps, driving the waiting soldiers back into the shelter of the entrance doors to Ford's Theater. Only their horses remained in the street, standing patiently with lowered heads and glistening sides in the April downpour.

# PART FOUR

★

Headquarters, Department of Washington
22d Army Corps,

Washington, D. C., April 14, 1865

Colonel Nichols:

I have sent to arrest all persons attempting to leave the city by all approaches. Have telegraphed to troops on the upper Potomac to arrest all suspicious persons—also to Gnl. Slough at Alexandria and Gnl. Morris at Baltimore—All our own police and detectives are out. No clew has yet been found by which I can judge what further steps to take. Can you suggest any?

*Respectfully,*

C. C. Augur

## 4

BOOTH was dead sober now. The effect of the liquor he had drunk at Surrattsville had long since worn off. His horse had fallen, flinging him to the ground screaming with terror and pain. He had lain in the road, digging his fingers into the gravel, sobbing angrily and cursing at the ill luck that had ruined his careful plans for escape. Herold had picked him up and put him on his own horse which had a steadier gait than the nervous-footed little mare. After that, Booth let Herold take complete charge. Fortunately, the boy knew the country well. He had often been through it on hunting trips and he could find his way even on the back roads at night.

Miles and hours had been lost because they had had to turn aside from their straight course through Port Tobacco to Virginia in order to get medical attention for Booth's injured leg. The pain had become constant, and the jolting of the horse was an unbearable racking torture that had affected his whole body. He

175

was convinced now that his leg was broken—no sprain or wrench could hurt like this. He was compelled to go more slowly, and he sat on the horse with his shoulders hunched and his teeth clenched. He kept changing his position in the saddle, trying to relieve the strain on the muscles of his leg.

His mind was obsessed with only one idea—to get to a doctor and obtain relief from this agony. He was almost oblivious of the danger of pursuit; he had forgotten his fellow conspirators; his mind was unable to plan any farther ahead than the doctor's house toward which he was riding. He knew that the country would be filled with troops in a few hours, but he would simply have to take his chances with them.

The place toward which he was bending every effort of his will was the home of Dr. Samuel Mudd. He had met Mudd during the previous autumn when he was exploring the roads of Southern Maryland, through which he had expected to take Lincoln to Richmond. He had tried to interest the man in his abduction plot—Mudd was the proprietor of a five-hundred-acre farm, and he had been a slaveholder who stood to lose a great deal if the North won the war. Mudd was influential in the district, and there was every reason to believe that he could be of great assistance in organizing the people there to help get Lincoln across the Potomac. At first he had seemed inclined to join in the attempt. Booth had spent a night in his home, telling him about his plans; he had

talked to him in Washington; he had tried in every
way to persuade him of the feasibility of his scheme,
but he had never quite been able to get the doctor to
go wholeheartedly into the plot. There was some curious incompatibility of temperament that kept the two
men apart. Mudd was coldly rational, fatally inclined
to weigh all the possible consequences of failure as
they would affect himself and his family. He made
reservations, sought to temporize and he was always
evasive. He was not the sort of person who would be
attracted to Booth's reckless and romantic temperament. He was impervious to his charm and to his im-
passioned arguments alike. Booth had finally come to
realize that the doctor had no use for him—and he, in
turn, had naturally taken a dislike to the man.

But he was the only doctor in the neighborhood,
and Booth was in desperate need of a doctor's services.
He did not quite know how to approach Mudd. He
was the kind of person who might conceivably have
been interested in the abduction plot because it offered
some material advantage to the South and to himself,
but he was not the sort who could be expected to approve of a political assassination even though it had
been inspired by the purest of patriotic motives.

Herold had stopped his horse and was waiting for
Booth to come up to him. "We're near the church
north of Beantown," he said softly. "You can see its
steeple against the sky up ahead there. It's not far

to the doctor's house now. How well do you know him?"

"Too well, I'm afraid. I'd rather go to a strange doctor if I could. I don't trust this one at all. I've had dealings with him before."

"What can he do? He don't know anything's happened yet."

"He will by morning."

"What do you want to do?"

"I don't know yet. . . ."

"Well, doctors don't grow on bushes around here. You better think up a good story to tell him."

They rode on silently. Booth forced his pain-racked mind to concentrate on the problem at hand.

"David," he said at last, "here's what we'll do. We won't tell him who we are at all. You do the talking —use fictitious names if he asks you who we are. Tell him my horse fell—that's true enough, God knows—and that I hurt my leg then. There's a gash on the shoulder of the mare, and my clothes are still filthy, so the story will sound reasonable enough."

"He'll know you when he sees you, won't he?"

"Not when I have this on, he won't." Booth reached into his pocket and pulled out the false beard he had taken from his costume trunk. He put it on and drew his shawl closely around his neck.

Herold looked at him in admiration. "That's a right smart trick. But what about your voice? He may remember you from that. I'd know it anywhere."

"You're going to do all the talking, David. At least I hope so. If I have to speak, I can disguise my voice well enough. I haven't been an actor for nothing."

They went on for a few minutes until they came to a large open field. Beyond it, at the top of a long rise, a house was silhouetted against the dim western sky. They turned into the lane.

"Has the doctor ever seen you, David?" Booth asked suddenly.

"No, I can't say as he has. I've often been past this house, though."

"We'll have to take our chances. Don't forget what I told you. You do all the talking. If he asks me a question, you answer it. Tell him I'm too sick to say anything."

Herold rode up the lane ahead of Booth. A dog barked at the sound of his horse's hoofs on the stones. Booth followed Herold slowly and saw him dismount on the lawn in front of the house to tie his horse to a tree. The dog in the barnyard yelped frantically when Herold knocked on the door. Dogs from neighboring farms took up the cry. Booth rode up and sat motionless in the saddle. Herold pounded on the door again.

"What name will I tell him?" Herold whispered.

"Any name, you fool! What difference does it make?"

"But I can't think of a—"

"Watch out! Someone's coming to the door."

A man in a nightshirt appeared in the doorway. He peered out apprehensively.

"What do you want? Who are you?"

"My friend here hurt his leg when his horse fell and threw him," Herold said nervously. "He's afraid it's broke. He can't stand on it. We thought maybe you could fix him up."

"Well, bring him in and I'll look at it."

The doctor walked out on the lawn. With Herold's help, Booth was lifted off the horse. They carried him into the parlor, where they put him on a sofa. The doctor left the room to get a candle.

Booth stretched himself out gratefully on the sofa and turned his face toward the wall. "Keep talking to him, Davy, so he doesn't get a chance to talk to me."

The doctor returned. The light from the candle he was carrying threw his thin sharp features into relief. Herold looked at him curiously to make sure he had never seen him before on one of his frequent visits to the neighborhood. Fortunately, the long face, with its unusually high forehead and short beard, was entirely strange to him.

Mudd put his surgical kit down on the floor and bent over Booth.

"It's his left foot that's hurt," Herold said hastily. "He had an awful fall. The horse was going fast when it happened. He's near fainting from the pain of it, I guess."

The doctor took hold of the boot and gently tried to pull it off. Booth groaned with pain.

"I'll have to cut the boot off," Mudd said. "The ankle must be swollen. Perhaps we'd better take him upstairs. He'll be more comfortable on a bed than he will on this sofa, and I can work better there."

"We're in an awful hurry, Doctor," Herold said. "We've got to—"

Booth immediately spoke to Mudd in a voice that was so unlike his own that Herold started when he heard it.

"Certainly, Doctor, if you think you can work better upstairs, we should by all means go there. I'm afraid that this is not a minor injury—I think the foot is broken."

"I'll get my wife to carry the candle while we help you up," Mudd said politely. He left the room and went toward the rear of the house.

"I thought you didn't want to let him hear your voice," Herold said to Booth in a whisper.

"I didn't do so badly, did I?"

"No, you didn't. I thought for a minute that someone else was talking. What do you want to let him take you upstairs for, though? We've got to get out of here in a hurry."

"Not before I get this foot dressed," Booth said irritably. "I can't travel while it hurts like this."

The doctor came back with his wife, a stout matronly woman who was very solicitous about the injured stranger. Mudd and Herold carried Booth up the stairs. The bedroom in which they placed him was the same one in which he had slept when he had spent a night with Mudd trying to persuade him to join the abduction plot.

The doctor opened his bag and took out a knife. Mrs. Mudd stood at the bedside holding the candle. Booth felt the false beard slipping away from his face. He pulled his shawl up closer in order to conceal what was happening. The doctor bent over him, inserted the knife into the boot at a point halfway down the calf, and then skillfully slit the soft leather along the front of the leg as far as the instep. The boot slipped off easily now. He stripped off the sock. The ankle was swollen and inflamed.

Mudd took the foot in his hands and manipulated the bones carefully. Booth clamped his teeth tightly together.

"It's pretty bad, I guess, eh, Doctor?" Herold said sympathetically. "It looks awful sore."

Mudd put the foot down gently on the bed. Booth let the air rush into his lungs again.

"It's bad, all right," Mudd said, rubbing his face vigorously. "It's broken—that's sure. Pott's fracture. The fibula—just above the ankle. It's not serious, of course, but I'm afraid it will be several weeks before your friend will be able to use his foot again."

A sudden wave of terror swept over Booth. Good God, not able to use his foot for weeks! He had suspected that he had broken a bone somewhere, but the actual seriousness of his predicament had not been brought home to him until this minute. Federal cavalrymen would be covering every road in the State by morning, and gunboats would be sent down to patrol the river.

Herold was protesting that it would be impossible for them to stay. Booth heard him say that they had to get back on the road—that it was a matter of life and death. He interrupted Herold quickly, in order to stop his frightened babbling. In his consternation Booth forgot to disguise his voice.

"If I must stay, I must stay. Perhaps I can get a carriage tomorrow. If you will be kind enough to let me spend the night here, Doctor, I shall be very grateful. I can't travel on horseback in this condition."

Mudd looked at him with a puzzled expression on his face. "Of course," he said slowly, "you must stay. I'll put some splints on your foot. You'll feel better when it's bound up. I'll go find something to use for splints."

He kept staring at Booth's muffled face. Finally he turned to his wife and asked her to come down with him to help look for splint material. They left the room, and Booth heard them whispering together as they went down the stairs.

Herold stood by the bed, shifting his weight from one foot to the other. He tried to say that he thought

183

the doctor's suspicions had been aroused, but Booth angrily waved him to silence.

Mudd said nothing when he returned. He dressed the foot with great care, strapping it up in homemade splints. Then, after a few words of instruction to Herold, he left the room and padded down the stairs, still expressing no curiosity about his patient.

The firm support of the splints soon quieted the pain. The bed was a luxury Booth had never expected to have that night, but he knew that he might have to pay for it with his life. Still, he might as well enjoy this comfort while he had it. He lay back and put his hands under his head. The night was nearly over. There was a faint streak of dawn through the windows that faced east, and the birds had begun to murmur restlessly in the trees.

Herold went down to put the horses away, leaving Booth alone with his recollections of the great scene that had already become history. The day that was now dawning would mark the beginning of a new era in the history of the Confederacy. He had conferred a great future upon the Southern States—a future that would be resplendent with glory and power. He had made this night forever memorable to his people.

He was faced with only one problem now—his own escape. He would spend the day here at Mudd's and start out at night again. There were people along the Maryland shore he could trust, if only he could get to them. Samuel Cox, for instance. Cox would surely help him. Booth had never met him personally, but John Surratt had told him that the Confederate spy system had often used Cox's house as a stopping place for its men on their way to and from the North.

This Dr. Mudd was certainly a queer sort, he thought. He must surely have recognized him, yet he had said nothing, asked nothing. Perhaps he was questioning Herold now. Damn the fellow! Why couldn't he be more human? He was the only Southerner Booth had ever met to whom he would be afraid to trust himself after what he had done for the South this night. Why, he was a Southern hero now, and any true Southerner should consider it an honor to help him!

He sighed and dug his arms into the soft pillow. He had taken the false beard off and hidden it away. It had not been a very successful disguise. He had been uncomfortable with it on, and he had been constantly afraid that it would slip off. Certainly he could not risk using it in the open daylight. Stage make-up was effective only in the theater. He would have to find some other method of transforming his appearance.

He wondered what had happened to the others. Had Lewis Paine succeeded in killing Seward—and did he get away? He felt reasonably sure that Surratt had shot Grant. Surratt was to be depended on to carry his mission through to the finish. And Atzerodt? Where were they now?

God, he was tired! I have actually done it, he said to himself, as his eyes closed. I have actually done it. No matter what happens now, what I have done can never be undone. I have killed Lincoln. The shaggy head fell forward as the bullet from his deringer hit it. I have killed Lincoln, he kept saying to himself. I have killed Lincoln!

---

## Saturday, April 15. Noon

---

Again he was standing on the stage at Ford's Theater, and he could see, somehow, beyond the footlights into the house where the audience was seated. Every person there was in some way familiar to him. The members of his family—except his mother—were sitting in the first row of the orchestra. Edwin was looking at him gravely; his brother Junius was there, and so were Asia and all the others. Around them were seated all his friends. Even people he had met only casually were in the theater.

In the right-hand stage box was a life-sized manikin moved with strings and wires. It had the face of Lincoln. The long stiff arms gesticulated wildly, and the jaw, hung on springs, opened and shut senselessly like the mouth of a ventriloquist's dummy. The sight of the thing enraged him. He raised his pistol and fired at it. It collapsed and fell forward with its grotesque head coming to rest on the edge of the box, and its great gorilla-like arms hanging down toward the stage, swaying lightly. The doors at the back of the orchestra pit burst open. Federal troops in perfect military formation began to march down the aisles. The building shook with the regular tread of their advancing feet, but he stood firm upon the stage and spoke to the audience in words of heart-stirring eloquence.

And then from the box, where the simulacrum of Lincoln hung motionless, came the sound of a woman crying. He looked up and saw his own mother there. The soldiers immediately began to run forward, lowering their bayoneted rifles. The audience stood up, shouting and screaming. Through the theater a great wind began to blow, bringing the darkness with it and drowning out the pandemonium with its own vast wailing.

He was on a moor now, riding alone through the night. He could see nothing, but he was aware of the moving shapes of mounted men around him, for he could hear the hoofbeats of their horses, and the sounds of voices crying his name passed from one part of the darkness to another. The long single syllable seemed like the call of an animal, rising and falling, eerie and far away. Then it was very close to him, becoming insistently louder, and he felt himself floating up a deep well of blackness into a sudden strange gray light. He was in a bedroom, and Davy Herold was bending over him, shaking him and whispering his name.

Herold stepped away from the bed, grinning foolishly. "I thought I'd better wake you up," he said. "It's nearly noon. You said you wanted to get out of here. I had my breakfast long ago. I never went to bed at all. The lady said she'd bring you something to eat."

Booth stared dazedly around the room. There was another high-backed bed in it, and a brightly colored religious print looked down at him from the wall. There were rain drops on the windowpanes, and the sky was gray and foreboding. He tried to sit up. He felt a sudden throb of pain in his leg. It drove away the last dull fragments of sleep from his mind, and he knew that he was a hunted man who must think and plan his escape.

There was a knock on the door. Mrs. Mudd entered with a tray. Booth turned his face toward the wall and groaned.

"He isn't feeling so good, ma'am," Herold said. "Maybe you have some brandy. That would fix him up."

Mrs. Mudd put the tray down on the edge of the bed. "No, I'm sorry," she said gently, "we haven't any brandy in the house. I could give him some home-made whiskey, though. We have plenty of that."

"Thank you," Booth said, without turning around,

"but I really don't want anything at all. I'll be all right in a little while, I'm sure."

She looked at him helplessly for a moment and then went out of the room, closing the door quietly.

"Davy, we have to leave this house as quickly as possible. I'm afraid to stay here now. I had hoped to wait until tonight before starting out, but I'd hate to trust these people if they find out what has happened, and news may reach here any minute. The Government will probably offer some sort of reward for us. That doctor is sure to discover who I am— he'll know me if he gets a good look at my face. I slept in this very bed only last fall."

"Don't worry," Herold said. "I've already arranged with him to take me over to his father's house to see if we can borrow a carriage. We'll be able to get out of here, all right. Nobody in this neck of the woods knows what's happened yet."

"Be careful what you say to him, Davy. He's a sly sort. . . . That woman is coming back here again. Keep her out of this room, for God's sake! I don't want any more of her sympathy."

Herold stood in the doorway to prevent Mrs. Mudd from entering the room. She timidly handed him some oranges and then turned to go down the stairs again. "The doctor is ready to ride out with you," she told him. "He thinks he ought to look at your friend's foot before he goes, though."

Booth cursed softly. "Let him come up if he has

to," he whispered to Herold, "although I don't know what good he can do." He put on the false beard again and drew the blanket up close. Mudd came into the room dressed in his riding clothes. Herold hovered around the bed, nervous and apprehensive.

"How do you feel now?" the doctor asked. "Foot still hurt?"

Booth mumbled something in reply.

"Frankly, I don't think you ought to be moved from here before that bone knits. Let me have another look at it. You're perfectly welcome to stay, you know."

Booth pushed his foot out from under the covers. The doctor felt it gently.

"There's no reason to open the bandage," he said. "You simply need time to let the break heal."

"We've got to go on, Doctor," Herold said anxiously. "I can take him to the home of a girl I know down here. We wouldn't think of—of—imposing on you. I'm sure my friend will be perfectly comfortable there."

The doctor shrugged his shoulders. "Very well then. I'm afraid we'll have trouble finding a carriage for you, though. Tomorrow is Easter Sunday, and all the carriages around here will be needed for church." He pulled the covers over Booth's foot. "Is there anything I can do for you meanwhile? I'm having one of my men make a pair of crutches for you. You'll need them in order to move around at all."

"How much do I owe you for your services, Doctor?" Booth asked in a voice muffled by the blankets.

"We can worry about that later," the doctor said genially. "There's no need—"

Booth reached under his pillow and took out a purse. From it he extracted twenty-five dollars in bills and thrust them at Mudd.

"I always like to pay as I go," he muttered. "Will you do your best to get me a carriage? I'll pay well for one."

Mudd drew himself up stiffly. "You don't understand. This is not a question of money. If there's a carriage to be had, I'm sure that any one of my neighbors will be glad to lend it to you. Unfortunately, I shall need my own for my family. . . ."

"Maybe we'd better get started, Doctor," Herold said. "My friend—"

"I'm sorry if I have offended you, Doctor," Booth said earnestly. "I merely meant to say that I am in urgent need of transportation and that I should be glad to recompense anyone for the use of a carriage for a day or so."

Mudd reluctantly took the bills and put them in his pocket. The muscles on his thin cheeks tightened.

"Very well," he said coldly. "Thank you for paying me so promptly. I shall do my best to get you a carriage."

Booth motioned to Herold to remain behind as the doctor left the room.

"Davy," he whispered, "ask the lady of the house to let me have some hot water and soap—and the doctor's razor, if she will. I'm going to shave off my mustache. That's one identifying mark I can get rid of easily."

The afternoon passed slowly. A Negro servant brought the crutches to Booth and cut them down to fit properly. They were simply pieces of wood with a crossbar at the top, but with their assistance he was able to move around the room, swinging on one leg. One of the doctor's old shoes was split open to fit over the swollen foot.

Booth managed to shave himself, and he looked in the mirror to see how much of a change the absence of his mustache made in his appearance. He was disappointed—his face looked almost the same. Then he lay down on the bed and waited impatiently for the carriage to arrive. The rain had stopped, and the sky was beginning to lighten.

He could hear the peaceful sounds of cattle in the barnyard and the soft noises of a hen industriously clucking to herself. If only this confounded doctor were a more friendly person—and one he could trust —he could stay here while the troops scoured the countryside. It would surely be possible to hide a man away on a farm as big as this.

Suddenly a dog barked. Someone was riding up

the long driveway. Booth reached for his crutches as a horse thundered up to the house.

He was standing up, pistol in hand, when Davy Herold burst into the room. "We've got to go fast," he shouted. "There's Federal soldiers in Bryantown, and that damned doctor knows who you are!"

"He knows——?"

"Sure he does. I waited for him outside the town. He came riding back and told me about the troops being there. They're after us, and he knows it. Said so. He's hopping mad, too. Said you abused his hospitality, coming here with blood on your hands. He doesn't want the troops to find you in his house. He's out on the road now, so he can warn us if they come this way."

Booth was furious. "Abused his hospitality, eh? What in hell did he expect me to do? Lie down in the bushes and die? God damn him! A fine Southerner he is." He stopped and asked suddenly: "David—the carriage—did he at least get me a carriage? I can't ride with this foot."

Herold shook his head. "We couldn't get one. We tried at his father's house, but the— You've got to ride! They're coming after us! You couldn't use a carriage anyway—we've got to take to the swamps. They'd catch us sure on the road."

Booth felt his body sag down on his crutches. Mounted troops after him now, and he would have to try to get away from them on foot in a country

193

where every household would have been warned against him.

"All right, David," he said. "Let's get out of here. You lead my horse. I'll walk."

Herold had both horses ready in a few minutes. Booth put the clumsy mass of false hair on his face and pulled his shawl up around it. He started down the stairs awkwardly on his new crutches. Halfway down, he felt the beard slipping from his face. Mrs. Mudd was standing in the hallway, watching. Quickly he drew the shawl around the lower part of his face. He managed to reach the bottom of the stairs without further accident. He explained to the bewildered woman that he would have to leave immediately, and then, without further ceremony, he hobbled out into the dooryard.

The ground was still soft from the rain, and the ends of his crutches sank into it. He simply could not tolerate the idea of riding again. Herold's horse plodded down the driveway, the empty-saddled mare behind it. Booth followed at a painfully slow pace. They turned into the road toward Bryantown. The doctor was nowhere in sight.

"It's only a little way down this road before we can turn off," Herold said. "Once we're in the swamps we'll be all right, but we've got to get off this road quick. Can't you ride—even a little ways?"

Booth shook his head determinedly. "I don't think

194

I could stand it. It was torture last night." He swung along on his crutches, swearing at his own clumsiness. "Keep that carbine ready," he warned Herold, "and watch the road ahead. I have to keep my eyes on these damned ruts."

After what seemed to be an interminably long time, Herold finally pointed out a wagon track leading into the woods. Booth turned into it gratefully. He was sweating from the exertion, and his armpits were already beginning to get sore.

The Zekiah Swamp, which they were entering, was a long but narrow piece of marshland on either side of a little stream that flowed into the Potomac. They had to cross only its extreme northern end, but the ground near the water's edge was so soft that Booth soon found himself stuck fast, unable to move. One of his crutches slipped away from him, and he fell into the mud, cursing hoarsely and shouting at Herold to come to his aid.

"You'll have to ride now," Herold told him as he led the horses toward him. "You'll stay here till the turkey buzzards get you if you don't." The horses' feet went deep into the black mud and made loud sucking noises as they pulled out. "I don't see how it'll hurt you any more than walking, if you let the horse go slow."

He helped the almost hysterical Booth get up on the little mare. The injured man's face was drawn and pale, and his clothes and hands were covered with

195

slime. He tore off the bedraggled beard and flung it into a puddle of stagnant water.

"You don't look so good," Herold said commiseratingly. "Your face seems awful white without your mustache."

Booth took out a handkerchief and cleaned off the gum which had held the beard in place. His horse began to go forward, floundering in the mud. Booth winced with pain every time his foot was thrown against the animal's side.

Herold picked up the crutches and mounted his own horse. They rode ahead slowly and waded into the sluggish waters of the stream. Booth's mare, trying to mount the opposite bank, threw her rider violently backward. He stifled an agonized scream, and dug his nails into the saddle leather while the horse struggled to reach firmer ground.

Herold seized the mare's head. He got her up on shore and held her firmly until she was on hard footing again.

"Do you want to try to walk now?" Herold asked.

Booth sighed resignedly. "It's torture either way. Perhaps we can make better time if I stay on the horse."

They were in a dense woods. The trees, covered with climbing vines, loomed up darkly. The spring foliage was already lush, and the bright blossoms of redbud spotted the green background. Peeper frogs were beginning their evening chorus.

# Saturday, April 15

They rode on in the gathering darkness. Once Booth stopped to look at his pocket compass. They seemed to be headed in the right direction to go around Bryantown, toward the southwest, but he had only a vague idea of where he was. He felt that he was riding aimlessly, and he was afraid that he might suddenly find himself near the town. It was cold and damp, and he shivered as he sat in the saddle and tried to protect his leg from being brushed against trees and bushes.

Finally, there was a break in the woods. The cart track they had been following led into a road. They made their way along it in the darkness. Booth was sick from hunger, and he felt the need of brandy. After a long while they came upon a small building. It was a church, a rough wilderness structure, standing at the intersection of several roads.

"We're somewhere, I guess, but I don't know exactly where," Herold said in a husky voice. "I don't ever remember seeing that church before."

"I thought you knew this country."

"I thought so too. Maybe I have seen this place before, but it certainly looks different somehow at night. I don't know which one of these roads we ought to take."

"Well," Booth said firmly, "I'm staying right here until you find out. I'm not going to do any unnecessary riding. Help me off this horse. I'll wait for you here in front of the church. Take any one of these

197

roads you wish and ride till you get to a house. Find
out which way we should go to get to Cox's place.
And, for the love of God, try to bring back something with wheels on it. And get some food too. I'm
starved."

Herold seemed to be gone an unreasonably long time.
Booth was lying on the steps of the little church with
his face turned up to the cloudy sky. His horse, teth-
ered to a tree, was standing near him. Sometimes she
would move in the darkness, thrusting her head inquiringly toward him, or she would stamp impatiently on the ground with one of her steel-shod
hoofs.

The idea began to form in his mind that Herold
might be deserting him. Certainly the boy would
have a better chance to escape if he were not bur-
dened with a crippled fugitive for whom the whole
Federal army must now be searching. Nearly a whole
day had passed since the fantastic episode in the theater. The country must be in a turmoil with the news.
Yet it was so quiet here, not forty miles from Washington. In Bryantown the troops were waiting. . . .
He remembered the little hotel there with its long
porch, and the houses that were clustered around it,
half-hidden in the shrubbery. He wondered whether
the soldiers had visited Mudd's house yet, and then it
suddenly occurred to him that he had left his boot
there, lying under the bed. He knew that his name

was written inside it. If the soldiers saw it they would concentrate their search in this section. Thousands of them would be sent out to comb every thicket and gully. Many of them must be on their way already, for the Maryland peninsula was obviously the place to look for him. He had given his name to the sentry at the Navy Yard Bridge. Perhaps they would take it for granted, though, that he had reached Virginia by this time. They had no way of knowing that he had been held up by a broken leg. Why had he given his own name to the sentry? Why had he done so many things that now seemed obviously wrong? Christ, what a careless fool he had been!

The mare began to move about restlessly, straining at the halter. Booth could hear steady hoofbeats approaching. He sat up to see who was coming. If it was a soldier he would have no chance of hiding from him, since he could not hope to move away from the steps. He would have to stay here and try to shoot first. There was a loud "Hulloa" as Herold galloped up to the church, crying: "I got a guide for you, all right. He knows where Cox lives and everything."

In a little while a man appeared on the dark road and came toward them hesitantly.

"This is Oswald Swann," Herold said. "He lives in a cabin near Bryantown. He knows this country well and he's willing to show us how to get to—to the place we want to go."

"Thank God for that," Booth muttered, looking

up at the vague form standing over him. He sensed immediately that the man was a Negro, although he had not spoken, and it was impossible to see his face in the darkness. "Did you bring me anything to eat?"

"Yes, suh. Some bread and ham— That's all I got, suh."

Booth took the food the Negro offered him and ate it eagerly. The ham was tough and stringy, but he was so hungry that he did not care.

"Did you see any soldiers around here today?" he asked, when he had finished.

"Yes, suh, dey went right past my house."

"Are they still in Bryantown?"

"I guess dey is—I didn't see 'em come back."

"What are they doing there, do you know?"

The Negro was silent for a moment. "Maybe dey is lookin' for someone," he said finally.

"Do you know where Mr. Burtle lives?"

"Yes, suh, reckon I do, but he's a long way off."

"And Mr. Samuel Cox—how far is his place?"

"Dat's a long way too. Muss be ten mile—maybe fifteen."

"Well, you take me there tonight, and I'll pay you well for it. I've hurt my foot and I can't ride very fast, so you won't have any trouble keeping up with us. We'll walk the horses all the way."

He had been a fugitive for only twenty-four hours, but already he knew the terrors of a fugitive's life. He was in constant fear of meeting anyone. Every sound, every light or sudden motion was a danger signal. The world was suddenly filled with people who were his enemies, men who would shoot him on sight if they knew who he was and what he had done. He would have to live from now on like an outlaw, forever prepared to meet violence with violence. His hands, which had already killed, must be ready to kill again.

He seriously considered the idea of shooting his Negro guide as soon as he had finished with his services. Tomorrow the fellow might tell others that he had shown the way to Cox's house to a man with an injured foot. The circumstances were suspicious enough to arouse even the apathy of a backwoods Negro. If he were to talk, word might get to the troops at Bryantown, and they would certainly ride down to Cox's plantation to investigate. If Booth were discovered there, he would bring disaster to his prospective host as well as to himself. It would be easy to take out one of his revolvers, ride up close and fire at the woolly head of the Negro. No one would hear the shot in this wilderness. The body could be thrown into the bushes. It might be weeks before it would be found. If he could shoot the President of the United States, he surely should not flinch at taking this insignificant Negro's life in order to protect his own. He must be absolutely ruthless now. He had been too easygoing in the past, too careless, too ready to trust others.

He rode on, his mind in torment. How was the South taking the news of Lincoln's death? What was happening in the North? Edwin was in Boston—would they permit him to play tonight after what his brother had done? Junius was out in the Middle West, in Lincoln's own country. . . . Had his mother been told yet? Surely the Government would send detectives to question every member of his family. And they would probably offer a big reward for him. How much would it be? A price on his head! Wanted: dead or alive, John Wilkes Booth, height five feet seven, black hair, black eyes, initials J.W.B. tattooed on right wrist. . . .

The Negro stopped. "Heah's where Mistah Cox lives," he said, pointing to a large white house surrounded by outbuildings and long paling fences. Everything stood out sharp and clear in the greenish moonlight.

The thought of getting rid of his guide occurred to Booth again. But now they were too near people who might hear the shot. Better see how Cox received them. He told the Negro to wait for them. Then they rode through the gate to the house that was standing quiet and austere in the night.

Booth's crutches pounded heavily on the floor of the long open porch. Herold raised the brass knocker on the door and let it fall with a solid thump that re-

sounded through the house. Several dogs in the barnyard had been growling uneasily; now they began to
bark. A light appeared in a window on the second
floor. A man stuck his head out and spoke to them
angrily.

"Are you Mr. Cox?" Booth asked in his suavest
voice.

"Yes. What do you want?"

"We were sent here by Dr. Samuel Mudd of Bryantown, and by Mr. John Surratt, who knows you, I
believe."

"Well?"

"I am in need of assistance, sir. I have hurt my leg
and I— Won't you come down here so we can talk?
I had rather not shout this matter aloud."

Cox disappeared into his room, and in a few minutes came to the door, a candle in his hand. He was a
man of about forty-five, thickset and stern-visaged.
He had pulled on his trousers over his nightshirt. He
stood in the doorway, examining his visitors. Booth
noticed that he had a small pistol thrust in his belt.

"Come in," he said finally. "It's damp out there
and cold. I have a chronic cough. I try to avoid the
night air."

They entered the house. Cox lighted a lamp and
motioned to a couch. Booth made himself comfortable on it and laid his crutches down beside him. Herold remained standing at the door.

"Well, sir, why were you sent to me?" Cox asked abruptly.

"Some time ago," Booth said, "you offered to participate in a plan to bring a certain person of high political importance in Washington through this country to Richmond."

Cox looked at him silently, neither affirming nor denying what he had said.

Booth went on: "That plan, as you know, never came to fruition. Richmond was taken by the Northern Army. General Lee surrendered his forces at Appomattox. The South was in desperate straits. Bold action became necessary. Last night, in Washington, an act of war was carried into the enemy's camp—"

"I have already heard of what took place," Cox said coldly. "I know that President Lincoln was shot while attending a play at Ford's Theater. Secretary Seward was attacked in his home—"

"Attacked? Is he still alive then?"

"He was this morning, I believe. Dangerously injured, but still alive."

Booth glanced quickly at Herold, but Herold had suddenly turned his face away and was studying a picture on the wall.

"And Grant?" Booth asked. "What did you hear about him?"

"Nothing. No mention was made of him or of any other officer of the Government. Why do you ask?"

Booth was silent. His mind was reacting swiftly to

the news of all these failures of his fellow conspirators. What had happened? How could Paine ever have left that house while Seward was still alive? What had stopped John Surratt. . . .

"You did not come here simply to bring me word of this assassination, I suppose," Cox said to him. "What do you want of me?"

Booth looked up at him, wondering if he could ask this man for shelter and protection. His manner was decidedly unfriendly. He seemed very different from the person John Surratt had described. "Do you know the name of the man who shot the President?" Booth asked slowly.

"Booze, I think they said—or Booth. Some such name, anyway."

"His name is John Wilkes Booth, sir. You may have heard it before."

"Booth? The actor?"

"Yes."

Cox was staring at him now. He got up from his chair and went across the room to the couch where Booth was sitting.

"Why do you tell me this?"

Booth examined his host's powerfully muscled face. There was no doubt that he was a person of indomitable will who could be of tremendous value if he would pledge his aid. Surratt had guaranteed the man's loyalty to the Confederacy. And he had to trust him—there was no choice in the matter now.

Booth summoned a ready smile, but he quickly became grave again under Cox's stern gaze. And then he said, almost in a whisper: "Because I am John Wilkes Booth, and I have come to ask your assistance as a loyal Southerner—"

Cox's face did not change. There was no evidence of surprise, no tinge of emotion in his voice as he spoke.

"And how do I know that you are John Wilkes Booth?" he asked.

"I don't think I shall have any trouble proving my identity," Booth said wryly. "Quite the contrary. Here—" He thrust out his hand with the initials J.W.B. tattooed on his wrist. "If you wish, I can show you papers with my signature, or—"

"Never mind," Cox said, motioning quickly. "I believe you. I was afraid for a moment that you might be a Yankee spy sent here to implicate me in this plot."

Booth smiled feebly.

"Why did you come to my house?" Cox demanded suddenly.

"Quite frankly, because it is near the Potomac River over which I must cross in order to get to Virginia. Also because I had been told that you have in the past been willing to endanger yourself many times by aiding the Southern cause."

The lamp was smoking. Cox walked over to it, carefully turned down the wick, and then drew a chair toward the couch. He sat down and stared at Booth.

"To whom else could I go if not to a friend of the Confederacy?" Booth went on nervously. "My life is in danger. Cavalry patrols are on all these roads. My leg is injured. I can travel only with the greatest difficulty. I must find assistance or I shall never get away alive."

"What do you want of me?"

"Help in getting across the river."

Cox's hands were gripped tightly around the arms of his chair. "Why did you do—what you did?"

Booth explained with great care the political necessity of his action. He analyzed his motives, stated his hope that a Confederate victory would result from the chaos into which he had thrown the Northern Government.

"And you think that what you have done will help the South?" Cox inquired.

"Of course," said Booth simply.

"You had no other motive—no personal reason?"

"None whatever," Booth said, looking at him coolly. "I should never have presumed to come to your house otherwise. I am not a murderer. I have done nothing that a soldier on the battlefield would not do. I do not regret what I have done—"

Cox suddenly seized the arms of his chair and stood up. His figure towered over Booth's.

"God damn you, you young fool!" he said in a terrible voice. "You think you're a hero now, don't you? You feel that you have done something for which the South should be grateful? Don't you realize that you have played into the hands of Northern politicians who have been waiting for a chance like this? Do you believe for a moment that Andrew Johnson is going to be more generous to the Southern States than Lincoln would have been? Or that any other Northerner can ever occupy the President's chair without remembering that his predecessor was murdered by a Southerner!"

Cox's face was livid. His hands were half-raised as he advanced toward the couch. Booth tried to stand up, but he had to sink back helplessly, unable to rise without his crutches.

"I don't expect generosity for my country—nor do I want it," he said. He tried to restrain himself, and he spoke with cold dignity. "I expect the Southern armies to fight now and win their own victory—"

"Fight with what?" Cox almost shrieked. "With their fists against guns or with their teeth against cannon? It takes money to run a war. Everybody knows that the South has none. Her currency is worthless. Her factories are gutted, her people starving, her ports blockaded, her Government in flight, her armies—or most of them—already surrendered. How in the name of God can she fight? With what? Are you insane? This war is over! It can't be started again now—there's nothing left to fight with!"

# Saturday, April 15

Booth reached for his crutches. "I am sorry, sir. I have been under a misapprehension. I had been told that you were a man devoted to the South. You talk like a man who is ready to rejoice in her defeat even before she has lost. I shall not trouble you—"

"Sit down!" Cox thundered. "You can't take refuge behind any silly nonsense like that. That's the sort of talk that has ruined us. All this damned blather about the Yankees being unwilling to fight; all this empty boasting about one Southern gentleman being worth a regiment of Northern shopkeepers is what has led us on blindly into defeat. It's time for Southerners to come to their senses!

"Wars, nowadays, aren't fought with dueling pistols. It's guns that win them—heavy guns—heavy masses of metal and heavy masses of men. We were in the right—the war was forced on us. We fought bravely for four long years, but the side with the superior wealth and greater numbers had to win eventually. Well, the Northerners have won. Are we to go on deceiving ourselves forever? They have won! The best we could hope for at this point was a satisfactory peace, and now you've destroyed even our chances for that with your damned dirty pistol!"

Booth's face was white and twitching. "God damn it, sir! I'll take words like this from no one. I came here in the belief that you were a loyal Southerner. I thought—"

Cox held up his hand and interrupted him, his

own anger subsiding as Booth's fury mounted. "Don't talk to me about being a loyal Southerner," he said. "I've risked a lot and lost a lot in this war, and I don't intend to be taken to task by a man who comes to my house as a common murderer—yes, a common murderer—and feels hurt that I don't congratulate him for committing murder."

Booth called Herold to his side and managed to get to his feet. Herold helped him get his crutches under his arms.

Cox ignored Booth's evident intention to leave his house. "And let me impress this upon you," he continued. "I hold no brief for Abraham Lincoln. Had he been killed by some natural means I would never have wasted a minute regretting his death. But he has been murdered—murdered in cold blood, and what you said about your doing nothing that a soldier would not have done is just so much nonsense, and you should know it. Furthermore, he has been murdered by a man who calls himself a Southerner. Such an act dishonors the South, and it will call down retribution upon our heads from the people of the North, who, at this crucial time, are more powerful than we are. This murder will have to be paid for in blood, in misery and in long oppression. It will take generations to wipe out its memory. God help the South now, and God help all of us, for we must pay for your madness!"

Booth was at the door. Cox followed him, never

stopping for a moment in his quiet vehemence. "I am sick of you romantic fools who go about believing that war is a matter of individual heroic deeds. God, I'm sick of you all—you self-appointed arbiters of destiny who think you can make the world over with a single stroke!"

He stepped out on the porch after Booth. "Right now," he went on, although Booth was paying no attention to him, "my adopted son, a young boy who should still be in school, is lying wounded somewhere near Petersburg, shot on one of the last days of the war. I have just learned where he is, and I had hoped to go down there to bring him back. I shall never be able to go now. I shall never be permitted to pass through country held by Union forces after what you have done. If that boy dies, his death will be on your head as much as if you had killed him yourself."

Booth did not even turn around. Cox looked at him bitterly as he stood there in the soft glow of the lamplight streaming through the doorway. As Herold approached with the horses, Cox spoke these last words to him: "I tell you I'm sick of all this war, and all you young fools killing each other and being killed, and I wish to heaven, sir, that you had never come to my house. In fact," he added with deliberate brutality, "I wish you had never been born!"

Booth handed his crutches to Herold without a word. Herold lifted him up to the saddle. As soon as Booth felt himself firmly mounted on the horse, he reached into his pocket and took out a penny. He threw the coin at the feet of the man standing on the porch, and cried out: "For your hospitality, sir—and grossly overpaid!" Then he wheeled his horse around and rode quickly to the gate, oblivious of the pain in his foot as the mare broke into a gallop.

The Negro was still waiting for him.

"Everything all right, suh?" he asked politely. "Mistah Cox goin' to put you up?"

"Damn Mister Cox! Here—take this for your services." Booth hastily counted out twelve dollars in bills and thrust them into the man's hand. "Get on home now," he said harshly. "You've been paid. Don't wait around here. Skedaddle!"

The frightened Negro hurried away. Booth's mind was in such a state that he had forgotten what a potential danger his guide might be. It did not even occur to him to warn the man to be silent. He waited, thinking of what Cox had said. He cursed his own folly for exposing himself to this petty farmer's attack. Herold was irritatingly slow. When he finally appeared he had several blankets thrown across his saddle.

"Where did you get those?" Booth demanded. "From Cox?"

"Yes, I—"

"I want no assistance from him. Take them back!"

"He's not so bad, really. He's just sort of wrought up about his boy, Harry. I told him that I used to go hunting with Harry, so he gave me these blankets. It's going to be cold out in the woods. I got some stuff to eat, too."

"I don't want anything from your Mr. Cox."

"He can get us across the river," Herold said eagerly. "He said he would. He told me that if we'd wait in a pine grove over yonder, he'd send someone tomorrow who would lend us a boat. And he isn't doing us any favors. He wants to get us out of this section, he said. He's afraid we might get caught near his place."

"There must be other people around here—"

"But we can't take any chances. We can't just go up to strangers and ask them. They might turn us in, especially if there's any reward—"

Booth was glumly silent.

"We might as well go to that pine grove," Herold said. "It's as good a place as any, and we'll have something to eat in the morning, if we wait there." He looked slyly at Booth and then urged his horse forward with a slight prod of his foot. He led the way toward a grove of trees about a mile south of Cox's house.

Booth followed him sullenly.

# PART FIVE

★

War Department, Washington, April 20, 1865

## $100,000 REWARD!

---

## THE MURDERER

of our late beloved President, Abraham Lincoln,

### IS STILL AT LARGE

### $50,000 REWARD!

will be paid . . . for his apprehension, in addition to any reward offered by Municipal Authorities or State Executives.

### $25,000 REWARD!

will be paid for the apprehension of

JOHN H. SURRATT, one of Booth's accomplices.

### $25,000 REWARD!

will be paid for the apprehension of

DANIEL C. HARROLD, another of Booth's accomplices.

---

*All persons harboring or secreting the said persons . . . or aiding or assisting their concealment or escape, will be treated as accomplices . . . and shall be subject to trial before a Military Commission and the punishment of DEATH.*

*Let the stain of innocent blood be removed from the land by the arrest and punishment of the murderers. . . .*

—EDWIN M. STANTON, *Secretary of War*

## Sunday, April 16

For the first time in his life Booth had to spend a night outdoors, sleeping on the ground like an animal, shelterless and cold. He lay huddled under his blanket, trying to remain absolutely still, for the slightest movement hurt his leg. He could still hear Cox's angry voice.

The night passed slowly. He felt that he would never be able to fall asleep, but he awoke suddenly into a world filled with light—gray, lead-colored light from a densely clouded sky. The ground was damp; heavy beads of dew clung to the grass, and the pine branches were laden with moisture. He felt stiff and cramped, chilled through and utterly miserable with pain and cold. His hands were so numb that his finger joints ached, but his face was flushed, and he could feel the first vague signals of fever stirring in his blood. He looked around at the barren landscape. Withered sedge, left standing from the year before, crowded in among the dwarf pines, and only the new

217

grass springing up under the dead growth carried any promise of spring. He shivered and drew his blanket more closely around him. Never before had he needed warmth and shelter and the kind attention of friends so much as he needed them at this moment, and now they were denied him.

He called feebly to Herold. The boy groaned and sat up, his little eyes squinting sleepily at the light. He arose and came over to Booth's side.

"I'm afraid my leg is going to give me trouble, David," Booth said, looking up with fever-brightened eyes. His hands plucked nervously at the edge of his blanket. "It seems to be infecting my whole system, and lying out here in the damp isn't going to do it any good."

Herold stared at him helplessly, not knowing what to say. His underlip pouted like a child's, and he looked as if he were going to cry. Booth wished fervently that Surratt or Paine had come with him. He was afraid to trust this irresponsible boy, and he was terrified at the thought of becoming so ill that the responsibility for their safety would devolve upon Herold. He felt a sudden dislike for the boy. He loathed stupidity, and he wondered why he had ever permitted himself to be surrounded with so much of it during this most important venture—he had actually exercised less care in selecting his fellow conspirators than he would have shown in arranging for a supporting cast in a theatrical performance. Herold was mumbling reassuring words to him. Booth closed his eyes to shut out the sight of his narrow-chinned un-shaven face that seemed particularly repulsive in the cold morning light.

"Mr. Cox told me that he'd send someone to us early this morning," Herold said. "Maybe——"

Booth cursed the mention of Cox's name. He asked Herold for the blanket he had thrown off, and then ordered him to look after the horses. In a few minutes the boy came running back excitedly, saying that Booth's horse had pulled the tie-rope loose and wandered away. Booth sat up, spitting out his fury in quick venomous words. Then he realized that it was futile to rail at this lumpish oaf who could not even understand the reason for his anger. He choked back his rage and explained quietly to Herold that he was to go in search of the mare and that he was to make no noise as he went through the woods.

Herold was gone for a long while. Booth lay quiet, the wrathful blood still pounding. He fumed at the evil mischance that had caused him to catch his spur in the Yankee flag—that one brief instant had overthrown all his plans, spoiled his chances for an easy escape. But for that he might be in Virginia now, among friends of the Confederacy. He could not travel with this broken leg, and he was terribly frightened at the prospect of becoming seriously ill out here in this horrible wilderness. He tried to force himself to throw off the paralyzing effect of the fever, but he felt weak and shaky, and he longed for the privilege of being sick in comfort and peace.

The heavy, moisture-laden clouds swept over the bleak pine barrens. There was an oppressive silence broken only by the occasional cawing of some distant crows. This was Easter Sunday, Booth realized with a sudden shock. Easter Sunday—the symbol of resurrection and renascent life. He shivered and breathed into his cold-stiffened hands.

He listened intently for the sound of Herold's returning footsteps, but he could hear nothing except the cawing of the crows. And then, from some place far away, came the sound of a shrill whistle. It was answered almost immediately by another whistle from a place much closer. He sat up and slid his revolver out of its holster.

In a few minutes he heard the voices of two men talking to each other as they approached the place where he was lying. He pulled back the hammer of his revolver with a sharp click. Then he recognized Herold's voice. He saw him returning, followed by a lanky middle-aged stranger who was leading Booth's mare.

"This is the gentleman Mr. Cox sent to us," Herold said. "His name is Thomas Jones, and he found your horse."

Booth released the hammer of his revolver and put the weapon under the blanket. Cox's emissary was a shabbily dressed farmer with a gaunt sad face. Long,

mournfully drooping mustaches emphasized the natural melancholy of his features, but the quizzical blue
eyes that gazed unabashedly into Booth's indicated
that the man was no helplessly subjected tenant
farmer.

"Who are you?" Booth asked bluntly. "Do you
work for this fellow Cox?"

"Not exactly," Jones said in a slow deliberate
drawl. "Sometimes I help him out with the planting,
but I wouldn't say I worked for him. I have a farm of
my own here. Sam Cox is my foster-brother. We
were brought up together." He pulled an old pipe
from his pocket and leisurely began to fill it with tobacco.

Herold put in an eager word. "Mr. Jones has a
boat. He can get us across the river. He says—"

Booth held up his hand for silence. "I want no
help from Mr. Cox or any of his friends," he said
stubbornly.

Jones never changed his blank expression, but he
said quietly: "Your friend here said you were sick.
You look pretty peaked. I thought I might be able to
help you somehow—"

Booth turned away from him wearily. He was so
thoroughly miserable that he no longer cared what
happened. The fever was already beginning to make
him feel lightheaded, and this Mr. Jones had an air
of unreality about him as he stood there, gray and insubstantial against the dark pines.

# The Man Who Killed Lincoln

"I couldn't let a sick man lie out here without offering to help him," Jones said.

Booth looked up at him, trying to fix the features that were wavering uncertainly. There was a queer little smile on Jones' ordinarily wooden face as he spoke. "So you're the man who shot Abe Lincoln, eh? Well, I must say there's plenty of folks around here who won't be sorry to see him gone. I don't hold with what Sam Cox said to you. Oh, he told me about it. Sam has an awful hot temper, you know. He says the first thing that comes into his mind. He'll always take the other side in an argument, and he'd just as soon be wrong as right. Sooner, sometimes, I think. And he's worried about his boy, of course. I wouldn't pay too much attention to what he said. He asked me to get you across the river, and he sent you something to eat." Jones took out a paper parcel and put it down beside Booth.

Booth wetted his dry lips with his tongue. "Can you get me something to drink? Some brandy—whiskey—anything. I must have a drink or I'll—"

Jones promised to bring him anything he needed. He began to talk to Herold in a quiet serious voice, and Booth heard him tell the boy that he must under no circumstances build a fire, shoot off a gun or let the horses get loose again. He showed Herold where there was a near-by spring, but he warned him to be careful, since it was sometimes used by people in the neighborhood.

"When do you think you can get me across the river?" Booth asked hoarsely. "I can't lie out here in the open. I've got to get shelter and medical attention."

"You'll have to wait here a bit until things quiet down, I'm afraid. There's too many Yankee soldiers around here now to take any chances. I'd invite you to my own house if it wasn't for the niggers there. You ain't any ordinary contraband, you know. Every nigger in the country is weeping and wailing for Lincoln. I wouldn't even trust my own men if they was to find out who you are."

Booth swore feebly, angered at the very thought of Negroes preventing him from getting shelter when he needed it most. He begged Jones to bring him the Washington newspapers and any others he could get. Then, half-embarrassedly, he thanked the man for his proffered services, and apologized as well as he could for his own discourtesy.

The day dragged on slowly. Booth fell asleep, occasionally muttering an incoherent phrase as his mind broke fitfully through the barriers of unconsciousness. Davy Herold sat on the ground beside him, industriously cleaning and polishing his carbine. Booth finally opened his eyes and stared up at the clouds drifting across the opening in the pines above him. He wondered how long it would be before he succumbed to the fever that was rising higher and higher in his blood. He turned his head and languidly watched his companion as he worked away at the gun. The boy seemed to be utterly absorbed in his task, oblivious of weather or danger. He began to whistle softly to himself as he rubbed vigorously at the steel with a bit of grimy cloth.

"David, have you ever wondered what it is like to die?" Booth asked suddenly.

The boy stopped whistling. His hand went on polishing mechanically. "I thought you was asleep," he said nervously. "I was just trying to clean this gun up a bit. Lloyd let it get rusty."

"Try your hand at these," Booth said, giving him his revolvers and bowie knife. Herold took them, spun the revolver chambers expertly, and then pulled off the percussion caps to examine them carefully, one by one. He loved firearms, and he was fascinated by weapons of all kinds.

"You didn't answer my question," Booth said.

"What question?"

"I asked you if you had ever wondered about dying."

"Why do you talk like that?" Herold said fearfully. "This ain't no time to be talking about dying. We got away, all right. We'll be in Virginia soon and everything will be fine."

"But did you ever wonder what it is like to die?" Booth persisted.

"Sure. I've seen people die."

"Have you ever imagined yourself dying?"

"Well, no—not exactly. . . ."

"What do you think it would be like?"

"Terrible, I suppose. Why do you want to talk about it?"

"Do you believe that there is a God, David? And do you pray to him?"

Herold looked down and rubbed away at the pistol. "Sure I do," he said slowly. "I always say my prayers before I go to sleep. I did last night even."

Booth made no attempt to continue the conversation. The simple, direct mind of his companion invited no subtleties of speculation.

"Don't forget to clean the knife, too," he said tiredly.

Herold put down the revolver and drew the dagger out of its sheath. "There's blood on it," he announced in an awed voice. "Is it Lincoln's blood?"

"No. It's the blood of that Yankee officer who was in the box with him."

Herold plunged the blade into the ground, thrusting the dark stains deep into the soil. The knife was soon bright again. He rubbed off the clinging particles of earth with his rag. Then he examined the shining blade carefully. " 'Liberty and Independence,' " he read out loud. " 'America—the land of the brave and the free. Sheffield, England.' "

"A most appropriate inscription," Booth said dryly. "England should know. If she had supported the Confederacy as she promised to do, the South would now be free."

He lay still, watching the wide panorama of the shifting clouds above him, and then he must have dozed off again, for he seemed, somehow, to be in Edwin's house in New York, and there were brightly chattering people around him, talking of the theater. He wanted something to drink, but his mother was in the room, and he hesitated to ask for brandy in her presence.

They were talking about the war, these people who switched gaily from one subject to another, and they seemed to be strangely oblivious of his presence, for he heard one of them mention his name. There was an abrupt and pregnant silence, and then someone who was mindful of the manners of good society changed the subject quickly, asking an innocuous question about the new bill at the Winter Garden. He walked out into the hall, in search of a drink of brandy. There was an odor of pine needles in the dark hallway, and it was extraordinarily cold there. He had to get a drink somewhere.

Brandy, brandy. The words "I shall die if I don't have a drop of brandy, yes, brandy," began to run through his mind like the refrain of a song. Where had he heard these words before? And then he realized that the phrase was the curtain line spoken at the end of the second act of *Our American Cousin*. Words from the play began to repeat themselves far down in the depths of his mind. "Don't know the manners of good society, eh? Well, I guess I know enough to turn you inside out, old gal—you sockdologizing old man-trap. Don't know the manners of good society, eh? . . ."

He was fully awake now, lying under the trees again. "David," he said gravely, "do you know the manners of good society? It's very important that you do because—"

Herold was looking at him with a frightened expression. The boy was standing up. His figure seemed enormous against the sky. *Brandy, yes, brandy. . . . Don't keep looking at me like that, you fool. Don't you know the manners of good society?* Booth felt suddenly that he was going to be very sick. His stomach was rising on him, and his mouth was dry. He wiped his lips with the back of his hand. *Don't know the manners of good society, eh? I shall die if I don't have a drop of brandy, yes, brandy, brandy. . . .*

"David," he mumbled, "for God's sake, get me some brandy. My throat is—" Voices chattering somewhere inside his own mind grew louder. He could hear them whispering . . . whispering . . . speaking the same words over and over again, until the monotony of their repetition called for an answer. Then he began to reply to them, arguing about the manners of good society, while Herold looked on helplessly, and the sky darkened slowly into night.

Booth awoke at daybreak after having slept for more than twelve hours. It was bitterly cold; the temperature had gone down nearly to the freezing point during the night, and there was a heavy dew on the grass. But the sun was shining. Its yellow rays were filtering through the rising mists, and the sky had only a few straggling clouds in it.

He tried to raise himself to a sitting position. The fever was still burning in his body, but his mind was clear now, freed from the constant stream of fantastic images that had tortured him all night long. His leg was terribly swollen, pressing against the tight splints Mudd had bound around it. He managed to sit up. The sudden change of position made his head feel as though the brain inside it were loose, jolted into quick pain by the movement. He put his icy hands against his face. His beard was beginning to grow out, and his skin felt oily and unpleasant to touch. He shivered violently as the cold air struck his body.

He saw that Herold was still asleep, and he noticed that the two horses were securely tied to trees. The place looked different in the sunlight, less gloomy, less terrible in its stark barrenness, and even the pale clay soil seemed to take on a more cheerful color in the mellow rays of the sun.

As he sat there, gazing around at the wilderness in

which he had passed another night, he was reminded
suddenly of his father. The old man had wandered
away from home one evening after an angry quarrel
with his wife. Booth had found him in the morning,
lying under a tree with his face upturned to the rising sun. He had an empty whiskey bottle in his hand,
and as soon as he was awakened, he complained bitterly of having a bad taste in his mouth, which, he
said, could be taken away only by having more whiskey to wash it down. Booth suddenly felt an odd
streak of affection for his father. The old fellow, for
all his tyrannical ways and sudden outbursts of temper, had often been amusing in his very waywardness.
Booth remembered their conversation that morning.
His father had explained elaborately that he had
gone into the woods to commune with nature, to greet
the coming of springtime with the proper libations.
Men slept too much in beds, he said seriously, and by
doing so lost contact with the feel of the earth against
their bodies—and anyway, they needed physical
hardship occasionally to help strengthen their souls.
He discreetly refrained from mentioning anything
about the quarrel that had made him leave the house,
and when he reached home he acted toward his wife
as if it had never taken place at all.

The old man had been dead for nearly thirteen
years. It was silly to keep on hating him now. He
must have had many good qualities—certainly his
wife, for all the tribulation he had caused her, was

still devoted to his memory, and people who had known him still mentioned him with admiration. Junius Brutus had already become a legend in the American theater—his fame had perhaps been enhanced by his strange antics. No one who had ever met him could forget the strong-willed old actor who had so often enraged managers, fellow actors and audiences in England and America by his sudden changes of mind and his quick belligerency.

Booth was brought back to the present with a start. A sound came to him from far away, rising thin and clear in the bright morning air. There was no mistaking what it was. He knew that he was listening to a soldier's bugle sounding reveille. He turned to Herold to waken him, but the boy was already sitting up.

"There are soldiers in the neighborhood, David," he said grimly. "I just heard a bugle blowing somewhere."

Herold reached for his carbine. "Jesus, I thought I dreamt that sound. What'll we do?" he asked in sudden panic.

"We can't do anything. If we ride away from here we might head right toward a searching party. We might just as well stay here and see what happens. They may not come this way at all."

Herold kept looking nervously around, as if he expected to see a troop of soldiers come crashing through the bushes any minute. Booth sat very still, a revolver in each hand.

230

Time passed slowly. Booth's head finally sank down in abject misery. He longed for a bed, for refuge of some sort, and for surcease from this constant vigilance. Somehow he must get across the river, reach the comfort of a Southern home, where people would not be afraid to take him in. Meanwhile he waited, and he heard nothing more of the soldiers. More than an hour went by, and the sun rose slowly above the tops of the pine trees. Finally, he heard a voice calling in the distance. Herold got up, cocked his gun and slipped noiselessly into the underbrush. Booth raised his head and sat still, balancing his revolvers in his hands, trying to look through the spaces between the scattered pines.

Then he heard a whistle. It was the same whistle that had announced Jones' arrival on the previous morning. He felt relieved, but he still kept his pistols ready until Jones rode into the camp accompanied by Herold. Jones looked at Booth's hot flushed face, and he did not need to ask how he felt. He told him that he had brought him another blanket, a bottle of whiskey and plenty of food. Then he took some newspapers from his pocket and handed them to Booth.

"There's a lot of soldiers in the neighborhood," he said casually. "You'd better lie still today and keep a sharp lookout."

"Yes, I know," Booth said, tearing open one of the papers. "We heard a bugle only a little while ago.

Did you see them anywhere? How did you get through? Why did you make so much noise?"

"I was just doing a little innocent hog-calling. Soldiers wouldn't pick up a man for calling hogs to come in and get fed, would they now? I'm a good hog-caller, too. It's lucky there wasn't any hogs around in these here woods or I'd have brought 'em right along with me."

Booth spread out the big sheets of *The National Intelligencer*. The front page, which was always given over to advertising, carried no indication that anything unusual had happened. In fact, at the top of the page, as he noticed with a shock, there was an announcement stating that on Saturday evening, April 15th, a benefit performance would be given for Miss Jennie Gourlay at Ford's Theater. It was unthinkable that this play could have gone on as scheduled. The paper evidently had not had time to take out the advertisement. Booth turned the sheet hastily. There were heavy black rules lining the news columns on the second page. He scanned the description of Lincoln's death, and then sought eagerly for something about himself. Finally, he found his own name. There was a brief account—all too brief, he thought. The paper did not seem to be quite sure of the facts about him. Perhaps it was deliberately playing him down. He looked at the *Intelligencer* first, because this was the paper to which he had sent his letter explaining the reasons for his act. Surely Matthews could not have failed to deliver his message.

He turned the pages of the other papers over frantically. Several of the New York papers did not even mention his name, and they did not seem to be at all certain as to who had done the actual shooting.

He could not find his letter anywhere. He picked up the *Intelligencer* again and studied it more closely. His eyes still kept searching the pages for the letter, but there was no mention of it. He saw a dispatch from Stanton which said that it had now been "ascertained with reasonable certainty" that John Wilkes Booth had been engaged in the crime. The trunk he had left in the National Hotel had evidently been searched, for Stanton referred to a letter from O'Laughlin which had been found there. And then he read a notice stating that a ten-thousand-dollar reward had been offered by General Augur, and he wondered whether Jones had seen it too.

He read that a knife had been found on F Street between Ninth and Tenth. This mystified him considerably, for it was certainly not his. He noticed that his horse had been traced to Pumphrey's stable, and he derived a bit of amusement from a statement that Surratt was believed to be Seward's assailant.

And then he saw a headline ROUTE PURSUED BY THE CRIMINALS, and under it he read: "About eleven o'clock last night, two men crossed the Anacostia Bridge, one of whom gave his name as Booth, and the

other as Smith. The latter is believed to be John Surratt. . . . Last night a riderless horse was found, which
has been identified by the proprietor as having been
hired from his establishment. Accounts are conflicting as to whether Booth crossed the bridge on horseback or on foot, but as it is believed he rode across, it
is presumed he changed his horse."

He read about the riderless horse with growing bewilderment. Then it occurred to him that it must have
been Lewis Paine's. But why had Paine abandoned
his mount?

There was no trace of the letter. Had Matthews
actually delivered it? Had he opened it—and destroyed it? Or had he been searched by the Federal
police? Had the Government found it? And if they
had, why were they suppressing it? Was the world to
be kept deliberately in ignorance? How could anyone be expected to understand what he had done if his
words of justification were never allowed to see the
light of day?

Jones had unwrapped the bundle of food he had
brought with him. Herold handed some bread and
ham to Booth, and poured out lukewarm coffee in a
tin cup.

"Can't you get me some Southern papers?" Booth
asked petulantly. "I must find out what the South is
saying. So far I have seen no evidence of her taking
advantage of this opportunity to press the war—"

234

# Monday, April 17

"But the war's all over," Jones said with a puzzled air. "General Lee surrendered. How can—"

Booth looked up angrily at Jones. "Don't tell me that the war is over," he said. "I have sacrificed my career, my family, perhaps my life, in order to help the South. The least the South can do is to help herself now. There must be—"

Herold suddenly jumped to his feet, signaling for silence. He stood at attention like a well-trained hunting dog, his mouth full of bread and meat on which he had stopped chewing.

There were sounds in the forest, sounds of many horses' hoofs moving at a light trot. A man's voice rang out. The horses broke into a canter, and a troop of cavalrymen rode past, so close that Booth could see the flashing of steel in the open spaces under the trees. In a moment they were gone. The woods were silent again. Herold began to chew on his food with a broad grin on his distended face.

Jones, who had been holding the muzzle of his own horse firmly in his hands, released the animal and drew a long breath. "I reckon you'll never have a narrower one than that," he said, smiling. "Did you see the way that mare of yours was pulling at the halter? I thought sure she was going to give us all away when she heard them cavalry horses."

He explained to Booth that he must get rid of the two horses before they betrayed him by neighing.

Booth suggested that he take them away with him immediately.

"I don't want any part in killing 'em," Jones said gravely. "I just couldn't bring myself to do it. I'll show Mr. Herold where to take 'em into the swamps, so there won't be any traces of their carcasses."

Jones had gone, taking Herold and the two animals with him. Booth hated to see the little mare led away to her death. But her presence was endangering his life, and he could not afford to indulge in sentimentality.

He helped himself to some whiskey and then read and re-read the newspapers Jones had brought. He realized now how badly the conspiracy had been bungled. He still could not understand how Lewis Paine could have left the Seward house without first making sure that his victim was dead. The papers said that Seward's life had been saved by a steel collar which the surgeons had placed on his neck to support his fractured jaw. But Paine should have noticed it—certainly he must have felt that his blade was striking against metal rather than flesh. And then there are, of course, plenty of other ways of killing a man besides cutting his throat.

He had expected nothing of Atzerodt, so his defection did not surprise him, but Surratt's failure was inexplicable. The papers reported only that General Grant had been reached by a telegram at the Delaware River ferry, and that he had returned immediately to Washington. There was no mention of any attempted attack on him.

Everything had gone wrong—except the killing of Lincoln, and Booth felt that that had succeeded only because he had done it himself. It seemed incredible to him, though, that the authorities in Washington could have been so stupidly slow in realizing that it was he who had shot Lincoln. The early editions of the newspapers expressed only uncertainty and bewilderment. He wondered, too, why the Government had been so long delayed in getting an organized pursuit under way. Perhaps Surratt's mysterious forces had done more than cut telegraph wires. Why, for instance, had the sentry let him cross the bridge after he had given him his name and a rather poor excuse? The sentry had whispered something to the Sergeant in charge, he remembered, and then they had let him go through. What had the sentry said? The men at the bridge almost seemed to have been expecting his arrival. And yet he had told no one that he was going to use his own name. He had not known it himself until he had blurted it out to the sentry. Of course, he had mentioned to Surratt that he was going to use the Navy Yard Bridge. Had Surratt told someone to expect him there? Who were these men who were able to accomplish so much in the enemy's city, and why had Surratt been so obdurate in refusing to tell him anything about them?

He knew that Lincoln's death had been desired by
many people. He recalled the rumors concerning
other conspirators who were supposed to have been
working toward the same end that he himself had ac-
complished. Had Surratt in some way managed to
tie the two conspiracies together and utilize both
forces at once? What were Surratt's connections? If
he could command such power, why had he so cautiously refrained from acting himself?

And then, while these suspicions were rising
through his mind, he heard two distant shots, and he
knew that the horses had been killed. He was isolated
in this wilderness now, and he could depend only on
Jones to get him out. It would be impossible for him
to reach the river while the woods were full of soldiers. He might have to wait here for days.

Certain things he had done unthinkingly—or left
undone—now began to disturb him. Why had he ever
been fool enough to accept the help that had been offered to him through Surratt without insisting on
knowing its source? He sensed that the people who
had been interested in his actions were well organized
and capably directed. They had succeeded in conceal-
ing their identity even from him. He did not mind
taking upon his own head all the guilt for the assassination, but he did want to be sure that the people
who had worked with him had done so for reasons
that were as pure and patriotic as his own.

This was not the first time that these suspicions had

occurred to him, but hitherto he had suppressed them, for he had either been too eager to see his plot against Lincoln carried out, or he had been too occupied with the activity of escape to give them attention. Now that he was alone, so that he could think and analyze, he regretted his carelessness and his haste. He determined to write down again his motives for what he had done. If he were to be killed he wanted to leave the world some evidence of his intentions, for he began to be afraid of the unknown alliance he had made. He still resented the fact that his letter to *The National Intelligencer* had not appeared.

He took out his notebook and opened it to a blank page. The book was a diary for 1864, but he had never bothered to use it. On the page to which he turned he had once written *Te amo*, and below these romantic words he now put the date "April 13, 14, Friday the Ides." He had only a hazy idea of what the word "Ides" meant, but he liked the expression because of its association with Brutus and the death of Caesar.

"Until today," he wrote, "nothing was ever thought of sacrificing to our country's wrongs. For six months we had worked to capture. But our cause being almost lost, something decisive and great must be done. But its failure was owing to others, who did not strike for their country with a heart. I struck boldly and not as the papers say." [He resented more than anything else the imputations that he had acted liked a cowardly cutthroat, taking his victim unawares. He felt that what he had done was justified because he had shot his man in a public theater without any attempt to conceal his own identity.] "I walked with a firm step through a thousand of his friends, was stopped, but pushed on. A colonel was at his side. I shouted *Sic semper* before I fired. In jumping broke my leg. I passed all his pickets. Rode sixty miles that night, with the bone of my leg tearing the flesh at every jump."

He stopped and read over what he had written. He did not notice his unconscious exaggeration in the statement that he had ridden sixty miles, nor was he aware of the fact that he had carefully refrained from mentioning Lincoln's name. He went on, holding his pencil tightly in his hand, writing with the concentration of a schoolboy who seeks to justify some misdeed in a letter to a sympathetic friend. And, like a schoolboy, he took it for granted that his reader would know to whom he was referring when he said "he" and "his" and "him."

"I can never repent it, though we hated to kill. Our country owed all her troubles to him, and God simply made me the instrument of His punishment. The country is not what it was. This forced Union is not what I have loved. I care not what becomes of me. I have no desire to outlive my country. This night (before the deed) I wrote a long article and left it for one of the editors of the *National Intelligencer* in which I fully set forth our reasons for our proceeding. He or the gov'n—"

A whistle sounded shrilly somewhere in the pine woods. He hastily put his notebook away and replied softly to the signal. Davy Herold walked into the clearing. His feet were covered with partially dried mud, and his face was hot and perspired.

"That's as nasty a job as I ever had to do," the boy said unhappily. "Them poor damn-fool horses just stood there and watched me put a pistol to their heads—" He rubbed his hands on his coat sleeves. "I left 'em in a bog. I hope they get covered up quick by the mud before the turkey buzzards start coming down."

"Or before some of those Yankee soldiers find them there," Booth said quietly.

Herold sat down heavily, searching Booth's face. "I wonder if we did right in shooting 'em," he said in a troubled voice. "We'd sure be in a tight fix if we had to move out of here in a hurry."

Booth lay back, supporting his head on his hand. Far above him in the blue sky two turkey buzzards were soaring in wide circles. He watched them drop down over the woods where the dead horses were. Then another black spot appeared, and, beyond it, still another.

He lay there and watched the buzzards marshaling their forces in the sky. He said nothing about them to Davy Herold. He remained absolutely still, and he could feel the fever rising again as the day waned. He knew that he was going to have another bad night, but he had some whiskey now to help him through it. He uncorked the bottle and drank heavily. After a while he felt drowsy. As he closed his eyes, the ground suddenly seemed to rise in a whirling motion, carrying him up into space. He was swept around in long, slow gyrations, moving ever upward. From the void around him voices began to speak in a soft, hardly audible jabber, and then they gradually became louder. Soon they were calling to him insistently in a horrible subhuman chorus. He had to answer them, and the sound of his voice, arguing with them one-sidedly, rose into the quiet afternoon air.

Herold, listening to him, sat and shivered, and he did not even notice the distant black shapes that kept dropping down out of the sky.

---

### Monday, April 17. 11:15 P.M.

---

The door of the little house on H Street opened slowly, letting through a faint streak of light. The four officers standing on the porch could hear the woman make a quickly stifled sound before she asked them what they wanted.

Major Smith, who was in charge of the party,

spoke to her. His voice was as noncommittal as though he had come to pay a social call.

"Are you Mrs. Surratt?" he asked.

"I am the widow of John H. Surratt," she answered, tightening her hands upon the door as she leaned against it for support. It swung gently back and forth on its hinges, making the long streak of light widen and narrow as the door moved.

"Are you the mother of John H. Surratt, Jr?"

She seemed to be moving her lips as though she were praying. Finally, she answered in a voice which was so low that it could hardly be heard.

"Yes," she said. "I am. What do you want of me?"

The Major cleared his throat. "We have come to arrest you and everyone in your house." He stopped speaking and stood looking down at the streak of light across the porch. He hated dealing with women, and he felt embarrassed and awkward. "We will have to take you to General Augur's headquarters for examination." He cleared his throat again. "You will have to let us come in, for we have orders to search this house as well as to arrest you. I'm sorry——"

She opened the door slowly and stepped back toward the parlor entrance. The light from the dimly burning gas jet in the hallway fell on her face, and they could see that she had been crying.

"This house was searched on Friday night," she said. "Isn't that enough? What can you hope to find now?"

"I have my orders, madam, and they are to arrest you and search this house—thoroughly. Will you wait here with me while my men go through to make certain that we find all the occupants?"

"There are only women here now," she said, sitting down on the sofa in the parlor. "Four of us—and a colored maid in the kitchen."

Smith nodded to his men, and they scattered themselves through the house. He watched the woman on the sofa closely, but he made no attempt to question her, for that was no part of his duty. She sat quietly, her head lowered and her lips moving again in prayer.

His men came in, bringing the women with them, one after the other.

"Do you want the colored wench in the basement?" an officer asked.

Smith shrugged his shoulders. "She probably doesn't know anything about what happened here. Let her stay there. Now, ladies, will you get ready? I have to take you to General Augur's headquarters."

"May we have a carriage?" Mrs. Surratt asked. "It's a damp cold night, and I don't want my daughter and these other ladies to—"

"Of course. Go out and find a carriage, Rosch," Smith said to one of his men. Then he turned to the women. "You'll need your hats and coats. I'm going to let Mrs. Surratt go upstairs to get them for you. Mr. Samson here will have to go along with her. I have had very careful instructions about—"

"—about not letting anyone have a chance to destroy evidence?" Mrs. Surratt said.

"Exactly, madam," Smith said, smiling slightly. "Now, if you will go to get these ladies' things—"

She left the room, followed closely by the detective. Smith stood with his aide, Captain Wermerskirch, in heavy silence. The bell on the front door clanged loudly. Wermerskirch opened the door to admit another man from headquarters. The three officers stood waiting like privates on sentry duty until Mrs. Surratt came down with the clothing. While the women were putting on their wraps, the bell rang again.

"That's your carriage, ladies," Smith said. "Will you open the door, Mr. Morgan?" he said, speaking to the officer who had just arrived.

Morgan, who had remained near the front door, immediately opened it. A tall man, who was wearing a white patch of cloth as a cap, stood on the porch. He carried a pickax over his shoulder, and he was dressed like a laborer, except for the fact that he wore shabby riding boots.

"I guess there's some mistake," the man said, trying to back away from the door.

"Whom did you come to see?" Morgan asked.

"Mrs. Surratt, but—"

"This is Mrs. Surratt's house. Come right in. She's at home."

"I think there's some mistake, sir. I won't bother her now. It's not important."

"What did you want to see her about?"

"She sent for me to dig a gutter in her back yard, but I can come back tomorrow. She's probably busy now."

"Oh, no, she's not. If she sent for you she'll want to see you. Come in."

The man shuffled through the doorway. Morgan noticed that his boots were stained with mud, and that his trousers, which were tucked into his boot-tops, were wet. The white cloth on his head was evidently a piece torn from the drawers of his underclothing. He was certainly a curious visitor for a presumably respectable lady to be receiving in the middle of the night.

Morgan began to question him about his means of livelihood and his acquaintance with Mrs. Surratt. The man said that he was a street laborer who slept where he could, and that he made a scanty living by digging. He was a Southerner, he admitted, but he had left the South rather than fight in the Confederate Army. He had his oath of allegiance with him, he said, pulling out a much-folded piece of paper to show to the officer.

Morgan opened the document and read it. The name "Lewis Paine, Fauquier County, Virginia" meant nothing to him, but a phrase written in at the end of the printed form immediately caught his eye.

"It says here that you are to go north of Philadelphia and remain there during the war," Morgan said suspiciously. The country was flooded with these minor evaders and petty offenders; it was hardly worth making any efforts to arrest them, but this one had walked right into the arms of the law. They would have to hold him for questioning, at least.

"The war's over, ain't it?" Paine said easily. "And anyway I couldn't make a living up North."

Morgan handed the document back to him. "You'd better wait here," he said. "I want to see if Mrs. Surratt knows who you are."

He went to the parlor door and spoke to Major Smith. Mrs. Surratt was kneeling on the floor, leading her little flock in prayer. Smith waited for her to finish.

"There's a man here who says you sent for him," he said as soon as she got to her feet. "I want you to look at him. He's out in the hall."

She walked to the doorway and peered nearsightedly at the giant standing there with his absurd cap on his head. She raised her hands, apparently frightened. "Before God, I never saw him until this minute, gentlemen. I'm glad you were here when he came. He seems to be a rough-looking brute. I should be afraid to meet him alone."

Smith stood looking at the impassive face towering over him in the dimly lighted hallway. "I guess you'd better send him along to Augur's," he said to Morgan.

"They may want him for something there. You never can tell these days who's wanted for what."

---

## *Wednesday, April 19*

---

Booth was stretched out upon the very spot where he had lain for four days. All day Tuesday he had been very sick—so sick that he could hardly remember the day at all. He was better now, although he was still affected by the fever that burned in his veins. And his mind was rational again; he had even been able to read the newspapers Jones had brought.

The papers had been unpleasant reminders of what was happening in the outside world. He had read them with disgust—and fascination. He hated what he read, for the papers were universally condemnatory, but he had to see what they were saying. He had been particularly outraged by some Confederate officers on parole in the North who had gone out of their way to denounce him publicly. Their action made him feel that he had sacrificed himself for people who were unworthy of what he had tried to do for them. He was infuriated by the fact that many of the Northern newspapers had seen fit to describe him as a second-rate actor, a fellow of no ability who was not to be taken seriously as an artist. He resented these spiteful criticisms of his acting even more than he did the personal abuse that was appearing everywhere. He felt that it was unfair to use such tactics, for these same papers had often praised his acting in the past.

Naturally, he could not talk about this to Herold, who was too stupid to understand the sensitive mind of an artist, but he did discuss with him the news reports of the great man hunt that was covering half a dozen States. They had pored together over the accounts which described how the Potomac was being patrolled. They elaborated plans and ways to cross a river on which every fishing smack and pleasure boat was being stopped for examination.

They read how the North was marshaling the services of thousands of sailors, soldiers and police who were desperately eager to capture them for the enormous rewards that had been offered. Jones had told them that the little town of Port Tobacco was filled with troops. Yesterday, at Brawner's Hotel there, a detective had approached Jones, saying that he would pay one hundred thousand dollars for information leading to Booth's arrest. And it was a bona-fide offer, Booth knew, for Jones had described to him the man who had made it, and from the description he was able to recognize his old friend, Captain Williams of the Washington cavalry police—the officer he had encountered on the sidewalk in front of Ford's Theater just before he went inside to fire the fatal shot.

The effect of that single shot was spreading now

with dreadful swiftness. Millions of Northerners were seeking him everywhere, suspecting every stranger of being John Wilkes Booth. He had read that they were on the point of capturing him in Tamaqua, Pennsylvania—that he had been seen crossing the border to Canada. The whole country was in the frenzy of a witch hunt for him, and he knew that he could be safe only with men like Jones, loyal Southerners who would spurn offers of fantastic wealth rather than sell out one of their own.

The effect of his shot was spreading; its thunder was rolling across the land. He was vividly aware of what was taking place in Washington, for he knew that this was the day on which the North was holding the funeral of the man he had killed.

He had read the plans for the elaborate ceremony. He knew at what time it was to begin, the names of the officials who were to attend, the route the long procession was to take through the streets of the city. And he knew that at this moment, in the bright sunshine of a spring afternoon, they were carrying the body of Abraham Lincoln out of the White House.

This was the end of his enemy's reign. But much as Booth had hated him, he could feel no exultation at the thought of Lincoln's funeral. The possibility of his own death was too close to him now.

The long hours of lonely silence were beginning to eat away at his belief in his own invincibility. He realized that even he himself could die.

Jones had brought the papers again, and Booth roused himself from his sick lethargy to read them. It seemed to him that he did nothing but read newspapers. They came to him, one day's issue after the other, and these printed sheets, more than anything else, had marked the passing of time while he had waited there in the thicket like a wounded animal, hoping that the chase would pass him by. And the news these papers had brought to him had been a series of disappointments, a crescendo of disaster that was still rising. He had read of the arrests of his friends—one after another they had been caught, Mrs. Surratt, Paine, Arnold and O'Laughlin—and he was afraid that it was only a matter of time before Atzerodt and John Surratt would be captured too. He feared the headlines of each day's paper, and his fears were always justified, for every day brought him more news of the collapse of his conspiracy, and he saw the men and women he had involved in it being dragged closer and closer to the scaffold.

The big white sheets with their small type ranked in column after column of ill tidings were in front of him always, and he read them through, studying even the little advertisements that kept on placidly appearing while history's thunder crashed. He was lying on his back, reading a description of Lincoln's funeral. The sky was covered with clouds again, and

251

there was a threat of rain in the mist-laden air. The world around him seemed to be more silent, more motionless than it had been when the sun was shining. The trees stood deadly still, holding their branches with limp quietness under the lowering gray clouds.

He read of the procession which had marched along the Avenue in yesterday's sunshine, carrying Lincoln's body from the White House to the Capitol where it was now lying in state under the great dome. He saw the thousands and the tens of thousands of people who had come to the city to line the streets. He heard the slow sullen firing of the minute guns and the steady tolling of church bells; heard the dirges of the military bands; saw the great black hearse towering over the heads of the multitude. And he could feel the passion and the fury of the crowds in the streets, for these people, he knew, had come not only to mourn, but to call down vengeance upon the head of the man who had slain their leader.

He was keenly aware of their hatred; it filtered through the conventional wording of the news dispatches, and it was apparent in the editorials he had read in paper after paper. He knew that men had been beaten and hanged for being incautious enough to remark that Abraham Lincoln had met a just death. He knew that mobs everywhere were hunting down people whose sympathies for the South were only suspected. He knew that newspapers, whose policies had been directed against the President, had had their offices sacked and burned, and their presses thrown out in the street. The North was striking out blindly in its wounded rage, making others the butt of its wrath, because he, the archconspirator, could not be reached.

It gave him a shock of horror to realize that if he were now to walk through the city of Washington where he had once been idolized, he would surely be torn to pieces by the very people who had formerly admired him. Vengeance—vengeance and persecution were all that he could expect now. And he was afraid, more afraid than he had ever been before. These outraged Northerners would never rest until they had tracked him down. He had to muster every last effort to get away from his present hiding place. It was too dangerously near the North.

He must get out of this accursed wilderness immediately. He had lain here for days while the Yankees had had a chance to consolidate their forces and organize their pursuit. He must reach Southern territory quickly. He was surely well enough to travel now.

He called Herold to him, and told him that he must go through the woods to find Jones and arrange for the use of his boat. They could wait here no longer. He was determined to cross the river that night.

It was dark by the time Herold returned with Jones. Booth had fallen asleep, and he awoke with a start to find the two men bending over him. His fever had risen again, and he felt sick and shaken as soon as he tried to sit up.

He spoke to Jones, telling him that he must cross the river at once, no matter what the risk might be. There was impatience in his voice, impatience and fear so great that Jones did not even try to dissuade him.

Herold gathered their few scattered belongings together and rolled them up in their blankets. Jones helped Booth stand on one foot, and then they lifted him up on the back of the old mare that Jones had brought from his farm. Booth sat in the saddle, hardly conscious of what was happening to him. He felt the horse move forward with a lurch, and he knew that he was starting forth on his journey again. Wet branches brushed against his face, and the horse stumbled once or twice in the darkness, but Booth paid no attention to the road he was traveling. They went on silently for what seemed to him to be a very long time.

He heard Jones whispering to Herold that they were approaching a public road, and that they would have to use great care in proceeding along it. Herold held the horse while Jones went on ahead. In a few minutes the sound of a whistle came to them faintly. Herold led the horse through the woods to the edge of the road, and Jones advanced again to signal when the way was clear. This procedure was repeated many times, so their progress was very slow.

Suddenly Jones was at their side, telling Herold they were approaching a Negro shanty that was close to the road. They went forward cautiously, watching the dim light burning in the cabin, but no one noticed them, and then they were in complete darkness again, moving down the road. Jones stayed with them, for there was another house to pass—the house of a white man who kept a pack of hunting dogs. They came in sight of it, and they could see lights burning in the windows. They listened fearfully for the dogs, but they got past without disturbing them. In a few minutes they were able to turn off the road into the woods. Jones took the halter from Herold and led the horse down a narrow track toward his own farm. In a little while they came upon a clearing where a barn stood looming above the trees.

Jones tied the horse to a tree near the barn, and told them to wait until he could bring something to eat. Booth looked down at Jones' face as it was turned toward him, a dim white spot in the darkness, and he spoke to him in a pleading voice. "Can't you take me into your house and let me have a cup of hot coffee there?" he asked, and his voice broke, for he knew that what he was proposing was impossible, and that he was speaking out of his own despair. He knew that Jones would tell him that there were Negro servants about the place who would be sure to give him away if they saw him. He expected the answer that Jones must give, but he was sick and irrational enough to be disappointed when he heard the actual words. His head sank down dispiritedly; he sat very still, his eyes closed, and his mind then began to turn within itself, seeking to escape from the hard realities of the night and the danger and the cold.

He never lifted his head all the while that Jones was gone. He was in a semi-conscious state, almost asleep. When Jones returned, Booth took the food he offered without a word, and ate it in silence.

Jones led them down a lane toward the river. After a few hundred yards they came to a fence that blocked their way. The horse was brought alongside the fence, and Booth was lifted off on the far side. He was given his crutches, and with Jones and Herold on either side of him, he made his way slowly across the open fields.

As he approached the river he could hear the wind blowing over the wide stretch of water with a deep hollow sound. From the top of the bank at the end of the farthest field he looked out into a black void. He trembled in the night wind as he stood there, terrified.

They got him down the bank, step by step, making painful progress in their slow descent, but at last they reached the shore. Jones took them to the place where his boat was hidden. With Herold's help he got the little skiff out of the weeds and into the water.

Booth was placed in the bow, where he lay down,

trying to shield himself from the wind. Jones took the oars. Herold pushed the boat off and jumped into the stern. The waves slapped noisily against the bottom as Herold's weight threw the bow up. Jones pulled at the oars, and in a few minutes they were away from the shore.

The boat crept slowly across the water. Jones rowed silently and skillfully, sending the boat forward with a steady motion of the oars. As soon as they got out of the shallows, the surface became less choppy, and the boat rode more easily over the surging water. The bluffs on the Maryland side made an irregular splotch of black against the sky. Booth peered over the gunwales, vainly trying to see the low-lying Virginia shoreline on the other side of the river.

Suddenly Jones stopped rowing and let his oars remain outstretched, floating on the water. He whispered excitedly to Herold. The boy twisted around to see what was behind them. He muttered to Jones. Jones leaned forward on the oars and pulled on them. The boat shot quickly ahead.

"What is it? What's the matter?" Booth asked nervously.

"There's a gunboat on the river," Jones said curtly. He rowed quickly, turning back toward the shore.

Booth pulled himself up to look over the side of the boat. Far behind them he saw a long dark shape on the surface of the water, and as he watched it, it seemed to be moving toward them. Then a tiny spot of fire flashed against it, and the crack of a rifle came across the water. Another spot, and then another appeared, followed by almost simultaneous reports.

Jones pulled frantically at the oars. The gunboat was under way now, and as the rowboat approached the shadow of the dark bluffs, a huge blot of flame appeared against the shape that was following them. There was a roar and then a heavy splash ahead of them. Herold put his hands on the oars and helped Jones pull.

The boat ran up on the beach with a rush. Jones and Herold leaped out. They picked Booth up and carried him into the bushes at the foot of the bluff; then they hauled the boat up on the shore and dragged it into the shelter of the underbrush.

Jones ran over to Booth and spoke to him hurriedly. "You'll have to wait here. We're going to climb up on the bluff where they can't see us. Don't move if they come near you, and they'll probably pass right by. That's the only chance you have, for you certainly can't try to get away."

Booth heard the two men clambering up the face of the bluff. In a few seconds the sound of the wind had drowned out the noise of their feet on the rock and gravel, and he heard only the ceaseless wash of the water on the shore. He waited, resisting the temptation to sit up and look out over the river. Then he

heard voices, and he knew that the North was groping blindly for him in the dark.

Men came along the beach toward him. They were
apparently afraid to use a light, lest they attract shots
from ambush. He heard them go past him, speaking
to one another. There was a long silence, and then he
heard them as they returned.

He held himself absolutely still as they approached. He could hear them talking together, but
they spoke in voices that were so guardedly low that
he could not make out what they were saying. Finally,
they were gone, and there was only the sound of the
wind and the waves. After a long while he heard
Jones and Herold scrambling down the bluff, and he
knew that they must have seen the small boat pull
back to its mother ship.

His body relaxed, and he slumped down, burying
his face in his hands.

---

## Friday, April 21

---

Jones had been unwilling to try the river again that
night, since he felt sure that the gunboat would still
be lying somewhere in the darkness to intercept them.
He had rowed back along the shore, keeping in the
shadow of the bluffs until he reached the meadow below his farm. They had landed there, and he had led

them up the steep path to an isolated place on the side of the cliff where the laurels grew thickly. It was nearly dawn by the time he left them, and the two fugitives were tired and discouraged when they finally lay down to get some sleep.

The wind kept blowing, and there was no protection from it in this exposed position high above the river. Booth spent the night shivering with cold, and the morning brought another cloudy sky from which occasional gusts of rain fell.

The wind still howled around the face of the bluff, bending the laurel branches before it. Far out on the surface of the river the whitecaps were breaking as the wind caught up the water and hurled it into spray. Through the drifting mists Booth could see a boat anchored in the middle of the river. He took the spyglass that Mrs. Surratt had brought to Lloyd's tavern and inspected the ship. It was a gunboat—there was no mistaking it.

He sat with his back against the steep wall, gazing despondently over the wide panorama. Herold woke up and asked if Jones had been there yet to bring them something to eat. When he heard Booth's indifferent answer, he rolled over to go to sleep again, shielding his face from the drizzling rain.

Hours passed. Booth remained motionless, sitting in a dull stupor, expecting his fever to rise again, for his leg ached and his whole body was numb. Jones finally arrived, bringing provisions and the inevitable papers. Herold got up and ate the food eagerly. For the first time Booth was not interested in what the papers had to say. He turned the rain-spotted pages idly. He was tired of reading about Lincoln—Lincoln lying in state in the Capitol—Lincoln starting on his funeral journey—Lincoln everywhere, eulogized and mourned. He put the papers away in disgust and began to talk to Jones about his plans for attempting another crossing as soon as it was dark.

Jones refused to accompany them. He felt that it would be too difficult for him to get past the gunboat and then return again. If Booth wanted his boat he would gladly donate it to the cause of the Confederacy. He would even come to them after dark to show them how to cross, but he wouldn't go himself. His absence during the night had been noted, and he could not afford to take any more chances now that the war was over. He had already lost nearly everything he owned.

Booth cut short his apologies and assured him that he was fully prepared to cross the river alone. He looked down at the tossing water and asked Jones if he thought there was any chance of better weather by nightfall.

Jones studied the sky gravely. "Well, this river can change mighty fast. It may be all smoothed out before dark—and then again, it may not."

Booth drew his blanket more tightly around himself and reached for the fresh bottle of whiskey Jones had brought. "We cross tonight, no matter what the weather is like," he said.

Herold ventured the opinion that they ought to leave as soon after dark as possible. Jones warned him that the evening tide might take them out of their way. Herold would have a hard pull, and it would probably take at least two hours to cross while the tide was coming in. Booth said curtly that they would make an early start.

As soon as Jones had gone, Herold promptly went to sleep again. Booth sat still for a long while, looking moodily at the mist-covered river. Water dripped off the laurel leaves, and his blanket was soaked, but the rain had finally ceased. He wiped his wet hands, took out his notebook, and opened it to a page where he had drawn a crude calendar, marking off the days as each one passed. He drew a line through April twentieth. He had made up the calendar only until June eighteenth, and he wondered where he would be by that time. In Mexico probably, he thought, or dead. And he mouthed the word, speaking it sharply between his teeth—dead, dead, dead. . . .

He was still free from fever; his head was clear, but he was tired and depressed. He kept thinking of his predicament, and he felt that the world had misjudged him. Even the South was not appreciative of what he had done—everything had gone wrong, and he looked forward with dread to the long journey before him. Perhaps it were better not to try. Death was easy. It had been easy for Lincoln. No pain, no consciousness of suffering—only a brief moment and then the peace that came forever, blotting out all memory, all pain. He had already suffered more than Lincoln had. He toyed with the thought of a self-inflicted death. After all, he had promised himself that he would die by his own hand rather than be captured. Perhaps he would be only anticipating if he were to kill himself now.

And he thought, too, of what might happen if he were to return to Washington to give himself up. It would be a dramatic thing to do—something that would make everyone realize that he was not a criminal, but a man of principle. He might even be able to defend himself successfully in court. There were surely many extenuating circumstances, and if he were to tell about the hidden conspirators who had worked with him through John Surratt, even the hostile Northern Government would have to acknowledge that he, John Wilkes Booth, was at least not alone in his guilt.

It angered him to think that all the calumny and bitterness had been concentrated on him, when there were so many others, equally guilty with him, who were unsuspected, and who would probably never be caught.

But he knew that he could never surrender himself. He had given his word not to reveal anything about his secret associates, and it was impossible for him to denounce them, even if he wanted to, for he had no idea who they were. Nor could he ever walk into the city of Washington to give himself up, because he knew that he would never reach the military headquarters alive.

His position was hopeless, and he knew it. There was nothing for him to do but to press on toward the Mexican border, fighting his passage every step of the way if necessary. Only the courage born of despair was left to him. He remembered how he had always felt when he played the closing scenes of *Macbeth*. He knew now what it was like to have death close in around him. He must summon that last wild flood of energy which comes to a man who is ready to fling himself on his enemies' swords.

He felt the boards under his feet again, and the painted walls of Dunsinane Castle rose up into the darkness of the high arch overhead. He stood alone in the center of the stage, the audience waiting breathless to hear his words. *They have tied me to a stake; I cannot fly, but bear-like, I must fight the course*— Fight the course! That was all that was left to him—to die fighting. He turned the pages of the little notebook until he came to a blank one. He took out his pencil and began to write:

*Friday,* 21.—After being hunted like a dog through swamps and woods, and last night being chased by gunboats till I was forced to return, wet, cold, and starving, with every man's hand against me, I am here in despair. And why? For doing what Brutus was honored for—what made William Tell a Hero; and yet I, for striking down an even greater tyrant than they ever knew, am looked upon as a common cutthroat. My act was purer than either of theirs. One hoped to be great himself; the other had not only his country's, but his own, wrongs to avenge. I hoped for no gain; I knew no private wrong. I struck for my country, and her alone. A people ground beneath this tyranny prayed for this end, and yet now see the cold hands they extend to me! God cannot pardon me if I have done wrong; yet I cannot see any wrong, except in serving a degenerate people. The little, the very little, I left behind to clear my name, the Government will not allow to be printed. So ends all! For my country I have given up all that makes life sweet and holy—to-night misfortune upon my family, and am sure there is no pardon for me in the heavens, since man condemns me so. I have only heard of what has been done (except what I did myself), and it fills me with horror. God, try and forgive me and bless my mother. To-night I will once more try the river, with the intention to cross; though I have a greater desire and almost a mind to return to Washington, and in a measure clear my name, which I feel I can do.

I do not repent the blow I struck. I may before my God, but not to man. I think I have done well, though I am abandoned, with the curse of Cain upon me, when, if the world knew my heart, that one blow would have made me great, though I did desire no greatness. To-night I try once more to escape these bloodhounds. Who, who, can read his fate? God's will be done. I have too great a soul to die like a criminal. Oh! may He spare me that, and let me die bravely. I bless the entire world. I have never hated nor wronged any one. This last was not a wrong, unless God deems it so, and it is with Him to damn or bless me. And for this brave boy, Herold, here with me, who often prays (yes, before and since) with a true and sincere heart, was it a crime in him? If so, why can he pray the same? I do not wish to shed a drop of blood, but I must fight the course. 'T is all that's left me.

Jones came to them just as it was growing dark. He told Booth that he need have nothing to fear from a shore patrol—Federal troops were being withdrawn from the vicinity because a report had been received that the men they were looking for had been seen in St. Mary's County on the eastern side of the Peninsula. Jones had been in the near-by village of Allen's Fresh when this news had reached the commanding officer, and he had seen the cavalry ride away a few minutes later.

Herold packed up their things again, and Booth was helped down the path to the river's edge. Jones then led them to a sheltered cove, where they spread out Booth's map on the sand. Jones lighted a candle he had brought and shielded its flame from the river side with his hat. He showed them the direction they must take in order to cross to a convenient landing place on the Virginia shore. He urged them to make for Machadoc Creek. A Mrs. Quesenberry, with whom he was acquainted, lived near there. She could put them in touch with his brother-in-law, Thomas Harbin, who could be depended upon to help them.

Jones told Herold how to allow for the incoming tide, and he explained to Booth how to compensate for the changing currents. He held the candle over Booth's compass while he pointed out their course on the map. As he talked, the wick sputtered and dripped wax on the plush-lined compass case. Light from the candle, reflected upward, shone on the faces of the three men with a faint glow. Herold was crouched down on the sand, trying to memorize the curving shore lines on the map; Jones was bent over him, his thin hollow-cheeked face spectral in the dim light; Booth stood leaning on his crutches, watching the two men lay out the course that was to determine his future and make possible his escape.

Finally, Jones put out the candle. He brought the boat around to the cove and helped Booth get into it. Booth looked up at him as he stood there, a shadowy figure in the darkness, and he held his hand out to this man who had befriended him and refused the enormous rewards offered for his capture.

"There is nothing I can say to you that would be adequate to express my appreciation," Booth told him. "I can't offer you anything that—"

Jones gripped his hand and silenced him good-naturedly. "Don't worry about thanking me," he said. "You just keep a sharp eye out for that gunboat and don't make any noise. The wind is going down.

Even a slight sound will carry a long way over open water."

"The least I can do is to pay you for the value of this boat. You may never see it again."

"Well," said Jones slowly, "it is a good fishing boat."

"We'll leave it in Machadoc Creek—if we ever get there. But in case we don't, please take this to cover its cost." Booth counted out eighteen dollars and thrust them into his hand.

Jones pocketed the money, and then, as Herold lifted the oars and whispered good-by to him, he pushed the boat away from the shore.

The sky was heavily overcast and the night was absolutely black. A flash of distant lightning brightened up the clouds for an instant and showed them the wide expanse of water around them. There was nothing in sight on it. The gunboat was evidently still far upstream.

After a long while, Booth began to feel uneasy about their progress. It was so dark that he could see nothing, and there were no stars to guide him. He struck a match, holding it under his coat to hide the flame, and studied his compass in the brief flare. They seemed to be moving in the right direction, but it was strange that it should take them so long to cross.

He waited patiently, straining his eyes for a glimpse of the shore line, but he could see nothing

268

except black water everywhere. Suddenly Herold stopped rowing, leaned forward and whispered to Booth that he thought he heard men's voices.

Booth listened. The sound of voices came to him distinctly. Two men near them somewhere in the darkness were talking to each other. At first he thought that they might be on the shore, but he realized almost immediately that he was hearing the voices of sailors on the gunboat. He fancied that he could even see a dark shape on the water. In a few minutes the voices became fainter as the tide kept sweeping the rowboat upstream, and then he could no longer hear anything at all. Herold continued to let the boat drift.

"What do you suppose happened?" he asked Booth finally. "How did we get near them? They were way up the river. Do you suppose they started coming downstream?"

"We're off our course," Booth said curtly. "Start rowing and see if you can't pull into the shore somewhere. We'll have to wait for daylight and make for Machadoc Creek then."

Herold began to row again. In about twenty minutes the boat slid noiselessly into some soft mud and stopped. Herold pushed it along with one oar until he reached the riverbank. The shore was heavily overgrown with rushes that were dry and brittle from their long exposure to the winter. He got out and

269

dragged the boat in among them, where it would be concealed from the open river.

"We might as well wait here," he said. "They won't be able to see us behind all these rushes."

---

## Saturday, April 22

---

The sky lightened gradually into the dawn of another gray day. The shores of the river took on shape around them, and Booth saw that they had landed in an inlet. It was too much to hope that they could have come into Machadoc Creek blindly in the darkness, but it was at least possible that this might be one of its neighboring inlets. He consulted his map and noticed something that puzzled him. Then he took out his compass. The needle pointed up the inlet. All the openings on the Virginia shore near Machadoc Creek ran from west to east.

He woke up Herold and told him that they were probably lost, and that it was essential to find out just where they were. Herold offered to go ashore on a reconnoitering trip. Booth studied the map gloomily while he was gone.

The boy came back in a few minutes with a sheepish grin on his face. "Do you know where we are?

We're still in Maryland in Nanjemoy Creek. I've hunted ducks in this very inlet."

"Are you sure?" Booth asked. "All these river shores look pretty much alike."

"There's a house back there a ways," Herold said laconically. "It's owned by a Colonel Hughes. He used to let me hunt here."

Booth located Nanjemoy Creek on the map. He began to curse when he saw that they had simply traveled across the wide mouth of the Port Tobacco River, and that they were even farther away from their goal than when they had started.

"It was that gunboat that put us off," Herold said. "And besides you were steering. I just rowed."

"Around in circles evidently. Well, don't stand there grinning like a fool. What are we going to do now? We have nothing to eat. We can't possibly put out on the river again until nightfall. What are you going to do about it?"

"Get something to eat," Herold said promptly. "Colonel Hughes will fix us up. He's a real Southern gentleman."

Booth sighed. "I hope so. Don't tell him any more than you have to. Tell him you were out fishing and got lost."

Herold went off and returned nearly an hour later, looking well fed and contented. He had a package of food under his arm, and he was carrying a bottle of whiskey. "This'll help us pass the time away," he said. "The Colonel told me that if we could catch the outgoing tide after midnight it would practically carry us right down to Machadoc."

Booth opened the parcel of food. More ham. He was sick of the sight of ham. These tidewater farmers seemed to eat nothing else.

Herold stepped heavily into the boat and sat down on the rowing seat. "Colonel Hughes let me have a copy of yesterday's paper. I thought you might want to see it. It says that George Atzerodt was arrested and—"

Booth seized the paper eagerly. He read the account of Atzerodt's capture, and he noted that the final words were: "It was with difficulty that the soldiers could be prevented from lynching him."

On the same page was printed a notice headed: "One hundred thousand dollar reward for the assassins." Fifty thousand dollars was offered for his own arrest, twenty-five thousand for Surratt's and twenty-five thousand for Herold's.

"Did you see this reward notice, Davy?" he asked softly.

"Yes, I saw it." Herold evaded his gaze.

"They spelled your name wrong, Davy, but I hope that your Colonel Hughes has a short memory for names. You didn't remind him, of course."

Herold spat in the water. "Hell," he said reflectively, "you've got to trust somebody. He knows who I am, all right."

"Does he know I'm here?"

Herold looked at Booth uneasily. "Yes, I reckon he does."

"What did he say to that?"

"He said he hoped we got across the river tonight. He—"

"He'd just as soon not see us near his place any longer than he has to, eh?"

Herold grunted.

"God damn these Southern gentlemen!" Booth pounded his fist on the side of the boat, denouncing his countrymen as ingrates and cowards. Herold shrugged his shoulders and curled up on the bottom of the boat to go to sleep.

Booth lost all track of time, and it was not until the clouded sky began to grow dark that he was sure that night was at last falling. He felt sick and feverish again; his leg was so swollen that it seemed that it must burst the bandaged splints, but he was impatient to get started across the river. He knew that he still had hours to wait, but he could not sleep. He lay on the bottom of the boat, listening to the water slap gently against its stern.

The wind died down, and the surface of the water gradually became very still. The tide kept rising, creeping up along the river banks. They finished the food Herold had obtained, and they waited for the tide to turn.

The hours passed slowly. Several times Herold had to push the boat farther up on shore as the water rose. He placed a stick in the mud and kept feeling it in the darkness so as to be able to tell when the tide changed. At last he announced triumphantly that he was sure that the ebb tide was beginning. He pushed the boat into the water and rowed out of the inlet into the main stream.

Booth listened to the steady plash of the oars. The boat went forward with a hardly perceptible motion in the quiet water. When they were well out on the river, Booth lit a carefully concealed match in order to see his map and determine their course around Mathias Point.

After a long stretch of rowing with the tide, they found themselves near a low marshy shore that was hardly visible in the darkness. Booth felt reasonably sure that they were on the Virginia side of the river this time, and when he saw the shore line bend around in a long curve to the south, he was convinced that they had reached their goal at last.

They went along slowly, but finally Booth became afraid that they might pass Machadoc Creek in the darkness. He told Herold to put the boat ashore until they could see where they were.

Booth roused himself from a fitful sleep on the bottom of the boat to see the first faint signs of light in the wide sweep of sky. The river banks began to emerge from the darkness and take on form and definition. The water was glassily quiet; there were no boats in sight anywhere, and there was nothing moving except the mist that drifted lightly over the surface. The shore was flat and desolate with no signs of human habitation on it as far as the eye could see. Farther inland to the south there were groves of trees. Mrs. Quesenberry's house was probably among them somewhere.

He woke Herold, and they started on their voyage again. They followed the muddy banks of the river downstream, observed only by some large white birds which stared at them solemnly from the shore. In a little while they passed the opening of a small stream which Booth identified from his map as Gambo Creek, and then they came in sight of a broader inlet which he was sure was Machadoc.

As they rounded the shore line they saw the dirty gray sail of a boat moving down the creek toward them.

"Fishing boat coming out for shad," Herold said. "Maybe we'd better not—"

Booth examined his map hastily. "There's probably a lot of traffic in this creek," he said. "We might

275

go back to Gambo Creek and enter there. We can get to Mrs. Quesenberry's by crossing overland in back of her house."

Herold swung the boat around. "I don't care where we go so long as I can get something to eat," he said unhappily. "I hope the lady is a good cook."

They went back along the shore and had almost reached Gambo Creek when the fishing smack sailed out on the open water. It turned down the river, paying no attention to them, but as Booth looked across the shore, he could see the sail of another boat following the first one.

Herold pulled on the oars and hurried into the shelter of the little creek. Then he rowed upstream leisurely until the creek narrowed at a place where a log bridge spanned the water. He brought the boat to the shore under a big walnut tree, and helped Booth get out on the bank.

The ground around the creek was very soft, and Booth knew that he would have trouble if he tried to walk through it with his crutches. He persuaded Herold to set out alone for Mrs. Quesenberry's house to see what kind of reception they could expect from her.

Booth stretched himself out under the tree. The day was evidently going to be another cold and cloudy one, but he was in Virginia at last. He had crossed the Potomac! This soil was Confederate soil—this river-bank marked the northern boundary of his own country. His native state of Maryland, loyal as she had been to the South during the war, had never been in a position to come out openly on the Confederate side. But Virginia had been the capital of the South, and here, if anywhere, he could hope to meet men to whom the honor of their country still meant something.

He leaned against the tree trunk, stretching his wounded leg out carefully on the grass. He felt weak and exhausted, but he was not hungry. His body, thrown off its normal balance by his wound and his fever, seemed to be living a life of its own, and food meant nothing to it. His temperature was still high, and he was lethargic and heavy, but he knew that he could never relax for a minute until he reached a place of safety.

The tide was entering the creek. Water rose slowly over the mud flats at the edge of the marsh, and seabirds waded in the shallows. Booth nodded tiredly as he waited for Herold to return. The boy seemed to be taking a long while—as always—to run this simple errand. He wondered what kind of story Herold was telling Mrs. Quesenberry. He must warn the irresponsible fool not to go blabbing to everyone. . . .

The tide rose higher, bringing the rowboat almost up to the level of the log bridge. Booth shifted about impatiently. Finally, he heard Herold calling to him, and the boy came in sight, muddy and forlorn, a downcast expression on his face.

"I had to wait a hell of a long time for the old lady to come home," he explained.

"Yes— And what did she tell you?"

"She's afraid of— Well, she just doesn't want to help us, I reckon. That's the long and the short of it. She didn't even give me anything to eat. Said she'd send Harbin over later if she could locate him."

Booth sighed. "Did you at least find out who else lives in this stinking bog? There must be other people near here. Maybe they have a more highly developed sense of hospitality."

"There's a farmer named Bryant somewheres around. Mrs. Quesenberry's daughter told me about him before the old woman came home."

"Help me up. I'll walk."

Booth swung along painfully on his crutches. He could never get used to walking with them. They got in his way, and the slowness of his progress irritated him. The ground was soft and spongy, making every step difficult. He muttered angrily at his own clumsiness.

After a short while his patience was exhausted. He was hot and sweating. His armpits ached, and his foot pained him terribly from the constant exertion. He stopped, limped over to a tree stump, and sat down.

"You'll have to go on alone, Davy, until you find out where this Mr. Bryant lives. I've taken all I can stand. I don't want to go wandering around like this, trying to find a man we're not even sure will help us. You go ahead and come back for me when you've found him."

Herold went off alone. Booth waited, sitting disconsolately on the tree stump. The underbrush around him was filled with flowering shrubs, and the air was heavy with their fragrance. The weather had become warmer, and there were birds singing in the trees.

He sat very still. The birds came close to him, and a rabbit ran out in the path. The omnipresent crows were flying overhead, cawing harshly as they passed.

This was Virginia, he thought. The richness of the soil, the lush flowering underbrush, and the languorous spring air were all typical of the warm spirit of the South. Here he would be sure to find friends. These people above all others should understand him. Yet he had met with a rebuff from the first person they had approached. What could he expect of the next one?

He saw Herold come down the road with a white-bearded man. This person was promptly introduced as the Mr. Bryant they were seeking. Bryant walked up to the stump on which Booth was sitting and stood slouchily in front of him. He was a seedy-looking farmer, down at the heels, shabby and emaciated.

Booth spoke to him politely, explaining that he

was a wounded Confederate soldier who was trying to avoid the Federal forces that were patrolling the river.

"Seems to me," Bryant said, "that every soldier in the Confederate army has passed by here by now, and every danged one of 'em has asked me for help."

"I'll gladly pay for your services," Booth said hastily. "I'm not asking for charity—"

"I know you're not. Your brother here told me you could pay, or I wouldn't have bothered to come down here."

Booth looked up at the narrow little eyes that were studying him. He took out some money and showed it to Bryant. "I can't walk, as you can see," he said. "I must get some means of conveyance. If you have a horse I'd like to hire it."

Bryant looked at him reflectively. "Where do you want to go, and how much would you pay?"

"First I want to go to the nearest doctor to get my foot dressed."

"There's a Dr. Stewart has a place 'bout eight mile from here. He's a queer sort though. May not want to pay any attention to you, and then again, he might. He's got lots of money, so he can do pretty much as he likes."

"Is his place on the way to the Rappahannock ferry?"

"Sort of—not too much out of the way, at any rate."

"All right. Get your horse and hitch it up. I'll—"

"Hold on there. I ain't got any carriage. Just horses."

"Not even a farm wagon?"

"No, sir, it was done commandeered."

"So I have to ride?"

"Unless you want to walk. That won't cost you nothing." Bryant tittered, and then his face took on its usual expression of blank indifference.

"Get your horse ready," Booth said. "I'll ride."

"And what was you thinking of paying? Money ain't worth much now, you know."

"Ten dollars would seem to me to be a fair price," Booth said.

"That's ten dollars gold. I don't want greenbacks, and I don't take no Richmond bills at all—not any amount."

Booth agreed to pay him in gold. Southern currency was no more valid than the promises of its people, he thought bitterly. A degenerate people, defeated and discouraged, thinking only of saving their own skins now. This money-cautious farmer was typical of them. God, there must be some decent men left in this State. If he could only find one of them!

He hobbled along the road to Bryant's cabin, a miserable little shack presided over by a housekeeper, a scrawny Negress. Herold asked for something to eat, and Bryant sold him some soggy biscuits and three cold slices of bacon for a dollar. Booth refused the food disdainfully, and urged Bryant to get his horse saddled.

Then there were difficulties. Bryant couldn't leave his farm until he had attended to the day's chores, since it would be impossible for him to get back before nightfall. He offered Booth the privilege of resting on his bed until he was ready to leave, and he told him that there would be no charge for it.

The afternoon was nearly gone before they finally got away from Bryant's house. Thomas Harbin, sent to them by Mrs. Quesenberry, appeared just as they were leaving, but they had no need of his services, and Booth dismissed him curtly.

The sky was beginning to lighten for the first time in days, and Booth felt that the fair weather was a promise of better things to come. The horse plodded along the road as the sun sank down in a crimson cloud bank. It took them several hours to cover the eight miles, and it was shortly after dark when they finally reached Dr. Stewart's house. They rode across the wide lawn, and Booth waited in the saddle while Bryant went in search of the doctor.

In a few minutes Dr. Stewart came out of the house, striding across the lawn, with Bryant following him, expostulating as he ran along to keep up. The doctor greeted Booth with obvious annoyance in his voice, and asked him what he wanted.

"We are Marylanders," Booth said slowly, trying

to see the features of the man to whom he was speaking. "I have broken my leg and it needs attention badly. That's why I came here."

"I'm a physician—not a surgeon. I doubt whether I can be of much assistance to you."

"My leg has already been dressed by a doctor who put splints on it. Dr. Mudd of Bryantown, Maryland —perhaps you know him?"

"Never heard of him," Stewart said. "I'm not acquainted with many people on the other side of the river. I'll look at the dressing if you like, but frankly, I've had very little experience with fractures. They're out of my line entirely."

Booth sat still in the saddle. He was so unfavorably impressed by the doctor's reception that it hardly seemed worth while to dismount. It did not seem possible that any man with a medical education could be so ignorant of such a simple thing as a fracture.

"I don't want to impose upon you," Booth said, "but I understand that there is no other doctor anywhere near here."

Stewart shrugged his shoulders. "Come into the house, if you wish," he said. "The least I can do is to look at the dressing. And I suppose you want something to eat, too. Every soldier who comes by here is hungry. I can't feed them all. There were some men here today from Maryland. I had to turn them away. There's a limit to what one can do, you know. We've had soldiers bothering us now for weeks. The whole country seems to be swarming with them."

Booth refrained from speaking the words that rushed into his mind. Herold helped him out of the saddle and gave him his crutches.

They entered the large and comfortably furnished house. The doctor's wife and several grown daughters looked up curiously at them. Booth became conscious for the first time that his clothing was torn and mud-spattered, and that his face was covered with a scraggly growth of beard.

Stewart led him into his own study and made a hasty examination of the wound, without, however, even offering to open the dressing.

The visible area around the bandages was inflamed, and the foot below the break was dark purplish. Stewart pressed into the flesh with his fingers. Booth winced and looked at the doctor inquiringly.

"It looks pretty bad, I must say," Stewart told him. "What you need, of course, is a complete rest. You ought to keep off your feet—lie still for a couple of weeks and let this thing heal."

Booth smiled bitterly.

"I'll see that the servants get you something to eat," Stewart said. "I can't offer to put you up here. As you can see, the house is already crowded. As a matter of fact, I have a paroled officer from the Confederate Army staying with me now. A friend of the family, of course."

# Sunday, April 23

Booth struggled to a standing position and put his crutches under his arms. "Of course," he said. "I understand. We won't trouble you. Mr. Bryant probably knows someone in the neighborhood who can put us up for the night. What do I owe you for this—er, medical examination, Doctor?"

Stewart was embarrassed.

"I wouldn't like to charge a Confederate soldier anything for a simple examination like that," he said. "Besides, there's nothing I can do for you, really. I'll see that you're given something to eat."

The doctor led them to the big kitchen and spoke briefly to one of the Negro servants there. Food was placed on the long wooden table for them. Booth sat, looking numbly at his plate. The ignominy of his position was too much for him. To be sent out to the kitchen like a common tramp! He swore softly under his breath at this uncivil Southerner who had treated him this way. He tried to pick at the food, for it was hours since he had had anything to eat, but he could not stomach it.

Stewart was talking to Bryant somewhere outside the house. Booth could hear the murmur of their voices, but the men were too far away for him to make out their words. This country doctor was evidently a suspicious sort of person who was trying to find out something about his unexpected guests. Booth sat at the table, so consumed with anger that he

285

could not even tolerate the sight of the food in front
of him.

He got to his feet and swung himself out of the
kitchen on his crutches without waiting for Herold
to finish eating.

Booth spoke to the doctor abruptly, choking back
his rage, and asked him if he knew of a house where
they could spend the night. He was told in the doctor's usual dry, noncommittal voice that the only
place he could suggest was the cabin of a William
Lucas, Negro freedman, who lived only a short distance away.

"I wouldn't ordinarily send a white man to a nigger's cabin," Stewart said with an attempt at an apol-
ogy, "but it's the only house near here at all. You've
spent nights in worse places when you were in the
army, I suppose. We can't be choosers now, with this
war and—" Stewart finished lamely, glancing at
Booth who was watching the cheerful glow of light
in the windows of the doctor's home.

Booth quietly asked Bryant to bring his horse, and
then let himself be lifted up to the saddle without
saying a word. Herold came out of the kitchen, wiping his mouth. Booth thanked the doctor elaborately
for his hospitality and rode off through the woods.
The anger which he had been nursing broke out as
soon as he got away from the house. He began to
curse Stewart.

He stopped his horse. He could not leave this place

without expressing to its owner some idea of his own contempt for him. He made his two companions wait while he took out the candle stump Jones had given him. He lit it, opened his notebook, and wrote a message for the doctor on one of its pages:

Forgive me, but I have some little pride. I hate to blame you for want of hospitality, you know your own affairs. I was sick, tired, with a broken leg, and in need of medical advice. I would not have turned a dog from my door in such a condition. However, you were kind enough to give us something to eat, for which I not only thank you, but, on account of the reluctant manner in which it was bestowed, I feel bound to pay for it.

It is not the substance, but the manner in which kindness is extended, that makes one happy in the acceptance thereof. "The sauce to meat is ceremony; meeting were bare without it."

Be kind enough to accept the enclosed five dollars (though hard to spare) for what we have received.

He paused and read over what he had just written. It seemed absurd to pay this cold-blooded doctor five dollars for the miserable food he had given them. Two or three dollars would be a too-generous price for what they had received. He had to think now about conserving his money, for, when the small amount he had with him was exhausted, there was no way of getting any more.

He turned to a fresh page and laboriously copied

out the note, changing the sum mentioned, after some consideration, to two and a half dollars. Then he signed it: "Yours respectfully, Stranger."

He gave the note and the money to Bryant to leave at the doctor's house on his way home. Then he took the bottle of whiskey that Colonel Hughes had given to Herold and finished all the liquor that was left in it.

It hit his empty stomach with terrific effect. His ordinarily great capacity for drinking large amounts of strong liquor had been impaired by his weakened physical condition. The alcohol went to his head almost immediately, and he was reeling in the saddle before they had gone even a short distance. He felt lightheaded and giddy, and he hardly realized where he was when Bryant brought his horse to a stop in front of a little cabin on the edge of a field.

He sat in the saddle, clutching the leather, while Bryant pounded on the door. A frightened Negro voice answered, asking timidly who was there.

Bryant had some difficulty in identifying himself. Finally, Lucas recognized his voice, and opened the door, saying that he had to be careful because people sometimes got shot this way.

Booth was helped out of the saddle by Herold. As soon as he reached the ground, he took his crutches and started toward the cabin.

"We need a place to sleep," Booth said thickly. "Dr. Stewart sent us here." He looked up and saw the Negro still blocking his way into the house. "Get out," he snarled. "We need this place."

Lucas spoke to him imploringly. "You can't do this, sir. I'm a colored man, and I have no right to take care of white people. I have only one room in this house, and my wife is sick."

Booth stared at him coldly. "What do you mean— 'I can't do this'? Whom do you think you're talking to? Get out! And take your wife with you." He brushed past Lucas and staggered into the cabin. A Negress looked up in fear from the bed. Lucas followed him with an expression of frightened defiance on his face. "I tell you, sir, that I'll get into trouble if—"

"Get out of here, nigger, and take your wench with you. We're Confederate soldiers, and we don't stop to argue with niggers. Outside, damn you! And stop whining."

Lucas looked around at the three white faces. "Gentlemen," he said, "you have treated me very badly. I—"

Booth drew out his knife. "How do you like that?" he said, swaying slightly on his crutches. "Would you like to feel it shoved into your belly?" He thrust the blade toward Lucas. The terrified Negro cowered back against the wall.

"We understand that you have a team of horses," Booth said. "We'll want them in the morning to take us to Port Conway."

"Yes, sir, but I have some men coming here in the morning to help me plant corn. I'll need—"

"You'll what?"

"Yes, sir," Lucas said sullenly.

Booth turned to Bryant. "These niggers are getting out of hand," he said. "It's these dirty Yankees who have put ideas into their heads. This war has—" He tipped forward and almost fell to the floor. Herold rushed over to him, and supported him while Lucas got his wife out of bed.

Booth insisted that the bed clothing be removed before he would lie down. Herold swept the blankets to the floor and spread Booth's coat out on the bed. Lucas bundled up his wife in some of the rejected blankets and led her out of the house. Booth dropped down on the mattress and immediately lapsed into unconsciousness.

Herold paid Bryant the ten gold dollars that had been promised him for his services, and then he lay down on the floor beside Booth's bed with his revolver and carbine beside him. As he tried to fall asleep he could hear Lucas speaking to his wife in a low plaintive voice that came from somewhere beyond the doorstep. Herold grinned and threw his boot across the room. It landed with a solid thwack against the door, and then everything was silent.

# PART SIX

★

HEADQUARTERS, DEPARTMENT OF WASHINGTON
April 24, 1865

Commanding Officer, 16th New York Cavalry,
SIR:

You will at once detail a reliable and discreet commissioned officer with twenty-five men, well mounted, with three days' rations and forage, to report at once to Colonel L. C. Baker, Agent of the War Department, at 211 Pennsylvania Ave. Command of General C. C. Augur.

—J. C. SEWELL, *A.A.A. Gen'l.*

## Monday, April 24

Booth and Herold drove into the little town of Port Conway in the middle of the morning. Lucas' son had arrived at his father's cabin with the team shortly after dawn. He had immediately been pressed into service, and Booth had been driven across country, lying flat on his back on the floor of the wagon. At Port Conway they headed directly for the ferry wharf on the shore of the Rappahannock. The flat scow that was used to take passengers and horses across the river was lying on the other side unattended.

Young Lucas tied his horses to one of the pilings and patiently curled up on the seat of his wagon to go to sleep in the sunlight. Booth told Herold to try to find someone who could get the ferryman to bring his boat across the river. Herold returned in a few minutes with a man whom he introduced as a Mr. William Rollins, owner of the ferry.

"You can't cross for a while yet," the man said in

a slow indifferent voice. "The tide's too low now, and, besides, my man is out fishing."

"How long shall we have to wait?"

"Well, now, that depends." The ferry owner stared gravely at the mud flats along the water's edge. "The tide's beginning to come in now. It might be half an hour, or it might be an hour before there's enough water to float that scow."

Booth lay back in the body of the wagon and closed his eyes. The sun was pleasantly warm on his body, and he felt so utterly miserable that he was content to lie there until the ferry was ready to take him across. His leg hurt with a dull and constant pain, and the swelling around the ankle was so great that he had been alarmed at the sight of it when he got up that morning. His whole body felt drained of energy. The wound, perhaps, was poisoning his system. He knew that he would not be able to travel much farther, and he had reached a state in which he did not much care what happened to him.

He could hear Herold arguing with the ferry owner. The boy's quick excited voice contrasted strangely with the leisurely drawl of the townsman. There was an odor of fish in the warm air, and the mud flats smelled of decay and wetness. Booth felt drowsy. He wished that the sound of the men's wrangling voices would stop. He put his arm over his eyes to shut out the bright sunlight and tried to go to sleep.

He heard horses approaching. He tried to convince himself that they were probably farm horses, and that he need pay no attention to them, but they were stepping briskly with the sharp tattoo characteristic of cavalry mounts. He raised himself reluctantly on one elbow and peered over the edge of the wagon. To his relief, he saw three men in Confederate uniform riding up the long road to the wharf. His tired brain told him that he must get up and talk to them, for they might be able to help him, and he would need help to get through the unfamiliar territory on the other side of the river.

Herold was already scurrying down the road toward the men, and as they rode up, he walked alongside them, talking in his shrill high-pitched voice. When he heard Booth summoning him, he came over to the wagon, and one of the horsemen followed slowly behind him.

"They're from Mosby's command," he whispered. as he helped Booth out of the wagon. "They wouldn't tell me where they're going, but they must be headed south somewhere. Maybe we could go along with them."

Booth put his crutches under his arms and stood for a moment, blinking in the sunshine as the first of the horsemen rode up. He greeted him cordially, and the soldier, taking it for granted that he must be a wounded Confederate comrade, asked him what command he belonged to.

"A. P. Hill's corps," Booth said, using the first

name that occurred to him. "I understand that you gentlemen have been with Mosby. May I introduce myself? I am John William Boyd, and this is my brother David."

"Bainbridge is my name," the young soldier said, dismounting and holding his hand out to Booth. "I am very happy to meet you. May I introduce my companions?" He turned around to look for them, but Herold had already rushed over to them and was talking to them eagerly. One of the men was watering his horse, and he was paying very little attention to what Herold was saying. Suddenly Booth heard Herold speak the word "assassinators." The sharp sibilants cut through the quiet morning air. Booth saw the man who had been tending to his horse quickly pull the animal's head out of the water pail and begin to question Herold.

Booth swore softly and hobbled across the wharf, followed by Bainbridge. Herold was grinning at him with a silly expression on his face.

"This is Lieutenant Ruggles and—ah—Jett," he said with a frightened giggle. "May I introduce my brother, John William Boyd?"

Booth glared at him.

The soldier named Jett, who was hardly more than a boy, was looking at Booth in open-mouthed wonder. Lieutenant Ruggles stepped forward. He did not extend his hand, but said gravely: "If you are what this man says you are, you must be John Wilkes Booth."

"I am John Wilkes Booth," Booth said quietly. "What he told you is true." He stood, swaying on his crutches, watching the startled faces of the young soldiers. Bainbridge stepped around Booth and went over to his comrades.

"We can trust them all right," Herold said. "They're real Southerners. They've been fighting with Mosby."

Booth motioned to him to be silent.

"I hope we can trust you," he said, speaking to Ruggles. "I am in great need of assistance. I have no way of getting beyond Port Royal. Are you gentlemen acquainted with this neighborhood? I am afraid that I shall not be able to travel any great distance. I must find temporary refuge somewhere. My leg is in such condition that it makes it almost impossible for me to go on."

"I know most everyone around here," Jett said. "I reckon I can get somebody to let you stay in their house. Are you really the man who killed Abe Lincoln? We heard all about it."

Booth smiled. "I really am. And there's a big price on my head, as you probably know. I must place myself in the hands of people I can trust, or I shall never get away alive. I have just come from Maryland where the whole State is swarming with troops who are looking for me. I need not only assistance but concealment. The Northern Government is sure to search for me here. Can I depend on you, gentlemen?"

Jett looked eagerly at Ruggles. Bainbridge and the Lieutenant began to talk together in low voices.

Booth interrupted them, saying: "I am sorry that this decision seems to have been forced on you, gentlemen. I assure you that I had no intention of telling you who I am, but since my companion has been incautious enough to do so, I have no choice but to throw myself on your mercy—and on your loyalty to the cause for which we have all been fighting."

Herold sidled away from Booth and went to the edge of the wharf to look down at the water flowing past its timbers as though he saw something of great interest there.

"We can't very well turn you in for blood money," Ruggles said hesitantly. "We—well, we'll help you, I suppose." Jett nodded enthusiastically. Bainbridge cleared his throat and seemed to be embarrassed. Finally, he spoke in a quiet tone that expressed polite inquiry rather than disbelief.

"We were told," he said slowly, "that the persons who killed the President have already been apprehended. Of course we may have been misinformed, but I do think that— What I mean is—have you any—?"

"I understand what you mean," Booth told him

with a disarming and good-natured smile. "I have plenty of evidence of my identity." He thrust out his wrist with the tattooed initials on it. "These letters, of course, might stand for John William Boyd, but they also stand for John Wilkes Booth. Furthermore, I have here with me a bill of exchange on a Canadian bank made out to—" He unfolded the piece of paper and pointed to the name "J. Wilkes Booth." "If that is not enough, gentlemen, I can—"

Bainbridge held up his hand. "I am quite convinced. I hope you will pardon me for being so doubting, but these are times when it is best to make sure— Shall we sit down and talk this thing over? Jett, see if you can't get them to bring that old mud scow across. There ought to be enough water in the river to float it now."

Jett walked out to the end of the wharf and called lustily across the river.

"Bring that God-damned old flatboat over here, Peyt. We're tired of waiting. Get it over here fast or I'll put a bullet through its bottom—and yours, too, if you don't hurry."

"Yes, suh, yes, suh. Comin' right off." A Negro on the other shore moved out of the shadow of a tree and walked out on the deck of the scow.

Booth and the three men sat down on a bench alongside the ferryhouse. Herold remained standing at the edge of the wharf, watching the scow move slowly out into the stream.

"Well, gentlemen, there doesn't seem to be much that I can tell you at this point," Booth said, propping his injured leg up on the end of one of his crutches. "You see in me a man who has sacrificed everything for his country. I did what I did because I thought it would give the South another chance to win her freedom. It seems that I was mistaken—apparently the South has nothing left to fight with."

"That's right," Jett said. "We're through, all right. The Yanks have everything there is to get. The Colonel told us to go home."

"Nevertheless," Booth went on, "what I did was done only in the interests of patriotism. Believe me, sirs, there was nothing personal or even vengeful in my act. Consequently I do not think that I am unjustified in calling upon Southern people to aid me in the plight I am now in. There surely isn't a single loyal household that wouldn't give shelter and protection to a Confederate soldier who was fleeing for his life from his Federal pursuers. No man in this whole war has ever been sought as I am now, I assure you. The Northern Government is offering enormous rewards for my capture, and it has put thousands of troops into the field to find me. I take it that since you were all with Mosby you are not afraid of danger and excitement and risk. Well, this is your last chance to participate in one of the great adventures of the war. I am sure that I can count on you—you look like men of spirit."

# Monday, April 24

The three men were listening appreciatively to what Booth was saying. He could not have found a more receptive audience for his appeal. Mosby's Rangers were among the most reckless and daring soldiers of the South. They had been a group of irregulars who fought with guerrilla tactics, striking quick surprise blows against isolated units of the Federal forces, and they were famous for their hard riding and fierce fighting.

"Sure we'll help you," Jett said excitedly. "I'll bet the Colonel himself would if he had the chance. It was a damned shame he had to give up. We were never in better shape—and we got all our equipment from the Yankees. We never did surrender, you know. We just disbanded at Salem last Friday. Mosby's on his way south now to join Johnston."

These were the sort of men he should have had in his plot, Booth thought. He should have gotten in touch with leaders like Mosby and Early. Too bad that Morgan had been killed. A raid could have been staged against Washington simultaneously with his own coup. One swift move like that might really have turned the fast ebbing tide of the war back again.

The ferry was approaching the end of the wharf. Booth called Herold over and handed him ten dollars in greenbacks to give to their driver. The scow slid alongside the wharf with a grating sound, causing the whole structure to sway as it hit against the pilings. The three soldiers brought their horses out on the dock, and Booth was hoisted up into the saddle of Ruggles' horse.

The ferry was pushed out into the river. Booth sat upright in the saddle, looking straight ahead toward the shores of Caroline County and the few scattered houses that lined the river's edge in Port Royal. He had forgotten how sick he had felt only a short while before. He was crossing into the heart of Virginia now, and he was in the hands of friends.

The town of Port Royal proved to be less hospitable than Booth had been led to expect. Jett had gone to two houses where he was acquainted. The woman in the first house had consented to take Booth in, and then, unaccountably, had changed her mind. At the other house, the owner had not been at home, so they decided, after discussing the matter over a lunch which Jett had brought to the ferry landing, to press on toward Bowling Green. Jett knew a farmer living about three miles south of Port Royal whom he could ask to put Booth up. In case he refused, lodging could surely be found in Bowling Green, where there was an inn.

They headed south on the road that led to Richmond. Ruggles and Herold led the way on foot, and the others followed slowly behind them. Soon they were at the edge of the broad alluvial plain that stretched along both sides of the river. They entered a series of low-lying hills covered with dense woods. Booth noticed that the country offered ideal cover in case of pursuit.

In a little while they came to a lane leading off to the right. Jett stopped his horse and waited for Booth to come up.

"This is it," he said, pointing to a small frame house in the midst of a grove of trees. "I'll go in and talk to old man Garrett. He's got a son in the army himself."

"Maybe I'd better go on with the other fellows to Bowling Green," Herold said uneasily. "I've got to get me a pair of shoes. The bottoms are out of these."

"Whatever you wish," Booth said to him patiently. He knew that Herold was afraid of what he might say to him for having blurted out the word "assassinators." "Do you want some money?"

"I'll be back here tomorrow—soon as I get the shoes." He walked over close to Booth's horse. "I'm sorry for what I did—honest, I am."

"Forget about it," Booth told him cheerfully. "Perhaps it was all for the best. We're among friends now as a result of it."

He handed Herold some bills and rode over to the entrance of the lane. Jett and Ruggles had already gone on toward the house. Bainbridge and Herold stayed at the gate. Booth turned and waved his hat to them. He was in high spirits now. Refuge was in sight, and he would have a chance to rest. His newly found friends were standing on the lawn in front of the house, talking to an elderly man and two younger ones.

"It's all right," Jett called out to Booth as he rode up. "Mr. Garrett says you can stay here." Booth was helped off his horse and introduced to his hosts as John William Boyd.

The two boys, who had been presented to him simply as Bill and Bob, stood looking at him with frank curiosity. Bill, the elder, was dressed in Confederate uniform, and it developed from the conversation that he had returned from the army only three days before.

Booth examined the layout of the farm while his two companions talked to the Garretts. It was a perfect hiding place for him—far enough from the road for him to be able to see anyone coming, and close enough to the thick woods in the rear for him to be able to flee to them if necessary. There were several small outbuildings between the house and the edge of the woods. At the far end of the lane, leading in from the road, was a large weather-beaten tobacco barn.

A middle-aged woman came out of the kitchen doorway, wiping her hands on her apron. She pushed her way through the children who were playing in front of the house and came over to the little group of men, scolding them for letting the injured stranger remain standing.

"You, Willie Jett, ought to have more breeding,

even if my own rapscallions haven't." She helped Booth over to the porch and made him sit down. He thanked her with the grave courtesy that always endeared him to women.

"Where did you get hurt?" she asked solicitously.

"In the battle near Petersburg," Booth said easily.

"I suppose you're on your way home?"

"No, I've been back to my native State of Maryland already. They wanted me to take an oath of allegiance to the Federal Government when I got there, so I refused to stay. It's bad enough that our men had to surrender to the Yankees—to have to swear to support their Government is intolerable."

"I don't blame you," Bill Garrett muttered. "Those damned Yanks'll be comin' down here wantin' me to take their dirty oath, too. Well, I won't do it neither. I'd rather run away to the hills."

"So long as Johnston's army is in the field there will always be a place for Southern men to go. I understand that Colonel Mosby is on his way to join him."

"Ain't you heard?"

"Heard what?"

"Johnston's surrendered too!"

"Who told you that?"

"I heard it on my way home. He surrendered to Sherman."

Johnston's army in the deep South was the last force of any importance left to the Confederacy.

With his surrender there could be no question that the war was finally over. Lincoln's death could make no difference now—if anything, it would only make the North more exacting in its terms for peace. He had not only failed in trying to save his country—he had probably done her irreparable harm. What Cox had said to him was true. He was a fool and a murderer.

He slumped down on the porch, paying no attention to the conversation that was going on. Everything was lost now. Even his endless struggle to escape seemed futile. He looked down at his swollen foot. The pasteboard splints that Dr. Mudd had put on it days before were still in place, but they were mud-spattered and frayed. They were pressing tightly against the hot angry flesh, and he knew that gangrene might set in unless he got medical attention soon. His foot might even have to be amputated. . . . The thought made him wince. He would rather be dead than permanently crippled. He clenched his teeth together tightly and rubbed his hand over the rough beard that had grown on his face.

Jett was standing in front of him holding out his hand. "Good-by," he said. "We've got to be going on to Bowling Green. Get all the rest you can here. We'll be back for you tomorrow or Wednesday."

Booth took his hand and thanked him earnestly, and then he shook hands with Ruggles. "I'll never forget what you men have done for me," he said.

## Tuesday, April 25. Morning

They mounted their horses and were off to a quick start, using their spurs to make the horses leap forward. The Garrett children watched them solemnly, and then they gathered around Booth, standing in a shy circle not too near this man who was a stranger. William Garrett came over and sat down on the porch beside him in order to swap stories about the war.

## *Tuesday, April 25. Morning*

Booth had slept on a cot in an upstairs room with the two Garrett boys. The little house held an incredibly large number of people for its size, and it was so inconveniently laid out that there was no privacy for any of them. There were only three rooms on the second floor, and to get to his sleeping place Booth had to pass through his hosts' room and the room where the smaller children slept. The household, according to its custom, had gone to bed early and gotten up at dawn. Booth had tried to sleep later, but the shouts of the children playing in the dooryard had kept him awake, and he had come downstairs at what was for him a very early hour.

The morning had passed quietly. He had lain on the grass in front of the house talking with the children in his elaborately polite manner, and he had entranced them by the very simple method of treating them with as much respect as he would give adults. He had told them stories of farm life, and he convinced them that he knew enough about animals and hunting and country sports for them to accept him as one of their own.

At noon, Mrs. Garrett's sister, Miss Holloway, a young schoolteacher who was boarding in the overcrowded house, returned for lunch. She had seen Booth only for a few minutes on the previous evening, and now as she crossed the lawn, she stopped to speak to this mysterious stranger who had come to stay at the house.

He smiled graciously at her with the smile that he always used for very young girls and old ladies. It was a smile devoid of the direct implications of sex, yet it had about it a forecast of sexual experience to come, and at the same time an echo of experience long past. Women invariably thought it charming.

Miss Holloway inquired politely about his wound, and then, as if she were imparting a new and surprising bit of news, she told him that Bill Garrett, whom she had met on the road, had just informed her that President Lincoln had been killed.

Booth looked up at her in surprise. She was rather pretty, he thought idly, but perhaps a bit too countrified. "Do you mean to say that word of Lincoln's death has just reached this community?" he asked incredulously. "Why, he's been dead for ten days!"

# Tuesday, April 25. Morning

"We lead a very secluded life here," she said demurely, seating herself on a bench near him. The children crowded around her, watching silently.

"But you knew about Johnston's surrender, and I hadn't heard of that. It certainly must have taken place after Lincoln's death."

"Oh, that's something that Bill brought back word of from the army."

"But he hadn't heard about Lincoln?" Booth plucked nervously at the grass. "What do you think of it?—The killing of Lincoln, I mean."

"I don't suppose it'll do the South any good now," she said hesitantly. "I don't know much about such things, but I don't like to see people killed."

"What did you hear about it?"

"Not much—just that he was shot in a theater in Washington by some maniac."

"By some maniac?"

"That's what they said—at least I think so. I suppose the man must have been a maniac to kill him at a time like this."

"You don't approve——?"

"The war is over, isn't it? But why don't you tell me what happened? You probably know more about it than I do."

Booth looked down at the grass again. "I heard that the man who shot Abe Lincoln was a Southern patriot," he said. "And that he did it for reasons that were purely patriotic."

309

"Yes? He must have had curious notions about patriotism. Who was he?"

"He is an actor named John Wilkes Booth."

"Oh, an actor—"

"Why did you say that?"

"Say what?"

" 'Oh, an actor.' "

"I don't know. I thought he would be a soldier—or something like that."

"Tell me, Miss Holloway, did you ever see an actor?"

"No, I never did."

"What do you suppose an actor would be like?"

"Oh, I don't know," she said, giggling. "Always acting, I reckon. You know—strutting around, making fine speeches and talking big. Like Hamlet or Macbeth, maybe. I teach Shakespeare in my school," she added primly.

Booth picked a blade of grass and carefully tore it into strips. "I've seen lots of actors. They never seemed to me to be any different from other people. Many of them have become soldiers too, you know."

"I didn't question their bravery. I just said that I had never seen any actors, so, of course, it seemed to me that they would be different from other people." She smoothed out her skirts and looked at one of the children as she asked: "You've been in big cities a lot, haven't you, Mr. Boyd?"

"Yes," he said shortly.

"He's lived on a farm, too. He told us all about it," Annie, the oldest girl, announced eagerly. "He had a pony once, too."

"I'm going to visit Richmond now that the war is over," Miss Holloway said. "I never was there, and I want to see what a city is like. I was too young to go before the war, and of course, I couldn't go at all during the past four years when everything was——"

"I'm afraid you'll find Richmond a pretty dreary place now."

"Because of what the Yankees did to it, you mean?"

He nodded.

"I hope they didn't burn all of it. I do want to see what a real city is like."

"I hope you won't be disappointed," Booth said.

"Can I go to Richmond, too?" Annie asked. The other children clamored to be taken along.

Miss Holloway was trying to answer them all at once. Then she saw Bill Garrett approaching. She got up quickly and ran into the house, saying that she had to help her sister.

Bill came through the gate, swinging a pair of shoes by their laces. Booth got up unsteadily and put his crutches under his arms.

"Miss Holloway has been telling me that you have just heard of Lincoln's death."

"Yeah," the boy said indifferently. "Somebody down at the shoemaker's was talkin' about it. I reckon

# The Man Who Killed Lincoln

Old Abe had it coming to him. He did a powerful lot of wicked things in his time. They should have shot him long ago." He put his hands to his mouth and called to his brother. There was an answering shout from the back of the farm.

"Hey, Bob! Dinner," he yelled. "It's time to eat," he said to Booth. "I can tell Ma's ready 'cause I heard her open the oven door—it's busted and it makes a clatter." The children were running into the house.

They all sat around the big table in the kitchen. The news of Lincoln's death was the main topic of discussion. When Bill Garrett heard that a hundred-thousand-dollar reward had been offered for the capture of the assassins, his eyes glistened.

"I wish that man would come this way," he said, spearing a piece of bread with his fork. "I'd like to get that money."

"Would you really turn him in?" Booth asked calmly. "He probably did it for the sake of the South, you know."

"That's a lot of money."

"Even so—"

Mr. Garrett spoke up dispassionately. "Don't mind what he says, mister. He's young and foolish. He don't mean what he says. If I thought he did, I'd larrup the life out of him."

"I'd take a lot of larruping for a hundred thousand dollars, Dad."

"You'd get more than larruping," the old man said

312

grimly. "You didn't seem to learn much sense in the army or you wouldn't talk that way."

"He doesn't know what he's talking about," Annie said scornfully. She was just old enough to be allowed to enter into a conversation with adults, so she always took the side of her elders. "Anyway it's very unfortunate that Mr. Lincoln had to be killed right now."

"What's unfortunate about it?" Bill demanded belligerently. "He deserved what he got."

"His death actually may prove to be quite fortunate for the South," Booth said in a quiet voice. He traced a pattern on the table with his fork. "Johnson will be President. He's a drunken sot, and there's sure to be trouble ahead for the North with him in charge." He looked up at the faces watching him. "Why, there might even be a revolution if things get bad enough, and then the South will have a chance to win its freedom again."

"Seems to me we've had enough of wars and revolutions," Mr. Garrett said. "What we need is to be left alone, so we can grow our crops and tend to our own businesses."

Miss Holloway tried to act as conciliator. "Must we forever be talking of war and politics?" she asked plaintively. "It's a beautiful spring day, but no one has even noticed the weather."

"I noticed it all right," Bill Garrett said. "I was just telling Dad this morning that it looks like a good tobacco year, wasn't I, Dad?"

"M-m," the old man grunted. "Might be a good year if they hadn't killed off so many men. I don't know how we're going to get a market for the dratted stuff now. I tell you these wars are the ruination of trade." He gripped the edge of the table and looked around at his guests and the members of his family. "The ruination of trade," he repeated firmly. "And I've had enough of 'em."

Booth grinned and looked down at his empty plate. Mrs. Garrett hastened to press more food on him.

Herold returned during the afternoon with Ruggles and Bainbridge. Booth hobbled down the lane to meet them.

"We're on our way back to Port Royal for a visit," Ruggles said. "So we thought we'd drop your friend off here. Jett couldn't come along—he seems to be having some trouble with his girl. He's been away too long, I reckon. She's probably set her cap for someone else now."

"I got my shoes," Herold said proudly, holding up one of them so Booth could see it. "Pretty good ones, too. I'll need 'em, I guess. We've got a long way to go."

"A long way to go!" The words struck a chord in Booth's mind. A long way to go—across the whole South, wearing out Davy Herold's new shoes as they went, endless patrols to pass, countless chances of recognition and capture to be met. . . . He was tired, and he wanted only peace and rest—peace and rest. He sat down on the grass and leaned his back against the rail fence.

"They look like good shoes, Davy. I hope they carry you a long way." He turned to Ruggles and Bainbridge, who were standing in the lane holding their horses. "I wish I had some way of expressing my appreciation for all that you gentlemen have done," he said slowly. "I can say to you only that the South will remember and be grateful to you for the part you have played in helping me. Some day the story of what I have done, and why I did it, will be known to all the world—I am sure of that. The world can judge then. . . ."

"Why did you do it?" Bainbridge asked curiously. "I can't understand what you hoped to accomplish. A few months ago Lincoln's death might have helped us—but now—"

Booth looked away from them across the fields, where fluffy white clouds were drifting over the forest's edge. "Believe me, gentlemen, I did not know that the war was over—I was not convinced of it. I could not see the South giving up the struggle so easily and so soon. I thought that my act would give our people a fresh impetus to continue the war and win back their own freedom." He looked at the grave, questioning faces of the two young soldiers. "I was mistaken, it seems. The war was over. What I did has apparently been a useless gesture. Yet I don't regret it.

If ever a man deserved to die for the crimes he had committed, Abraham Lincoln did. He caused the deaths of hundreds of thousands of fine young men like yourselves. He destroyed the happiness of the people I loved. I have never felt that I was acting as a murderer, any more than a man who shoots a mad dog or a dangerous wild animal feels that he is taking life unjustifiably. I regret only that what I have done has had no directly useful result."

"And now——?" Bainbridge asked softly.

"Now I seem to have thrown my life away for nothing at all." He leaned tiredly against the fence and let his hands drop loosely at his sides. "You see what I have come to. I am a fugitive, almost alone, seriously injured, wandering in strange territory. . . . My only hope is to get through to Mexico, for my life will never be safe in any section where the Northern Government can reach me. My chances of getting there successfully are, I am afraid, rather slight. The North has started a man hunt for me which is unprecedented for its size and thoroughness. I will never be taken alive, though——I can promise you that. I must press on to the Mexican border, but I don't know how long I can keep going. I need medical attention badly, as you can see. This foot is becoming dangerously swollen. I have been compelled to keep moving on it, and the wound has been aggravated beyond the endurance of human flesh."

"Would you like to have me examine it?" Ruggles asked. "I've had some practical experience with wounds in the army."

"I don't think you'll be able to see much. The bone is broken inside—there is no surface lesion. I shouldn't like to have the splints taken off. They give me some support, and they were put on by a doctor. If you think you can tell anything from the condition of the inflammation—" He exposed the swollen purplish flesh. Ruggles bent over and looked at the wound. His face became very serious as he studied it. Then he felt the hot surface gently. Booth winced at the touch.

"You'd better get to a doctor," Ruggles said shortly. "I never saw any kind of fracture act like that. Maybe there's some kind of internal suppuration—if such a thing is possible." He stood up and looked at Booth commiseratingly. "You'll have to see a doctor—or you may have to have an amputation if you let that thing go any further."

Booth gripped his hands together, shivering and terrified. He covered the wound again. "I should have had a hard enough time getting away with a sound body," he said bitterly. "This damned foot has ruined my chances." He sank back against the fence again. "Have you heard anything of Federal patrols in this part of the country?" he asked. "Have they sent soldiers here, too?"

"They don't seem to have," Bainbridge told him. "There hasn't been a Yankee in Bowling Green since the battle of Richmond."

"They can't be such fools as to overlook this area —especially if they pick up my trail anywhere in Maryland. This is the only section I could get to from there. That will be obvious enough to them. Christ! I'm tired of this endless flight."

"We'll be all right now," Herold said reassuringly. "Why, I heard of a Confederate Maryland battery that's not very far from here—over toward a place called Guinea Station. If we can get to them, they can't refuse to help us—they're Maryland boys."

Booth shrugged his shoulders. "I'm sorry you gentlemen aren't going any farther south. I should like to have gone with you. I can buy horses around here, I suppose?"

"Horses are pretty scarce," Bainbridge said, "but you can probably manage to get a couple of them, because money is even scarcer. Everybody is stuck with Confederate currency, and nobody will accept it now."

Booth looked at the dark belt of forest that ringed in the open fields. If he were only in good condition, this would be a fine place to stay, he thought. He could never be taken here if he had both feet firm on the ground beneath him, for a nimble-footed man could easily slip away from the house to lose himself in the woods that stretched away on every side.

# Tuesday, April 25. Afternoon

Bainbridge untied his horse from the rail fence and put his foot in the stirrup. "We won't say good-by to you now," he said. "We'll stop in on our way back from Port Royal. We should be back before dark."

The two soldiers rode down the lane. Booth remained seated for a while, thinking moodily. Finally, he got up, took his crutches, and went back to the house with Herold.

"I hope these people can find a place for you to sleep tonight, Davy," he said as they walked along together. "I warn you that the house is already overcrowded. We'll have to move on tomorrow, I think. Tell me more about this Confederate battery. It might be the place we should head for."

They sat on the lawn, talking for nearly an hour. The sun dropped down to the tree level and the air became cooler. The Garrett cow came in to be milked. She walked slowly across the field, stopping every few feet to crop a bit of fresh grass. When she got to the fence, she put her head over it to look with momentary curiosity at the two strangers. Then she turned about majestically, like a ship in full stream, and went off toward her shed, vigorously switching her tail.

The homely farm animal ambling along placidly in the almost level rays of the sun, the brooding peacefulness of the partly plowed fields and the unpretentious farmhouse with its long porch and quietly smoking chimney—all combined to bring back to Booth the memory of his own home in Belair. The cow was a plain old brown cow, a trifle gaunt and bony about the hindquarters; the fields were gravelly and worked out; the house was little and somewhat shabby —a poor example of a type that was common among the lower middle-class planters of the section, and it was in no way comparable to the fine brick structure that his father had erected in the Tudor style of his native country. Yet all these things were symbols— symbols of a happier past that he had renounced. And these symbols were rising now to plague him. All his life he would see things like these that would serve to remind him poignantly of the loss of his own past. He paid no attention to Herold's elaborate and rambling discussion of his plans for their escape. He felt lonely and unhappy as he watched the sun sink down behind the trees.

Suddenly Herold gripped his arm. "There's horses coming—fast!" he whispered excitedly.

Booth listened. He could hear the beat of pounding hoofs. He struggled to his feet and loosened his revolver as two horsemen dashed into the lane. They were Ruggles and Bainbridge.

"The Federals are in Port Royal, and they're after you!" Ruggles gasped as he pulled his horse up short. "They're coming this way, too. You'd better get back in the woods—they may come in here."

"They're after you, all right," Bainbridge said. "We never got to Port Royal. We met a friend of mine outside the town who warned us not to go in unless we had our paroles. He said there were troops there searching for a man named Booth. They've had word you're down here, I reckon."

"We saw them on the road behind us when we came up the long hill," Ruggles added. "You'd better get out of here quick."

Booth looked around him with an assurance that he did not feel. "They'll have a hard time finding us here," he said. "David, run and get one of the Garrett boys. Perhaps we can buy their horse and leave immediately. We can go out through the woods in back."

Herold dashed into the house. Ruggles and Bainbridge wheeled their horses around. "We've got to be going fast too," Bainbridge said apologetically. "We haven't any parole papers."

They clattered down the lane as Herold came out of the house, followed by Bill Garrett and his father.

"I have just heard some news that makes it imperative for me to leave at once," Booth said to them. "I need a horse—two horses in fact, but I know you have only one. I am willing to pay a very good price for it. I will give you one hundred and fifty dollars in greenbacks for your horse. Will you sell him to me?"

The two Garretts looked at each other, puzzled by this sudden request. The horse was worth much less than the price Booth offered, but they immediately became suspicious.

"Well, now," the son said with a deliberation that

exasperated Booth, "I don't know. We need a horse here on the farm. There's still plowing to be done. Where did you want to go in such a hurry? Maybe I could drive you there."

"Guinea Station," Herold said promptly. "We want to get to Guinea Station quick."

"Name your own price to drive us there," Booth told him. "I'll pay it—I'll pay anything within reason, but for God's sake, hurry!"

Bill Garrett hesitated. His father spoke for him. "Why don't you name the price? You know what it's worth for you to get there."

"I have no idea how far it is. I'll pay you anything you want. Let's not stand here haggling about money. I don't care how much it costs. I've got to get out of here now! Get the horse, please."

The son turned to go toward the little shed in which the horse and the cow were kept. Booth was looking fearfully toward the road. "David," he said, "go with him and help him—"

Through the quiet air the shrill note of a bugle sounded.

"Good Jesus—it's the Federals!" Herold almost shrieked. "They'll be here in a minute. We've got to—" He seized Booth's arm and tried to propel him rapidly toward the rear of the farm. Booth stumbled and cursed his own awkwardness with the crutches that were holding him back at this one moment in his life when he needed most to move quickly.

# Tuesday, April 25. Afternoon

They did not even get as far as the tobacco barn when the sound of many horses' hoofs warned them that the troops were near the gate. Booth drew his pistol, and Herold was muttering one of the childish prayers his mother had taught him. They watched the narrow opening of the lane. Across it a body of men rode rapidly and continued along on the main road without noticing them at all.

"They—they went right by," Herold giggled nervously. "They didn't even stop!" He caught his breath in quick hysterical jerks. "They—they—they didn't stop at all!" He began to laugh uncontrollably.

Booth stood swaying on his crutches. Sweat had started out on his forehead, and his stomach felt sick. "We'd better go on into the woods," he suggested quietly to the hysterical boy. "They may come back. We'll be safer in there than out here in the open." He led the way, struggling across the rough stubble of the fields and pulling his crutches with difficulty out of the soft earth. He went several hundred feet into the woods before he stopped. Herold, by this time, had become calmer.

Booth sat down heavily under a tree and carefully put his crutches beside him. "I'd give anything in the world for a drink right now," he said. "A drink of almost anything—"

Herold grinned sheepishly. "I brought some whiskey back with me," he said, pulling a big flask out of his pocket. "Here it is."

Booth seized the bottle and wrenched out the cork. The liquor was raw and harsh, but his overwrought nerves were grateful for it. He handed the bottle back to Herold, who took an enormous swig.

The bottle passed back and forth for a while. It was beginning to get dark under the trees. Finally, Herold asked timidly: "Do you think they'll come back now?"

"I don't know," Booth said wearily. "We'd better wait here for a while and see what happens. Are there any towns between here and Bowling Green?"

"Not a one. It's a God-forsaken wilderness. The only bit of life on the whole road is a tavern halfway there."

"Well, if they don't come back soon, they've probably gone on to Bowling Green. How far is it?"

"Must be about twelve miles—maybe thirteen."

"They probably won't be back this way tonight, then. We'll have to get out of here before dawn, though."

They sat in silence for a while longer. Finally, Booth suggested to Herold that he go up to the edge of the woods to see if anyone was in sight. He waited anxiously until the boy returned.

Herold came back in a few minutes. "Seems to be all right," he said. "I didn't see anybody. Must be time to eat. I'm getting awful hungry. Maybe we could go to the house now. We've got to see about that horse anyway."

# Tuesday, April 25. Afternoon

Booth got up reluctantly. "All right, David. We might as well be on our way again. There'll be no rest for me anywhere now." He shivered in the cool evening air and pulled up the collar of his coat. They walked through the woods and across the open field to the farmhouse. The kitchen windows were already gleaming with light.

The family was inside, gathered around the table for the evening meal. Mr. Garrett opened the door. He stood with his arm across the entrance, and his face was grim and foreboding.

"We didn't save places at the table for you," he said curtly. "We didn't think you were coming back."

"We're hungry," Herold said dolefully. The light from the kitchen doorway threw his face into strong relief. He looked as if he were going to cry. "Besides, we wanted to talk to you about that horse."

Garrett studied the boy's wan face and then looked past him at the vague figure of Booth standing on his crutches in the darkness.

"All right, you can come in and eat," he said grudgingly. He lowered his arm. The children and Miss Holloway pushed around the table in order to make room. The two men sat down. Food was put on their plates, and everyone ate without speaking.

Booth's glib tongue failed him. He felt that the silence, painful as it was, was preferable to anything he could say. There was no other chance of getting food in this wilderness. He was hungry, and he ate the plain meal gratefully.

Finally, Mr. Garrett finished eating and pushed back his plate. He sat glowering at the two men, but he waited for them to be done with their food. Then he spoke and came bluntly to the point.

"What I want to know is why you were so scared of those Northern troops." He stared at the two lowered faces. "The war's over. Honest Confederate soldiers have nothing to fear from a squad of Yankees now. What have you done?"

"We haven't any parole papers," Booth said, after vainly searching his mind for a better excuse.

"That's not a shooting matter."

Booth leaned back in his chair and tried to smile. "Well, if you must know, we got into a slight brush with some Federals in Maryland. I told you that I refused to take the oath there."

"So they followed you all the way down here, eh?"

"Well, hardly that, I suppose," Booth conceded. "But I was afraid that if they caught us without parole papers they might send us back to Maryland, where they would know what we have done, of course. I assure you that we're not criminals—"

The old man muttered to himself.

"We're perfectly willing to leave. I don't want to stay where I'm not welcome. I have already offered to buy your horse—or hire it. We will go now if you will supply me with some means of transportation. It is obvious that I can't walk any distance."

"Guinea Station is a good ways off," Garrett said. "I wouldn't think of letting one of my boys start out for there at night. And I won't sell you the horse."

"Well, what do you want us to do?"

"I could take 'em over in the morning, Dad," Bill Garrett suggested.

"Maybe—but there's one thing sure—they can't stay in this house tonight!"

"Where do you expect us to sleep?"

"I don't care where you sleep. You can stay out in the woods if you want to. I reckon it wouldn't be the first night you had to spend under the trees."

"He's hurt bad," Herold protested. "He ought to be in a hospital. You wouldn't turn him out like that?"

"Couldn't they stay in the barn, Father?" Mrs. Garrett asked. "They'd have a roof over their heads anyway."

"All right, let 'em stay in the barn."

The two Garrett boys nudged each other under the table. "We'll see 'em out to the barn if you want us to, Dad."

Booth got up unsteadily. "I am sorry that your welcome is so easily withdrawn," he said. "I assure you that you have nothing to fear from us. I should much prefer to leave here tonight." He hesitated. Garrett looked at him stonily. "We aren't criminals. We—

327

Oh, well, what's the use? Will you let us have your horse early in the morning—before dawn?"

"You can arrange that with my son. Give 'em a couple of blankets," he told his wife. "You won't be so badly off," he said to Booth. "There's plenty of hay in the barn to sleep on."

---

## Tuesday, April 25. Late Afternoon

---

The twenty-five men from the Sixteenth New York Cavalry were tired—dog tired. They had been put on a boat the previous day and had been shipped down from Washington to Belle Plain, where they had landed at ten o'clock at night. Then they had been ordered to ride along the Virginia shore the whole night through, looking for a man with an injured leg and one other man with no distinguishing marks. They soon realized that they had been sent out after the President's assassins for whom enormous rewards had been offered. They had roused sleeping farmers and turned whole villages out for questioning. At first they had been enthusiastic, but even before the night was over they began to feel that they had been given an impossible task. The countryside was filled with wounded men of all sorts, and the local people were far from willing to give them much assistance.

328

## Tuesday, April 25. Late Afternoon

And then, in Port Conway, at the end of the morning, after hours of futile questioning, their officers caught the first scent of their quarry. They had met William Rollins, the man who owned the ferry there, and he had identified Booth and Herold from the pictures the commanding officer carried. He told them that the fugitives had crossed over to Port Royal on the previous day in company with Willie Jett and some other Confederate soldiers. He knew that Jett was going to Bowling Green because his girl lived there, and it was reasonable to suppose that Booth would be with him. Rollins had been pressed into service as a guide, and he had been arrested at his own request in order "to make things look all right to his neighbors." (He had to live with his neighbors and he knew how they would take his betrayal of a fellow Southerner.)

The whole troop was trotting dispiritedly along the road that led south to Richmond. The men rode in a half-dazed condition, seeing nothing, hearing nothing. They wanted only a chance to sleep, and they were ready to let the cash and the glory go. Booth, they thought resentfully, could be caught just as well the next day.

It was Conger who was driving them on. Lieutenant Doherty was the regular military officer in charge of the troop, but Colonel Everton J. Conger was its real head. He was a detective who had been detailed by Lafayette Baker of the Secret Service to go out

329

after Booth, and he was determined to let nothing, not even the protest of saddle-pounded muscles, stop him now that he was so close to his prize. Conger had been shot through the hips in a battle several years before, and his old wound troubled him on a long ride. But he sat up straight in the saddle, determined not to let anyone see that he was in pain. He had to make a good example of himself in front of these men, and besides, his second-in-command was Lieutenant Luther Baker, Lafayette Baker's own nephew, who had been sent along to report in person to his uncle how the pursuit was conducted.

The horses were even more worn out than the men. The officers had already been given a very unpleasant demonstration of the sad condition of their mounts. Conger and Baker had caught a glimpse of two men on the road ahead of them shortly after they left Port Royal. They had tried to overtake them, but their horses simply could not be made to move their tired legs fast enough to catch up with the fleeing men. The two officers had to give up the chase and fall back. They had kept the troops moving at a forced trot, but it meant continual spurring and lashing until everyone's temper was on edge, and Conger and Baker had quarreled when Baker's horse had bumped against the Colonel's. The soldiers had long since ceased to care about anything. They even found no satisfaction in hearing their own officers curse each other. It was

330

hardly remarkable that they had all passed by the entrance to the Garrett farm without noticing it.

It grew dark as they rode along. The road was deserted and there were no houses to be seen. Finally, they came to a clearing where there was a tavern called the Half-Way House. Rollins told them what sort of place it was. The officers decided to go in to question the tavern keeper. Doherty was instructed to keep his men in their saddles. Conger knew how difficult it would be to get them on horseback again if he once let them put their cramped legs down.

A group of hard-faced girls greeted Conger and Baker noisily as they entered the dingy barroom. Officers in uniform must have money with them, and money was at a premium in the wilderness. The girls almost mobbed them in their eagerness.

Conger pushed the girls roughly aside, in order to talk to the barkeeper, but the man only stared at him blankly when he was questioned.

He tried a different approach and appealed to the girls. "The men we are looking for," he said impressively, "are wanted for an attack on a young girl—a very young girl—almost a child. I am sure you will want to help us find them."

The girls whispered among themselves. "There were some men here yesterday," one of them said sullenly.

"What were they like? How many were they?"

"There was four of 'em—with only three horses. They went on to Bowling Green."

"Was one of them wounded—hurt in the foot?"

The girls looked at one another, and then their spokesman shook her head.

"Three of 'em went through here today on two horses," she volunteered.

"Perhaps they left him in Bowling Green," Baker suggested to his commanding officer.

"We'll go on," Conger said determinedly. "We can't take any chances of his getting away early in the morning. Go out and see that the men are ready." He thanked the girls politely and walked out into the darkness. Doherty and Baker were having trouble getting their men in formation.

Conger barked out angrily, and the squad finally got under way.

It was nearly midnight when they reached Bowling Green. The little place was asleep, and no one noticed the troop of armed men riding down the main street. Rollins led them to the town's only hotel, which stood dark and silent in the spring night.

Doherty told his men to dismount. Conger instructed him to post them around the building so no one could get away through the rear. Then he went to the front door and pounded on it with the butt of his pistol. The heavy strokes sounded hollowly through the big rambling structure, but no one answered. One of the soldiers came running around from the back, dragging a Negro boy with him.

The Colonel tried to question the frightened lad, who kept struggling in the soldier's grip, but the boy was so scared that he could only stammer incoherently.

"Where did you find him?" Conger asked the soldier.

"In back, sir, in a nigger shanty there."

Conger summoned several men and went around to the rear of the hotel. An old Negress was standing on the steps of her house berating the soldiers.

"Where's the owner of this place?" Conger demanded abruptly. "Why doesn't he come to the door?"

"It's a lady, suh. She's prob'ly most likely too skeered to come down."

"What's her name?"

"Mrs. Goldman, suh."

"Who's in there with her? Is there a man in there with a broken leg?"

"No, suh, I ain't seen none."

"Well, who's in there?"

"Jest two genlemen, suh—Mrs. Goldman's boy and Massah Jett. Her little girl's in dere too."

"Tell Mrs. Goldman to come out!"

"Whut you want, suh?"

"Call her out. She knows your voice. Tell her to

333

open the door, or we'll break it down. Come on—speak up!"

"Yes, suh." The woman cupped her hands and called Mrs. Goldman's name. "You better opun de door, honey, or dey's goin' to bust it in."

"Keep yelling," Conger told her. "I'll go around to the front."

The door was open by the time he got there, and Mrs. Goldman was waiting for him with a candle in her hand. "What do you want?" she asked quietly. "You have no right to carry on like this with peaceful people."

"We're looking for a man with a broken leg, and we have good reason to believe he's here. We are—"

"He's not here. There are no men here except my own son and a friend of my daughter's."

"Is William Jett here?"

"Yes," she said hesitantly, "he's here. He's my daughter's friend."

"I'll see this Mr. Jett. Show me his room." Conger pushed his way past her into the hall. Baker and Doherty followed him, and one of the soldiers placed himself at the doorway with his rifle in hand. "I must warn you, Mrs. Goldman," Conger said, waving his pistol, "that if any attempt is made to fire on us by anyone in this building, we shall burn the place down and take you all to Washington on capital charges. Lead the way, please."

The three officers followed her up the stairs. She

334

stopped at a door near the stair-landing on the second floor and knocked on it gently. "Willie, will you please come to the door? There are some men here to see you." She turned to the officers standing behind her. "Please don't make a disturbance, gentlemen. My son is in that room with Mr. Jett, who has been nursing him. He is seriously wounded."

"I want to see this son of yours," Conger said brusquely. "Are you quite sure he isn't wounded in the leg?" He took the candle from her hand and thrust the door open with the point of his revolver. Willie Jett was crouched in a far corner of the room, watching with desperate eyes as the men advanced toward him.

"Take your prisoner," Conger said to his two officers. They seized Jett by the arms and held him firmly. The Colonel went to the bed and bent over it to examine the face of a young boy who was lying there asleep or unconscious. He was breathing heavily, and his face was flushed and hot. Conger suddenly turned down the sheets. The boy's chest was swathed in bandages, and he was evidently in a bad way. The Colonel looked at his white thin feet and then gently pulled the sheet back again. "I'm sorry, madam," he said. "I had to make sure. . . . You'd better take us to another room now. I don't want to disturb your son."

Mrs. Goldman went out into the hall. "You can have any room you want—they're all empty," she said bitterly. "No one stays here now."

# The Man Who Killed Lincoln

Conger led the way to a room at the other end of the building. Baker and Doherty held the shivering figure of Willie Jett between them. The Colonel sat down at a little table in the bedroom and pulled Stanton's reward notice out of his pocket. "Just so you understand what we are here for," he said, "I will read you this." He began with great deliberation. " 'War Department, Washington, April 20, 1865. One-hundred-thousand-dollar reward. The murderer of our late beloved President, Abraham Lincoln, is still at large'...." He read on in a firm voice, stressing, when he came to them, the words: " 'All persons harboring or secreting the said persons, or either of them, or aiding or assisting their concealment or escape, will be treated as accomplices in the murder of the President and the attempted assassination of the Secretary of State, and shall be subject to trial before a Military Commission and—' " he stopped and looked straight into the eyes of the withering Jett, and then flung out the words—" 'the punishment of DEATH!' "

"Yes, sir. Yes, sir, I know what you want. I'll tell you—" The boy faltered. "Could I see you alone, sir? I—I can't talk with so many people around."

Conger laid his revolver down on the table in front of him and signaled to Baker and Doherty to leave the room. They withdrew, taking Mrs. Goldman with them.

"Well, now, son, you'd better tell me the truth,"

the Colonel said as soon as he was alone with Jett. "We know who you are, and what you have done in connection with a certain person. If you tell me what we want to know about him, I will see that nothing happens to you. If you don't—well, you heard what I just read to you."

"Yes, sir, I'll tell you anything you want. Honest, I will, sir."

Conger leaned forward. "Very well," he said slowly. "Where is John Wilkes Booth?"

"I left him at a farm near Port Royal—the Garrett farm," Jett said, lowering his voice.

"Near Port Royal?"

"Yes, sir, about three miles this side of it."

"We have just come from there."

"Did you, sir? I thought maybe you came from Richmond."

"From Richmond? No, we are from Washington. Tell me, is Booth still at that farm?"

"I think so, sir. His friend, Mr. Herold, went back there to join him today."

"So Herold is with him, eh? I want you to take us there—now."

"You're sure I'll be—you're sure I won't be hanged?"

"Not if you show me where he is—and if we get him all right."

"Yes, sir."

"Come on. Get dressed. We ride out immediately."

In a few minutes they were out on the street in front of the hotel. Some of the soldiers had fallen asleep on the porch.

"Get 'em up in the saddle," Conger said curtly to Doherty, "and see that this man's horse is brought around."

Doherty went from man to man, shaking each one to make him wake up. A soldier was sent for Jett's horse.

"There are still horses without men," Conger said irritably. "Where are the rest of your men, Lieutenant?"

"I'm afraid they've crept away to sleep somewhere, sir. I'll see if I can find them."

Without waiting for Doherty, the Colonel walked around to the side of the hotel. Several men were asleep on the lawn. He kicked them awake, cursing and shouting at them to get back to their horses.

"What sort of jelly-gutted soldiers are you?" he stormed. "I've found the man we're looking for, and you go to sleep on me like this! Get around there!"

He summoned the bugler and had the call sounded. Townspeople began to come out of their houses. At last the men and horses were ready, and they went riding off into the night. Jett sat in his saddle, overcome with his own misery. He knew that his people would never forgive him for what he had done, but he was afraid—afraid of the rope that the Colonel had dangled in front of his eyes. The troop broke into a gallop and went streaming along the road. The thin sickle of a new moon was rising above the trees.

---

## *Tuesday, April 25. Midnight*

---

Booth had been lying for hours on a pile of hay in the big tobacco barn at the rear of the Garrett house. He was unable to sleep. Herold was snoring gently. Booth stared into the darkness overhead. There were mice in the barn. He could hear the soft patter of their feet as they ran along the beams in the loft.

At no time since he had left Washington, eleven days before, had he felt the chase so near him. Even in the thicket in Maryland, when cavalrymen had ridden within a few feet of where he was lying, he had not really believed that they could take him. But now his pursuers were hot on his trail. Evidently the Government had traced him across the Potomac— and across the Rappahannock too, for that matter. It was horrible to have to lie here helpless, simply because old man Garrett's stubbornness had prevented him from getting a horse. He could be on his way now to the comparative safety of the Confederate battery near Guinea Station. The good luck that had followed him all his life seemed to have deserted him.

That instant when he had fallen on the stage, breaking his leg, was the very moment of his kind fate's departure, he thought.

He would have to get up early, well before daybreak, in order to leave this place before the troops he had seen on the road could have a chance to return. He wondered whether they would find any of his soldier companions in Bowling Green. It seemed unlikely. No one could possibly know of his connection with them.

An owl called somewhere in the woods. The night was filled with a chorus of insects and frogs, but this one mournful cry arose above the incessant monotone. Booth's thoughts returned to Belair, where an owl had lived in the woods near the house. He had often tried, as a boy, to locate the bird that he could hear calling so plainly from the trees, but he had never been able to find it.

He wondered where his mother was. He hoped that Edwin, or some of his brothers or sisters, had had enough sense to keep her away from newspapers and gossiping people. The news must have reached her long before this, of course, but she should not have to undergo the strain of reading the daily papers with their conflicting reports of his capture. Poor Mother! Such things were so far away from her quiet home life. And she had been so proud of him—so proud of the fact that he had never broken his promise to her not to enter the army and fight in the ranks.

## Tuesday, April 25. Midnight

He drew a long breath and pushed his head deeper into the soft hay. He must get some sleep or he would be in no condition for the long trip ahead of him in the morning. Thank God, his mother didn't know what a state he had come to—turned out of a miserable house like the Garretts' and made to sleep in the barn. . . .

He must avoid the road to Richmond—there were likely to be Federal patrols on it now. He would have to strike west into the mountains of Kentucky and Tennessee. It would be weeks before he could get to the Mexican border. He would be sure of a welcome in that country, though. Maximilian and the French were trying to create an empire in the wilderness there, and they were importing the first beginnings of European culture into that backward land. There might even be a theater in one of the larger cities— he could learn Spanish or French, if necessary. His father had given performances in Italian after a very brief preparation. What his father had done, he certainly could do. He could do anything in this world, he felt, if he put his mind to it. After all, he had succeeded in killing Lincoln just as he had planned, and he was still alive to tell the tale of his exploit.

He might rise to fame and power in Mexico. The circumstances were such that a young man of talent and reckless bravery could hope for almost anything there. Maximilian could help him obtain an entrée into the courts of Europe. The glittering life of the old world would be open to him after his conquest of Mexico. What he had done in Washington would eventually be forgotten. The world had a short memory, and was inclined to overlook past misdeeds when a man had made an international reputation for himself. He might even return to the United States some day in triumph. . . .

He wished that he could start this very instant. He wanted to ride through the cool night air toward his destination and his greatness. God damn this filthy barn and its niggardly owners!

The owl called again, and somewhere far away, a dog barked.

---

## Wednesday, April 26. 2 A.M.

---

Conger and Jett were riding at the head of the troop when they came to the entrance of the Garrett farm.

"I think we'd better stop for a moment here, sir," Jett said. "I'll explain to you how to reach the house. I don't have to go in there with you, do I?"

"You and Mr. Rollins can wait here with my sentry," Conger told him. "Tell me how the ground lies."

"Well, sir, you go ahead down this lane. The house

is in a grove of trees to the left. In the back there's a barn and some sheds. The woods come in close to all the buildings."

Conger instructed Doherty to wait at the entrance to the lane with his men, and then he and Baker rode forward to open the gates and examine the house. In a few minutes Conger came riding back. He called the men together and explained his plan of action to Doherty in their presence.

Then he sent six men to post themselves along the edge of the woods behind the barn, in order to prevent anyone from escaping through the rear. These men were sent on ahead. Doherty and the rest of the troop were instructed to ride slowly behind Conger, and to spread out in a circle around the house as soon as they passed through the inner gate.

"Remember that you're dealing with a desperate man," Conger said. "Keep your arms ready and be prepared to shoot quickly if necessary—but don't shoot unless you have to. We want to take him alive. Don't make any noise as you go in—I want to surprise the occupants of the house while they're still asleep. Follow me now, and walk your horses carefully."

He started down the lane with his silent troop behind him. The men held their rifles in their hands, so they would not rattle against the saddle holsters. Baker had already gone through the inner gate by the time they got there. They could see him dimly, standing on the lawn with his horse near the kitchen entrance. The cavalrymen quietly placed themselves around the house.

Baker mounted the steps to the kitchen door and hammered on the panel. A window on the second floor opened, and an old man's voice called out, asking who was there.

"Never mind who we are," Baker said to him. "If you are the owner of this house we want to talk to you. Light a candle and open this door."

Baker and Conger spoke together in whispers until a light appeared in the kitchen window. The door opened. Conger drew his pistol and told the old man standing hesitantly in the doorway to come outside. Two soldiers immediately pushed their way into the kitchen to search the house.

"Where are the two men who are stopping here?" Conger demanded.

Garrett raised his candle in order to get a better sight of the man talking to him. "They've gone," he said sullenly as soon as he saw the blue uniform. "They went away into the woods this afternoon."

The kitchen windows glowed with light as the two soldiers inside found a lamp and lit it. Voices murmured from the upper part of the house, and a child began to cry. Conger stepped closer to Garrett.

"Just where did they go in the woods?" he asked.

"I don't know—they just went. They came here without my consent, and they left without telling me where they were going. I don't even know who they are."

"Not very particular about your guests, are you, Mr. Garrett? Well, it may interest you to know then that those two men are the murderers of President Lincoln, and that anyone who shields them or abets their escape is incurring a capital charge. Now—where are they?"

Garrett's face, clearly lighted by the candle in his hand, showed no change of expression. "I know nothing about that. I told you they came here without my consent. I didn't want them to stay. In fact, I refused to let them sleep in my house. They—"

"I don't want any long story from you. Where are those men?"

Garrett remained silent. Conger turned and spoke to one of the soldiers standing behind him in the darkness. "Bring me a lariat rope," he said with sudden savageness, "and by God, I'll put this man up to the top of one of these trees! We'll see if he wants to tell us then!" He advanced toward Garrett, thrusting the point of his pistol into the old man's belly. "Bring me that rope and be quick about it. By Christ, I'll make this bastard talk if I have to yank his tongue out by the roots! The rope, damn you, the rope! Are you going to take all night unloosening it?"

Baker touched his arm. "They've found someone, sir," he said. "They're bringing him here."

Conger looked around, keeping his pistol against

his prisoner's body. Two of his soldiers were leading a young man dressed in Confederate uniform into the circle of light.

"Where did you get that rebel whelp? Who is he?"

"We got him in the corncrib, sir. He was hiding there."

"Maybe he's one of the men we are——"

"He's my son," Garrett said. "He——"

"Never mind," Conger roared. "I don't want to hear anything about him. He's here just in time to see his father lifted up to the top of a tree with a rope around his neck. Where's that rope, you God-damned fool?"

The soldier hastily held up a coil of rope which he had taken from his saddle. Bill Garrett tried to break away from the men who were holding him.

"You can't do that," he shouted. "He's an old man. He hasn't——" The soldiers choked off his voice. Conger walked over to him, motioning to his men to release him.

"You don't want to see him hanged, do you?" He waved his pistol in front of the boy's white straining face. "Well, maybe you'd like to tell us what we want to know." He asked, almost in a whisper: "Where are the two men who were staying here? Where are they?"

Bill Garrett looked at him without answering. Conger spoke to the man with the rope, never moving his eyes from the boy's face. "Take that rope," he said quietly, "and throw one end of it over a branch of this tree." The man started forward to obey.

"I'll tell you where they are," Bill Garrett said quickly. "Don't hurt my father. I'll tell you."

"Well?"

"They're in the barn. They're sleeping in the barn. We locked them in there, and my brother and I went out to sleep in the corncrib so we could watch them. We were afraid they'd steal our horse."

Conger lowered his revolver. "Lieutenant Doherty," he said, "summon your men."

Booth awoke from a restless sleep with a start. Everything was completely dark around him, and for a moment he did not know where he was. Then the dry sweet odor of hay, and the rustling beneath his head as he turned, made him realize that he was in the barn on the Garrett place. He was wide awake, staring into the blackness, and he was suddenly afraid.

He lay still, listening. Something had awakened him. He was trying to find out what it was. The insect chorus was still droning, but there was a new and strange quality to it now. It seemed to be fainter and farther away than it had been before. There was a zone of silence around the barn.

He felt the skin on his body tighten. He was cold, and he began to shiver, but he kept absolutely quiet, and he strained his ears to hear whatever it was that had awakened him. And then he heard it—the stealthy footfall of something moving in the grass near the barn. He raised himself carefully to a sitting position. He stretched out his hand to find Herold. He felt his shoulder under his hand. From somewhere in the distance, freighted with anguish, the sound of a young boy's voice crying indistinguishable words rose above the all-pervading insect noises, and then the voice stopped, cut off as though someone had clapped a hand over the protesting mouth. In the rear of the barn, and terribly close to it, there was a sudden snapping noise as if a dry branch had been stepped on by someone in the darkness. There was a whispered curse. A voice commanded silence in another whisper. Then Booth knew that his pursuers had caught up with him.

This was the end. He could never permit himself to be taken and marched back to Washington as a prisoner with twenty million people howling for his life. This was the end, and this body with its directing mind keenly awake and alive, was finished. He sensed that Death was in the barn, waiting for him in the darkness. His old ally had turned against him and was ready to claim his price.

Better to die now fighting than to be dragged away to the ignominy of the gallows. He remembered the bright image of John Brown's body, hooded and bound, swinging in the December sunshine. His hand tightened on Herold's shoulder, and he felt the boy's body stir into wakefulness.

"They're here, David," he whispered softly. "The barn is surrounded." Herold sat up, shaking off his hand.

"Who's here?"

"The troops we saw on the road today, I suppose. Anyway there are men outside. I heard them. Listen—"

There were voices speaking plainly now as people approached the barn. A faint glow of yellow light could be seen through the wide openings left in the walls so the air could circulate around the tobacco. The light grew stronger and the voices louder. Long streaks appeared on the barn floor, wavering and swaying unsteadily. The whole area outside seemed to be stirring with life. The streaks of light stopped moving and remained fixed. Men were talking in low voices at the barn door, and Booth heard the sharp click of a padlock being sprung open.

"The carbine, David," he whispered desperately. "Where is the carbine?" He felt the long cold shape of the gun thrust into his hands.

With a loud and terrifying noise the barn door began to thunder and shake as someone kicked against it again and again.

"Wake up in there!" a man's voice called. "We have come to arrest you, and we warn you that it will

349

be useless to try to resist. We have this place surrounded by armed men. Open this door!"

Conger and Doherty were stationing their men around the barn. The horses had been left at the house, and all the men were on foot. The Colonel had had a rail fence torn to pieces, and he was using the rails to mark the places where each man was to stand. He warned the soldiers to keep their guns in their hands, but he told them not to shoot unless the fugitives tried to force their way out of the building.

Baker had put the candle on the ground near the barn door, where it burned quietly in the still night air. Baker was standing with Bill Garrett in front of the door. No answer had been made to his challenge, but he could hear someone stirring inside the barn. Conger came over to him and told him to send young Garrett inside to tell the two men that they must surrender.

Baker cleared his throat uncertainly, and then he spoke out loud, trying to conceal the nervousness in his own voice. "We are going to send this young man in," he said. "You have been found on his place, and he is responsible for your presence in this barn. He is coming in to ask you to turn over your arms and surrender."

There was no answer.

"I don't want to go in there," Bill Garrett protested, "and I'm not responsible for their presence here. We had no choice in the matter. Those two are desperate men, and I'm afraid they'll shoot me."

"You go in there," Conger said determinedly, "or I'll shoot you right here and now. You gave them shelter. Now you disarm them."

Baker took the padlock from its hasp and grabbed Garrett by the arm. "I'm going to pull this door open now," he told him. "We'll stand clear of it for a second in case they try to shoot at the opening. If they don't shoot, you go in quick, and I'll shut the door behind you. Make sure you get their weapons. We won't let you out without them."

"I don't want to do it, mister. I can't help it if—"

"Shut up! I'm going to swing the door open now." Baker pulled at the door and hastily stepped back with it. The candle flickered and almost went out. He shoved young Garrett inside and slammed the door after him. They could hear footsteps as the boy walked hesitantly across the floor, feeling his way in the darkness.

"Damn you! Get out of here—you've betrayed us," a man's voice exclaimed in an angry whisper. Then a conversation took place in such low tones that the officers could not make out the words. Garrett came to the door and in a frightened voice begged them to let him out.

"Have you got the arms?" Baker asked.

"No. They wouldn't give 'em to me. I—"

"Then go back and get them."

"Let him out," Conger said. "They may try to harm the boy if he goes over there again. Open the door."

Baker swung the door open. Garrett scrambled out.

"They don't want to surrender," he said quaveringly. "I told you they was desperate. He cursed at me and said he was going to shoot me."

"Did you tell them who we are?" Conger asked.

"No, sir. They didn't ask me."

Conger spoke to Baker. "Tell them we'll give 'em five minutes to come out. If they're not out by then, we'll burn the place down."

"Yes, sir." Baker stepped close to one of the air spaces in the barn wall. Then he turned around to Conger. "Don't you think we ought to douse that candle, sir? He can probably see us out here, while we can't see him."

Conger hastily knocked the candle over and stepped on its still flaming wick. Baker put his face to the opening again.

"We know who you are in there," he said. "We'll give you just five minutes to surrender your arms and come out, or we'll set fire to this barn and drive you out."

The man inside the barn answered for the first time. Baker noted with satisfaction that he spoke in a well-modulated voice—a voice that was rich and resonant—an actor's voice.

"Who are you?" he asked. "Whom do you want?

We are guilty of no crime, and there is no reason—"

"Then you have nothing to fear. If you are innocent you will not be afraid to give up your arms and come out."

"But we don't know who you are. We don't know whether you are friends or enemies. It may be that we are to be taken by our friends."

Conger seized Baker's arm excitedly. "Don't tell them who we are," he whispered. "It's just possible that he may think we're rebels. If he does, take advantage of it. We may coax him out that way. You don't have to lie to him, but don't answer any questions as to who we are. Just keep insisting that they come out."

"Yes, sir, but it doesn't seem very possible to me. I think they're just trying to delay matters."

"Do as I tell you."

"Yes, sir." Baker went to the opening again. "It doesn't make any difference who we are," he said faithfully. "We know who you are, and we want you to come out. We have fifty armed men encircling this place. You can't possibly get away. Come out peacefully and you won't be harmed."

"Give us a few minutes to think it over."

Conger called Doherty and told him to inspect his men, to make sure they were all wide awake and in their appointed places. He waited patiently with Baker in front of the barn door. A whispered colloquy was going on inside. The two voices grew louder.

# The Man Who Killed Lincoln

One man could be heard berating the other, who answered him in a low whining voice. Finally, the man who had spoken to the officers before called out clearly.

"Captain," he said, "I know you to be a brave man, and I believe you to be an honorable one. I am a cripple—I have only one good leg. Give me a chance for my life. Withdraw your men a hundred yards from the door and I'll come out and fight you."

Conger spat on the ground in disgust. "Tell him to go to hell," he muttered. "We didn't come here to watch him put on a performance."

"We can't do anything like that," Baker said, speaking into the barn. "We came here to take you prisoner—not to lose men fighting with you. Surrender and come out."

"Fifty yards then," the voice pleaded. "Give me a chance."

Conger was furious. "Get him out, for Christ's sake, or I'll—" He burst into a string of barracks oaths that made the soldiers standing behind him grin sympathetically.

"The Colonel says you must surrender and come out," Baker said. "We can entertain no counter propositions. Surrender and come out, or we fire the barn and shoot."

"Very well then, my brave boys, prepare a stretcher for me!"

"Now what in hell does he mean by that?" Conger

asked irritably. "Is he coming out or isn't he? I'm getting tired of all this play-acting. Where's that boy we sent in?" He looked around for Bill Garrett. "Get some brush," he said when he found him, "and pile it up at the far corner of the barn. Don't be too quiet about it either. I want him to hear you putting it there. By God, I'm going to get some action! Go on, do as I tell you."

"Yes, sir, but—"

"God damn it! Do as I tell you."

The officers waited. They heard voices on the other side of the barn, and then young Garrett came stumbling back in the darkness.

"He wouldn't let me do it, sir. He threatened to shoot me if I didn't go away."

"Good—now we're going to start things." He spoke to Baker. "Give that idiot in there just two minutes to make up his mind. I'm going to fire the barn then."

Baker obeyed. There was no answer from the barn, but the wrangling between the two men inside began again.

Conger shouted to the soldiers. "Get ready for 'em now, boys. We're going to set the barn on fire. If they try to make a break—shoot fast!"

The whining voice in the barn was pleading desperately. Suddenly the other voice spoke out loud. "All right, Colonel, there's a man in here who wants to surrender."

"Let him come out then," Baker said quickly. "But he must bring his arms with him."

"Upon the word and honor of a gentleman, sirs, he has no arms. All the arms are mine, and I mean to keep them."

Conger growled.

"He has a carbine," Baker said. "We know he was carrying one."

"It's my carbine, unfortunately for you, gentlemen, and I don't intend to give it up. Do you want to let him come out? I swear to you that he is guilty of no crime."

"For Christ's sake, let the poor bastard out," Conger said. "I don't blame him. I'd hate to be in there with that lunatic. He seems to think he's still on the stage."

"All right, I'll open the door for him," Baker called out to the men in the barn. "Make sure he sticks his hands out first, though. We don't want to take any chances. Hands out first," he repeated.

"Grab him, and get him away from here," Conger said hurriedly. "I'm going around back and fire this barn. That'll drive the damned fool out."

Baker pulled the door open and crouched beside it, waiting. He could see a pair of hands thrust themselves out. He seized them hastily and yanked their owner outside. "Take him away and tie him up," he said to his men.

Almost immediately a faint glow appeared at the

side of the barn. There was a crackling sound. The light grew stronger. In a few minutes the whole side of the barn was ablaze. The fierce yellow light showed a circle of men standing with their guns half-raised. The flames swept up to the roof, leaping with terrible speed up the dry boards and curling out under the eaves.

Herold began to cry hysterically as he was led away.

Booth saw the first spark of fire in the corner of the barn. Before he could move, it had sprung into a flame and was lighting up the dark interior. Instantly the hay in that corner was a mass of fiercely burning flames. In the sudden illumination Booth could see the long bare shapes of the rafters and the undersides of the shingles on the roof. In front of him there was a pile of old furniture. From it he seized a table, and then, realizing that he had no chance of putting out the fire, he dropped it, and it crashed to the floor. He bent down to pick up the carbine, and he stood for a moment holding it and looking around wildly. He felt that there were men standing at every opening in the barn walls where the flames had not yet reached. They could see him now surely, and he could see nothing in the darkness outside.

He had the curious illusion that he was standing on a stage in some play that he had acted time and time again before. The light was coming from the footlamps, and the fire was stage fire, unreal and harmless. There was an audience beyond it, sitting somewhere out there in the darkness watching him, waiting to see how he would act in this old familiar part—this part in which the hero had to die with a brave speech on his lips as they rang the curtain down.

This was his last great moment. There must be no weakening now. He had to carry the affair off with a flourish, as Macbeth had done, and Hamlet—and Othello, whose death speech was the grandest of all. *Who can control his fate? Here is my journey's end, here is my butt, and very sea-mark of my utmost sail.* He knew the parts; he had played hundreds of death scenes; he knew all the appropriate words and gestures.

The flames had reached the roof. The heat was becoming unbearable. He backed away from it, still supporting himself on his crutches. In a few minutes the whole barn would be on fire.

This is the end—this is the last terrible moment, he thought. All the years of my life have led only to this. All the days of my childhood, all the nights of my youth, my triumphs, my conquests, the applause I have earned, the women I have won—all are to end in this. "He was trapped in a burning barn and shot to death by the soldiers who had tracked him down." Stop! They are watching me! There must be no self-pity now. I have this last part to act. Let it be said that he died bravely. Better to perish now, quickly and surely, by the hand that had killed Lincoln and changed the fate of nations, than to be riddled with bullets by a gang of Yankee hoodlums.

Now! Now! Be rid of this clumsy carbine. It thudded on the wooden floor as he threw it from him. The pistol—the pistol, smaller, surer, easier to handle. His hand felt the smooth heavy grip. There was a sound behind him—a sharp, metallic click that he heard even above the crackle of the flames. He whirled and saw the muzzle of a gun coming through one of the openings between the boards in the barn wall. Quick now, or they will have you! They are already closing in! Quick—point the pistol to the back of the head so the face will not be shattered by the terrible plowing course of the bullet. Quick now— only the hand of a Booth is worthy to kill a Booth!

The pistol against his skull—and then, with a roar, his world collapsed.

Baker rushed into the barn as soon as he heard the shot. He caught Booth's body before it slumped to the floor. Conger ran around the barn and followed him inside. Baker was turning the body over, trying to find the wound.

"What on earth did you want to shoot him for?" he asked Conger. "We could certainly have—"

"Shoot him? What in hell do you mean—shoot him? I didn't shoot him. He shot himself. Anyone can see that—look at the wound."

"No, he didn't shoot himself," Baker said firmly. "That just can't be. Someone shot him, and whoever it was should go back to Washington under arrest." He examined the neck of the limp body, and his fingers came away sticky with blood.

"It certainly looks to me as if he shot himself," Conger said. "That's just the way it would be if he had held a pistol to the back of his head and fired low. The bullet's gone right through, from side to side. Get him out of here, anyway. There may be some life in him yet, and this place is getting too damned hot."

The body was carried out and laid on the grass. Soldiers gathered around it in a little circle, looking curiously at the man who had killed the President of the United States. The barn continued to burn, and the flames lighted the scene with a flickering red glow. Conger took some of his men into the barn to see whether the fire could be put out, but the flames were already eating away at the rafters under the roof, so he returned to the place where Booth was lying. One of the women from the house had brought a pail, and Baker was sprinkling water from it on the white still face.

"He's alive, all right," Baker said, looking up at his superior officer. "I don't think he'll last long, though. We'd better take him away from here. This heat is— Wait a minute! He's trying to say something." He bent down close to the injured man and heard him say in a hardly audible voice: "Tell Mother—tell Mother—"

"Yes," he said gently. "What do you want me to tell your mother?"

"Tell Mother I died for my country," Booth gasped, and then his eyes closed, and his breathing became fainter.

"Pick him up and take him over there to the house," Baker said to the soldiers. "He may live for a while yet."

They lifted him up and carried him away from the fierce heat of the burning barn. As they went, the roof sagged down and fell into the burning mass within. A shower of sparks and heavy billowing smoke rose up into the night sky.

It was quiet and dark on the porch. Baker asked Miss Holloway for something on which to place the dying man. She brought out an old feather bed, and Booth was put down on it. Then a candle was lighted, and it burned fitfully on the floor, throwing a wavering and uncertain light on the faces of the men gathered around this outdoor deathbed. Blood kept oozing out of the wound, staining the cloth beneath the head with a dark soggy patch.

"Notice where the bullet hole is," Conger said. "Right behind the ear."

"I don't care where it is," Baker said irritably.

"He didn't shoot himself. Do you suppose we can go back and say that we let him—"

Conger whistled softly. "Of course, of course. You're absolutely right. He must have been shot." He turned to the soldiers standing on the lawn behind him. "Where's the man who shot him?" he asked. "I want to talk to him."

Everyone looked at him blankly. Then a man thrust his way through the little group. It was Boston Corbett, the sergeant who had been stationed at the rear of the barn.

"I did it, sir," he said calmly.

"He's crazy enough to have done anything," Baker whispered. "Let him say that he did it. The authorities have had a lot of trouble with him anyway, Doherty tells me."

"What did you do it for?" Conger asked the sergeant, who was standing rigidly at attention before him, as though he were being examined at a formal court of inquiry. "There was no need to shoot him, and you had orders not to do so unless he tried to escape. You must have had a good reason, surely."

"Providence directed me to do it, sir. I heard the voice of God."

"Humph!" Conger cleared his throat. "So you shot him, eh? He was trying to shoot one of us, I suppose, wasn't he? You saw him raise his gun?"

"Oh, yes, sir," Corbett said eagerly. "He was. He was going to shoot. I saw him and then I—"

# Wednesday, April 26

"That will do, Sergeant. I'll leave your case to Providence and the Secretary of War. Just see that you turn your arms and your command over to your corporal until we get back to Washington."

"He shot him right behind the ear, sir," one of the soldiers said. "That's the very place the President was hit."

Conger glowered at him. "More Providence, I suppose. Where's that boy we took out of the barn? Bring him over here and tie him to a tree where I can keep an eye on him."

Herold was led into the circle of light cast by the candle and tied by his hands to a tree near the porch. He hugged the tree trunk closely, trying to avoid looking at the motionless body that lay under the candle flame. He was praying, and his dirt-stained cheeks were tear streaked. Jett and Rollins were brought in by the sentries, and a man was sent to Port Royal to get a doctor.

Baker tried to see if Booth could be brought back to consciousness. He asked for some brandy and a handkerchief. Miss Holloway brought them to him silently. Baker moistened the cloth and squeezed some drops of the liquor into Booth's open mouth. Conger then took the handkerchief and dipped it into the cold well water. He washed Booth's forehead clumsily, and he wiped away the blood that had run down the side of his neck. He moved the candle nearer, and he saw that the dying man's eyes were open, staring at him and following him as he moved.

"Is there anything that I can do for you?" he asked.

"Turn me over," Booth whispered. "The pain is killing me. Turn me over on my face."

The two men laid him face downward on the feather bed. In a few minutes he was trying to talk again, his voice muffled by the soft stuff around his mouth.

"For God's sake, turn me back again. I'm choking to death. Is there blood in my throat, Colonel? I can't breathe."

Conger opened his mouth and examined it with the light of the candle. "There's no blood there, Booth. The bullet didn't pass that far forward. There's no blood there at all."

"But I can't breathe. I can't move."

"I know. I've seen men shot through the back of the head before. They become paralyzed and—"

He bent down over Booth's face, hesitating to say that men who had been shot through the cervical vertebrae always die, but there was no need for his hesitation, for Booth had slipped into unconsciousness again and his breathing had almost ceased.

The men stood waiting, and some of the tired soldiers dropped down on the grass to sleep. The sky slowly lightened in the east. The barn was still smoldering, and a long column of smoke rose up against the reddening clouds. The doctor arrived from Port

Royal, but there was very little he could do. One look at the gaping hole in the back of Booth's skull told him that.

Out of the welter of dreams and long-forgotten images, confused, unreal, filled with the sorrow of remembered happiness and made tumultuous with the terror of the present moment, Booth's mind struggled again into consciousness, and his eyes opened to behold the dawn. Around him the moving figures of men, and beyond them the large dark shapes of horses —everywhere about him, trembling in the morning breeze, the fresh green leaves of springtime hung like a veil before the sun.

He lay on the porch with his eyes staring upwards. His head was alive, but even through the frightful pain he could feel death encroaching upon him. His body was already dead, and he could not move his own hands. He had been dragged up from black unconsciousness to watch himself die, and he was pinioned down by paralysis so that he could not move or cry out or struggle against the terror that was enveloping him. His brain fiercely urged his hands to lift themselves, but there was no response. He remained absolutely still, weakened by the effort, and only his eyes blinked quickly as a last sign of life and will.

One of the officers bent down and spoke to him. Booth could hear the man plainly, although his voice seemed unreasonably far away. "Is there anything I can do?" he heard him ask, and he heard him repeat the question several times. He tried to move his own lips, but the breath from his dead lungs was so feeble that no sound came, and the officer finally stood up and began talking to someone else.

He must make them understand. He tried to attract the man's attention again by moving his eyelids rapidly, but no one noticed him. They were treating him like a corpse already, he thought bitterly. The horror of his anomalous position between life and death was so great that he wanted to cry. He felt a great longing for his mother. He tried to speak her name, but he was unable to push the breath out of his mouth. He closed his eyes, terrified and lonely. There were men all around him, but they were far away somehow, although he could hear the murmur of their voices.

He must speak to them, must hold communion again with the living. He struggled fearfully, trying to attract their attention by moving the still-responsive muscles of his face. He must speak to them. He must make them understand that he, too, was alive.

No one noticed him. He closed his eyes, feeling himself slip down into the darkness. And then he sensed that someone was bending over him, trying to listen to the beating of his heart. He opened his eyes and saw a man's face near his own. It smiled at him, and he made a superhuman effort to speak to it. The man moved his ear close to Booth's lips, listening for the faint, hardly breathed words. Evidently he heard, for he answered the request, and Booth saw his own dead hands lifted up suddenly from the porch where they had been lying. The limp, half-bent fingers were silhouetted above him, motionless against the sky. He saw his own hands, and he felt sick and frightened at the sight of them. He moved his lips again, shaping the words: "Useless, useless!" The man perhaps understood, for his face became grave, and he laid the quiet hands gently down on the porch.

The bright world was graying now. The sounds of the men's voices became fainter. Even the pain that had been gripping his head in a clamp was less noticeable. Suddenly, he realized that if he let himself slip now, he would never come back again. He opened his eyes with a start to see the morning sun again. And then he felt the dull grayness creep over him once more. The men were standing in a circle around him, watching his face. They had stopped talking. He saw their faces recede into the grayness, waver and become clear for a moment. He must have closed his eyes after that, because there was only darkness before him—darkness, and a slow rhythmical beating, and then—only darkness. . . .

# *EPILOGUE*

★

After mature consideration of the evidence adduced
in the case . . . the Commission find the said accused—

Of the Specification............... GUILTY

And the Commission do, therefore, sentence. . . .

## Thursday, July 6

THE great trial was over. It had begun on May tenth (and on that day Jefferson Davis had been captured). The old penitentiary in the Arsenal grounds had been converted into a court, and the eight prisoners were housed in the same building, hooded in canvas bags, stiff-shackled, and foot-chained to seventy-five-pound iron weights. They had been tried before a Military Commission of nine army officers and three members of the Judge Advocate General's office. They had been seated on a platform at the end of the courtroom with a soldier between each two prisoners. Day after day for weeks they had heard their lives sworn away by witness after witness. They had sat and listened—Arnold, the ex-commissary clerk; Mudd, the country doctor; Spangler, the crab-fishing sceneshifter; O'Laughlin, the once happy-go-lucky Irishman; Atzerodt, the Port Tobacco carriage maker; Paine, the professional soldier; Herold, the former druggist's clerk and partridge hunter; and in a corner by herself, Mrs. Surratt, widow, boarding house keeper, and mother of John Surratt who had escaped to Canada. And against her, Louis Weichmann, in fear of losing his own life, had spoken damningly, tightening the noose around her neck.

The warm days of spring had turned into the hot days of summer as the trial dragged on. The last sporadic efforts of Confederate resistance had been stamped out. The body of Abraham Lincoln had reached its final resting place in Springfield, Illinois. The Grand Army of the Republic, recalled from the battlefields to Washington, had marched in review down the long Avenue to the Capitol, and it had taken two days for its tens of thousands to pass. The war was over, and men were seeking the ways of peace again. There was only this one final nasty business to be gone through—but a good job had to be made of it, for the Commission was determined to brand the Confederacy forever as a reckless and desperate effort that had included murder in its plans as well as rebellion and warfare.

So the trial had been made a trial of the Rebel Government, and the charge had named Davis and the leaders of the Confederacy, in addition to these sorry-looking culprits shivering in the prisoners' dock. The opening days of the trial had been devoted to trying to establish Richmond's complicity, and the time of the Commission had been taken up with secret ciphers, details of rebel cruelty to prisoners, and accounts of rebel attempts to burn, plunder and spread disease into the cities of the North.

The prisoners had sat and listened to all this. Two hundred and sixty-five witnesses in all were examined in the course of the trial, and each one of them had spoken for or against the eight prisoners, but the prisoners had never been allowed to utter a word.

Now it was all over. The sentences had been fixed and approved by the new President. Provost Marshal General Hartranft and the nine officers of the Military Commission were at the doors of the prison to read their findings to the prisoners in their cells. And they had brought them word that four out of the eight were to be sentenced to imprisonment and hard labor, and that the other four were to be hanged by the neck until they were dead.

---

## Friday, July 7

It is fearfully hot in the courtyard of the prison. The sun beats down on the heads of the crowd, and the guards stationed along the tops of the walls are sweltering in their uniforms. The raw wood of the newly built gallows gleams whitely against the dark brick walls, and the heat waves shimmer over the platform where four empty chairs are waiting under the ropes. Down deep in the cool earth under one of the buildings in the prisonyard the body of John Wilkes Booth, wrapped in a soldier's blanket, lies in a secret grave. And next to the gallows are four freshly dug pits with the soil piled up around them bleaching in the sun. Four rough wooden coffins are stacked up in front of them. Under the platform four soldiers stand ready to knock away the props which hold up the hinged front boards that are to serve as a trap.

Now all eyes are turned to one end of the yard. A woman in black supported by two priests appears there. Behind her are four soldiers and an officer. Everyone is silent as she enters the yard. Then comes Atzerodt, looking nervously from side to side. He has a handkerchief on his head, and his wild disheveled hair sticks out beneath it. Four more soldiers follow him with their bayoneted rifles pointed stiffly to the sky. Behind them is Davy Herold, his face haggard and white, peering fearfully at the great gallows structure looming up above the crowd. And then Lewis Paine, striding along behind his guard as though he were marching to battle again. He seizes a straw hat from the head of an officer, puts it on his own head and walks defiantly to the gallows.

Mrs. Surratt has mounted the stairs to the platform. The others follow her. She is seated in a chair at the far end, and someone holds an umbrella over her head to shield her from the scorching sun. Paine is seated next to her. Then Davy Herold—and Atzerodt last.

# Friday, July 7

General Hartranft reads the order of execution in a low voice that can hardly be heard beyond the first few rows of the crowd. Three clergymen speak—one for Paine, one for Herold, one for Atzerodt. Finally, the prayers are finished. The two priests are silent as Mrs. Surratt desperately kisses the crucifix.

The prisoners are told to stand up. They are bound and hooded. The chairs are taken away. The executioner looks across the courtyard for General Hancock, who is to give him the word, but Hancock is still waiting outside the prison gate, hoping for a last-minute reprieve for the woman. Finally, he comes in.

"All is ready, Captain. Proceed," he calls across the yard.

"Her too?" the executioner asks.

Hancock nods, and a murmur runs through the crowd. Hancock claps his hands twice. The sound seems thin and faint in the vast expanse, but the executioner hears it. He gives the order. The soldiers under the platform obey his command. They knock out the supporting timbers. The hinged boards fall with a crash. The four living bodies drop, only to be stopped in mid-air. They swing at the ends of the ropes—they swing in dreadful little arcs in the sunshine, and it is a long while before they are still.

# ACKNOWLEDGMENTS

In the preparation of this book I have had to call upon so many people for assistance that it is impossible for me to acknowledge my indebtedness to them all here. I should, however, like to make special mention of Chief Clerk Edwin B. Pitts of the Judge Advocate General's office in Washington, who enabled me to examine at leisure the unpublished documents in the War Department archives. In fact, I should like to take this opportunity to comment on the courtesy with which I was treated everywhere in Government circles.

I wish to express my appreciation also to the librarians of the Library of Congress, of the New York Public Library, of the Rutgers University Library and of The Players Club Library; to Miss Marguerite LeHand for permitting me to visit the Lincoln Cabinet Room in the White House; and to Dr. Hendrik Willem van Loon, whose letters of introduction proved to be open sesames everywhere.

To Mr. Alfred F. Goldsmith for his unceasing search for material on the case; to Mr. Maxwell Nurnberg and to Miss Maria Leiper for careful readings of the manuscript; to Mr. I. N. Steinberg for his drawings; to Miss Katherine Buckles and to Mr. Joseph Spivak for unusual care in proofreading.

Above all, to my wife and to my sisters for their patience and help during the years of preparatory work.

And lastly, to Mr. Saxe Commins, editor of Random House, for his encouragement, for his constructive suggestions on the manuscript, and—most important of all—for his friendship which has been long and enduring.

376

# AFTERWORD

*in which the author discusses the sources used in writing this book, tells what happened to some of the people who were involved in the assassination, and comments on the still-unsolved mysteries surrounding the murder of Abraham Lincoln.*

## TOGETHER WITH A BIBLIOGRAPHY

# *Afterword*

The story I have told here follows carefully the actual
sequence of events as they occurred during the month of
April, 1865, when the termination of the long war between
the North and the South was sealed with the blood of Abraham Lincoln. History had set the stage and managed the
dramatic action so well that there was no need to invent plot
or characters—the story had been cast in a great tragic pattern, and the characters were in real life strange and remarkable enough to satisfy anyone.

Here, in fact, were all the celebrated types of romantic
fiction ready at hand. The man who was to die was the greatest figure in our country's history, and the time chosen for
his death was the peak moment of his career—the moment
when victory and peace were at last assured. And the man
who was to kill him was a perfect Byronic character, pale,
melancholy and extraordinarily handsome. John Wilkes
Booth was no common criminal. Neither poverty nor depri-
vation had played any part in shaping him, although he was,
of course, the product of his environment as much as any
slum-bred murderer. He was the result of a feudalistic
culture, and he himself was aristocratic by tradition—if not
by birth. Furthermore, he was thoroughly imbued with the
ideals of that tradition which taught that an outward show
of gallantry could suddenly be transformed into violence
when there was an end to be gained. Around him was a
supporting cast of villains ranging from the slightly gen-

# Afterword

teel John Harrison Surratt to the low-comedy clown, Atzerodt.*

The setting, too, was of exceptional interest. Wartime Washington, filled with spies and Confederate sympathizers, was a city in which anything could happen. It was a place filled with turbulence and color, even though it was still only an overgrown country town of shabby houses and unpaved streets. Almost every trace of it has been swept away. The Civil War capital has already become as much a part of the romantic past as Troy or Roncesvalles. In the very heart of this city, Booth, with his flair for the dramatic, picked on the interior of a theater, with the play in full progress, as the *mise en scène* for his astounding coup. Even fate, which is likely to be at least momentarily kind to those who play into its hands, gave him the lurid red glare of a burning barn to light up his grand finale. And he died, not instantly, of course, but in the lingering agony that enables an actor to wring out the last bit of juice from his curtain scene.

Plot, characters and setting were the free gift of history. I had only to take the material offered and weave it into a continuous narrative. The assassination has often been written about before, but it has been treated for its historical rather than its dramatic values. As a dramatic spectacle it has long been awaiting a revival, and the characters needed only an invitation to walk again on that unquiet stage where the action is never finished, and the lines have to be rewritten from generation to generation.

* Even the names of the people involved in the assassination were so perfectly suited to their parts that one would have difficulty in trying to improve upon them.

# Afterword

There was no need to invent anything in the telling of this story, other than conversation, internal and external, and that, with the few minor exceptions listed below,* is all

* These exceptions are:

1. Booth's encounter with the two soldiers at the very beginning of the story is fictitious.

2. Actually, John Matthews was inside the theater at the moment Booth fired the shot that killed Lincoln. I have placed him outside in order to show how bewildered the crowd was about the identity of the assassin. Matthews might easily have left the theater during the first part of the third act, since his presence on the stage was not needed until the third scene.

3. Atzerodt's meeting with the soldier in the barroom of the Kirkwood House is fictitious. He did enter the barroom a few minutes after ten o'clock, and left about ten-fifteen, but nothing is known of what took place while he was there.

4. Exactly what Samuel Cox said to Booth has never been established. Oswald Swann, the Negro who was waiting outside the house, testified that Booth came out cursing at Cox, so it is reasonable to assume that he had met with an unfavorable reception.

5. The case of John Surratt is such a complicated one that it will have to be treated at length. A discussion of his complicity will be found later in these pages.

----

For some strange reason everyone who has written about Booth's crossing the Potomac has taken at face value Jones' statement that Booth and Herold put out on the river for the first time on Friday, April 21. Yet Booth's own diary, in the entry for that day, says: "After being hunted like a dog through swamps and woods, and *last night* being chased by gunboats till I was forced to return, wet, cold, and starving, with every man's hand against me, I am here in despair." (Italics mine.) Also, the War Department archives show that Jones had been reported missing from his house on Thursday night.

# Afterword

that I have invented. Otherwise I have set down the story exactly as it happened, with scrupulous attention to details of time, place and incident. Fortunately, there are complete and reasonably accurate records available which cover almost every moment of Booth's movements from the night of the assassination until the day of his death. A brief description of them may be of interest.

The most useful sources were the stenographic reports of the Conspirators' Trial and of the Surratt Trial. There are two thousand pages of testimony in these volumes, taken down directly as spoken in court by people who saw Booth kill Lincoln or who came in contact with him during his flight. Even more important than these trial reports for firsthand evidence, though, are the original documents in the possession of the Judge Advocate General's office. These consist of hundreds of affidavits, letters and depositions of people connected with the case. Reference to these papers has enabled me to reconstruct the details of certain hitherto unpublished incidents in Booth's flight, particularly those which have to do with his passage through Virginia to the Rappahannock River.

The material in the Judge Advocate General's office also contains many statements made by eyewitnesses who were interrogated by Stanton's court of inquiry on the night of the assassination. Testimony of this kind is especially valuable, since it was recorded before the witnesses had a chance to elaborate upon their stories—or conveniently forget anything which might later seem embarrassing to their safety.

These accounts bring out many details that are not generally known about the case, and disprove others that have been solemnly accepted as true. For instance, careful examination of the reports as to what happened in Ford's Theater during the assassination shows that the general belief that Booth brandished his dagger as he ran across the stage, and cried out: "The South is avenged!" has no foundation in fact. Even Booth's own words in his diary indicate that this never happened. He was much too concerned at the moment with getting away safely, and it is reasonable to assume that the shock of the fall which broke his leg drove out of his mind any grandiose notions he may have had about delivering an apt curtain speech upon the stage.

In addition to these primary sources of evidence, there were a number of works that had to be consulted for information on certain minor details. Booth's visit to Dr. Mudd's house is adequately covered in the Conspirators' Trial reports, but a more complete picture of the household is given in *The Life of Dr. Samuel A. Mudd* by his daughter Nettie. Booth's stay in the thicket near Cox's house has been described by Thomas A. Jones, the man who helped the fugitives cross the Potomac. Jones wrote a little book about his experiences which he planned to sell at the World's Fair in Chicago in 1893. On the occasion of his first appearance there, some Union veterans in the audience tried to mob "the dirty rebel who helped Booth escape." Jones' venture was an immediate failure, and his book has consequently become exceedingly rare.

The pursuit of Booth by the cavalry patrol which tracked him down is fully related in Lafayette Baker's *History of the United States Secret Service*. There is additional material (Doherty's report) in the *Official Records of the War of the Rebellion*. Accounts have also been left by Ruggles, Bainbridge, Miss Holloway and William Garrett.

# Afterword

Reference to them will be found in the bibliography appended here.

In order to get firsthand impressions of the scenes that play an important part in the story, I traveled the road taken by Booth from Ford's Theater to Garrett's farm. Many of the places on Booth's rather isolated route have changed very little. The Surratt tavern still stands, although a real-estate development is rapidly being built up around it. Dr. Mudd's house may be seen at the top of a large sloping field that is a part of the actively worked farm belonging to it. The thicket where Booth lay in hiding has long since been stripped of its trees, but its location can, with some difficulty, be identified. The ferry between Port Conway and Port Royal has given way to a modern bridge, but the ruins of the ferry wharf can still be seen in the river.

On the day I arrived at the Garrett farmhouse (April 22, 1937), some Negroes from the neighborhood were just beginning to tear down the old building which was in an advanced state of dilapidation. A dense, junglelike growth of trees had sprung up in the dooryard; the porch on which Booth died had rotted away; no trace of the original tobacco barn was left, but a new barn had been built almost on the very spot where the old one stood. I drew plans of the house and photographed everything. The pictures I took were, I suppose, the last ones ever made.

In Washington I was shown the exhibits used in the trial of the conspirators—Booth's deringer (spelled with one R on the pistol itself); Booth's dagger with its curious inscription; Paine's dagger, chipped by the impact against Seward's steel collar; Booth's compass, still spotted by the candle grease which had dripped down on it when Jones showed

*Over the box-rail now to the stage, the light burning in his eyes, and a tearing sound as he jumps — one of his spurs has caught in the flag draping the box, and he is thrown off balance. . . .*

FROM A CONTEMPORARY PRINT

## FORD'S THEATRE

### TENTH STREET, ABOVE E.

| SEASON II. | WEEK XXVIII. | NIGHT 174 |
WHOLE NUMBER OF NIGHTS, 453.

JOHN T. FORD............................PROPRIETOR AND MANAGER
(Also of Holliday St. Theatre, Baltimore, and Academy of Music, Phil'a.)
Stage Manager........................................J. B. WRIGHT
Treasurer..............................................H. CLAY FORD

### Saturday Evening, March 18, 1865

# BENEFIT
### OF
# JOHN M'CULLOUGH

### ON WHICH OCCASION
### THE EMINENT YOUNG AMERICAN TRAGEDIAN,
### MR. J. WILKES

# BOOTH

Having kindly Volunteered his services, will render his Great Character of

## PESCARA!

W. H. Hamblin.......................as.......................Malec
(By permission of Messrs. E. L. Davenport and J. W. Wallack, Jr.)
Miss Alice Gray......................................Florinda
John McCullough......................as.......................Hemeya
C. B. Bishop..........................as.......................Caleb Scrimmidge

First time this season of Sheridan Taylor Knox's Great Tragedy of THE

# APOSTATE!

Pescara..................by..................J. WILKES BOOTH
Hemeya...................by..................JOHN McCULLOUGH
Malec.....................by..................W. H. HAMPLIN
Raoul.......................................MATTHEWS
Altava.......................................D. E. REILLY
Clamor.....................................CHARLES WARWICK
Gomez.......................................R. H. EVANS
The Cadi....................................W. J. FERGUSON
Gonzango...................................C. V. HESS
1st Moor....................................L. CARLAND
2d Moor.....................................J. PARKHURST
3d Moor.....................................L. DeBONAY
4th Moor....................................C. BYRNE
Florinda.....................................Miss Alice Gray

The Great Domestic Drama, founded upon fact, called

# JONATHAN BRADFORD!
### OR, THE MURDER AT THE ROADSIDE INN.

Caleb Scrimmidge.............................C. B. BISHOP
Jonathan Bradford.............................D. E. REILLY
Dan Macraisy..................................J. F. WHEELOCK
Jack.........................................R. H. EVANS
Mr. Hayes....................................MATTHEWS
Dexter.......................................W. FERGUSON
Rodpisk......................................L. CARLAND
Sergeant Fuss.................................C. V. HESS
Corporal.....................................J. PARKHURST
Juliet.......................................J. L. DeBONAY
Annie Bradford...............................Miss J. GOURLAY
Sally........................................Mrs J. E. SCOTT
The Childe...................................Misses NICHOLS and WATSON

# A GRAND SACRED CONCERT
### SUNDAY EVENING, MARCH 19, 1865.
## BENEFIT OF JAS. R. O'BRYON,
### OF FORD'S THEATRE.

---

## FORD'S THEATRE

### TENTH STREET, ABOVE E.

SEASON II.....WEEK XXXI.....NIGHT 191
WHOLE NUMBER OF NIGHTS, 405.

JOHN T. FORD.............................PROPRIETOR AND MANAGER
(Also of Holliday's St. Theatre, Baltimore, and Academy of Music, Phila.
Stage Manager........................................J. B. WRIGHT
Treasurer.............................................H. CLAY FORD

### Friday Evening, April 14th, 1865.

# THIS EVENING
The Performance will be honored by the presence of

## PRESIDENT LINCOLN

# BENEFIT
### AND
# LAST NIGHT
### OF MISS
# LAURA KEENE

### THE DISTINGUISHED MANAGERESS AUTHORESS, and ACTRESS
### Supported by
## MR. JOHN DYOTT
### AND MR. HARRY HAWK

TOM TAYLOR'S CELEBRATED ECCENTRIC COMEDY
As originally produced in America by Miss Keene, and performed by her
upwards of

### ONE THOUSAND NIGHTS,
### ENTITLED
## OUR AMERICAN

# COUSIN

FLORENCE TRENCHARD.........MISS LAURA KEENE
Her Original Character

Abel Murcott, Clerk to Attorney..................John Dyott
Asa Trenchard.....................................Harry Hawk
Sir Edward Trenchard.............................T. C. GOURLAY
Lord Dundreary..................................E. A. EMERSON
Mr. Coyle, Attorney..............................J. MATTHEWS
Lieutenant Vernon, R. N.........................W. J. FERGUSON
Captain De Boots.................................C. BYRNES
Binney...........................................G. G. SPEAR
Buddicomb, a Valet..............................J. B. EVANS
John Whicker's Gardner...........................J. L. DeBONAY
Rasper, a Groom
Bailiffs...........................................G. A. PARKHURST and L. JOHNSON
Mary Trenchard...................................Miss J. GOURLAY
Mrs. Mountchessington...........................Mrs H. MUZZY
Augusta..........................................Miss H. TRUEMAN
Georgiana.......................................Miss M. HART
Sharpe..........................................Mrs. J. H. EVANS
Skillet..........................................Miss M. GOURLAY

### SATURDAY EVENING, APRIL 15.
## BENEFIT OF MISS JENNIE GOURLAY
When will be presented BOURCICAULT'S Great Sensational Drama,
# THE OCTOROON.

Easter Monday, April 17, Engagement of the YOUNG AMERICAN
TRAGEDIAN,
# EDWIN ADAMS
### FOR TWELVE NIGHTS ONLY

### THE PRICES OF ADMISSION :
Orchestra.........................................$1.00
Dress Circle and Parquette..........................75
Family Circle......................................25
Private Boxes.................................$6 and $10
J. E. FORD, Business Manager.
L. Brown, Printer, Washington, D. C.

---

*Last billed*
*appearance*

*Last unbilled*
*appearance*

### FROM ORIGINAL PROGRAMS IN THE AUTHOR'S COLLECTION

*This theater was obviously the destined place*

*The front of the box had been draped with flags*

FORD'S THEATER PHOTOGRAPHED SOON AFTER THE ASSASSINATION

*All the years of his childhood had been associated with that house . . . .*

*"Here is my journey's end . . . all the years of my life have led only to this."*

THE BOOTH HOMESTEAD, BELAIR, MD.

THE GARRETT FARMHOUSE, PORT ROYAL, VA.

FROM PHOTOGRAPHS TAKEN BY THE AUTHOR

LEWIS PAINE
*placidly murderous giant*

DAVID HEROLD
*former druggist's clerk*

GEORGE ATZERODT
*Port Tobacco carriage maker*

MRS. MARY SURRATT
*boarding house keeper*

THE PRINCIPAL

SAMUEL ARNOLD
*ex-commissary clerk*

MICHAEL O'LAUGHLIN
*happy-go-lucky Irishman*

JOHN H. SURRATT
*Confederate spy*

EDWARD SPANGLER
*crab-fishing sceneshifter*

CONSPIRATORS

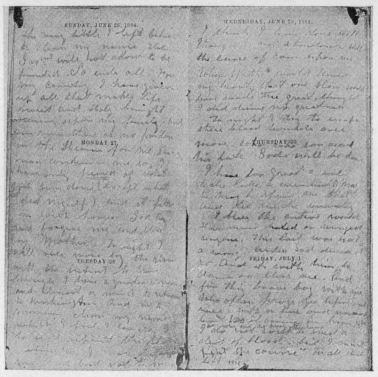

*He determined to write down again his motives for what he had done. If he were to be killed he wanted to leave the world some evidence of his intentions . . . .*

BOOTH'S DIARY

(*From the War Department Archives*)

*The body was carried out and laid on the grass*

BOOTH'S CAPTURE

*The conspirators were seated on a platform at the end of the courtroom*

THE CONSPIRATORS' TRIAL

*To be hanged by the neck until dead . . . .*

*They swing in dreadful little arcs in the sunshine,*
*and it is a long while before they are still*

him his course across the river; the boot which Dr. Mudd had cut from Booth's leg; and the maps the fugitives had used on their journey. The diary, faded and fragile, was taken from the safe in the Judge Advocate General's office and handed to me for close inspection. The photographs of Booth's sweethearts were still in the pocket in the back cover.

The Washington Weather Bureau kindly opened its files to me and made available its detailed records of the weather during the period covered in this story. It was interesting to note that on the bottom of the page for April 15, 1865, the clerk had made a special entry—the only human touch in all that technical record. He had written: "The city is draped in mourning for President Lincoln's death."

The Library of Congress supplied me with newspapers for April, 1865, so that I was able to gather much useful information from accounts written at the time by journalists in various cities. All the material quoted in this book is, of course, authentic.

I have concentrated attention on Booth in the telling of this story because it has always seemed to me that the central character in the drama of the assassination was not Lincoln, but Booth. Obviously Booth has been remembered in history only because of his connection with Lincoln, but this book has been concerned more with drama than with history. In the dramatic tragedy of the assassination, Lincoln had the passive role; Booth the active one. Lincoln was delivered to his fate unknowing, unheeding, blind. Great as he was and important, in this scene he had only one function, and that was to die. Booth, however, had to think, to plan, to act in the full conscious realization of what he was doing, and although his mind was perhaps disordered, he was certainly not so mad that he did not have to weigh beforehand all the possible consequences of his deed to himself and to others.

Lincoln never heard Booth creep up behind him. As a conscious, thinking being, he died the instant the shot struck him. His existence for nine hours afterwards was existence only in the physiological sense of the term.

He had been living for more than four years under the constant threat of assassination, and he had finally become used to it. He had been brought into Washington secretly for his first inauguration, because word had leaked out that he was to be killed as he passed through Baltimore. He had been shot at during a ride in the country, and a Southern gentleman had advertised in a Confederate newspaper that he would subscribe a thousand dollars toward a fund to subsidize an assassin. The White House had been flooded with letters that sometimes became obscene in their hatred. After Lincoln's death some of these letters were found in his desk. He had written on the envelope containing them the single, significant word: "Assassination."

His life had been filled with the threat of death, but, fortunately, when death came he was unaware of its arrival. Yet he had long brooded over his fate and had had many premonitions of it. Herndon, his law partner and biographer, says of him:

He always contended that he was doomed to a sad fate, and he repeatedly said to me when we were alone in our office: "I am sure I shall meet with some terrible end." In proof of his strong leaning towards fatalism he once quoted the case of Brutus and Caesar, arguing that the former was forced by laws and conditions over which he had no control to kill the latter, and, vice versa, that the latter was specially created to be disposed of by the former.

In Springfield, just after the Presidential election of 1860, Lincoln experienced one of these strange manifestations of his destiny. He saw a double image of himself in a mirror—one image real and lifelike, the other pale and shadowy. He was convinced that this meant that he would live through his first term safely, be re-elected and meet his death before the end of his second term.

Even more remarkable than this was a dream which he had only a few days before he was killed. He told it to Mrs. Lincoln and to Ward Hill Lamon, his friend and bodyguard. Lamon recorded it in Lincoln's own words:

About ten days ago, I retired very late. I had been up waiting for important dispatches from the front. I could not have been long in bed when I fell into a slumber, for I was weary. I soon began to dream. There seemed to be a death-like stillness about me. Then I heard subdued sobs, as if a number of people were weeping. I thought I left my bed and wandered downstairs. There the silence was broken by the same pitiful sobbing, but the mourners were invisible. I went from room to room; no living person was in sight, but the same mournful sounds of distress met me as I passed along. It was light in all the rooms; every object was familiar to me; but where were all the people who were grieving as if their hearts would break? I was puzzled and alarmed. What could be the meaning of all this? Determined to find the cause of a state of things so mysterious and so shocking, I kept on until I arrived at the East Room, which I entered. There I met with a sickening surprise. Before me was a catafalque, on which rested a corpse wrapped in funeral vestments. Around it were stationed soldiers who were acting as guards; and there was a throng of people, some gazing mournfully upon the corpse, whose face was covered, others weeping pitifully. "Who is dead in the White House?" I demanded of one of the soldiers. "The President," was his answer; "he was killed by an assassin!" Then came a loud burst of grief from the crowd, which awoke me from my dream. I slept no more that night. . . .

Most remarkable of all, though, was the recurrent dream which Lincoln had had all during the war, and which came to him on the night preceding his assassination. At the Cabinet meeting held on April 14, word was expected any minute of the surrender of Johnston's army to Sherman. Gideon Welles, Secretary of the Navy, who was present at the meeting, put down Lincoln's comment in his diary:

The President remarked it would, he had no doubt, come soon, and come favorable, for he had last night the usual dream which he had preceding nearly every great and important event of the War. Generally the news had been favorable which succeeded this dream, and the dream itself was always the same. I inquired what this remarkable dream could be. He said . . . that he seemed to be in some singular, indescribable vessel, and that he was moving with great rapidity towards an indefinite shore; that he had this dream preceding Sumter, Bull Run, Antietam, Gettysburg, Stone River, Vicksburg, Wilmington, etc.

"I had," the President remarked, "this strange dream again last night, and we shall, judging from the past, have great news very soon. I think it must be from Sherman. My thoughts are in that direction, as are most of yours."

# Afterword

The killing of Abraham Lincoln was doubly tragic in its implications. One was the great but impersonal tragedy of a nation deprived at a crucial moment of a much-needed leader; the other was the personal tragedy of an impressionable youth who had been led by passion to kill the one man in that nation who might have done something to ameliorate the sufferings of the people in the Southern States. Booth not only sacrificed his own life in the attempt—he defeated his own purposes, for by killing Lincoln he prepared the way for the exploitation of the people of the South that has persisted through generations to our own day. It has even been suggested that Booth must have been in the pay of the Northern faction that was opposed to Lincoln, since his action threw the balance of power into their hands, but the charge has never been substantiated, and Booth's own words indicate that he may have been a fool but that he was surely not knowingly a traitor to his own cause.

His deed showed the uselessness of the attentat as a political weapon. Even when an assassin kills a man who is really a monster, the political system which has permitted such a creature to flourish will, hydra-headed, immediately throw out a new crop of tyrants to replace the old. And, when a great and good man like Lincoln is cut down, the loss is an irreparable blow to both factions concerned.

What Booth did had an immediate effect on the destinies of our country. On the night of the assassination, the United States was left without a government of any kind, for the terrified officials who gathered around the bed of the dying war President were not a government—they were only a roomful of human beings who had come to see a fellow man die, and most of them were mortally afraid that they might meet his fate at any moment, since it was then generally believed that the assassination was only a part of a vast rebel plot to seize the city of Washington and paralyze the nation. For nine hours, while Lincoln lay unconscious, hysteria and madness reigned in the national capital, and the incomplete and long-delayed telegraph messages that were sent out only added to the confusion everywhere.

Booth's senseless act paralyzed the North as he had hoped it would, but the South was in no position to enter the field again. The war that he had expected to see continued merely fizzled out, and the South had to pay for his crime.

But the far-reaching political effects of the assassination have been ably dealt with by many historians. I have been concerned here only with the personal issues that involved Booth and his fellow conspirators, so I have necessarily had to make the narrative end with the death of its main characters. Yet I cannot help believing that some readers who have followed this account to that final scene which took place in the bright July sunlight of a Washington prison-yard must feel that there is still more to come, that some of the people lived on, and that what happened to them afterwards might possibly throw some light on the tragic events of the assassination itself.

Booth's sudden coup affected not only the destiny of a nation—it had strange and violent repercussions in the lives of many people, important and unimportant. For the Lincoln murder case, of course, did not stop with the hanging of the conspirators. It went on, winding like a dark thread through the unhappy administration of Andrew Johnson, blighting the career of Edwin M. Stanton, and touching with tragedy the lives of other governmental officials who

# Afterword

have had no part in the story here. Suicide and madness followed in its wake. The ghosts of the men who had plotted against Lincoln walked through the postwar years, and the survival of one conspirator made it necessary to try the case all over again.

Of the conspirators who had been named as parties to the crime in the Government's charges, only one escaped. This was John Harrison Surratt, the most mysterious and intangible of all the queerly assorted people who played a part in the assassination. His career is baffling, not for lack of evidence, but for its multiplicity and its strange contradictory nature. There are reasonably definite records of the movements of all the other characters during the period immediately before and after the assassination, but Surratt is a will-o'-the-wisp, a curiously elusive creature who seems to have been endowed with the incredible ability of having been in two widely separated places at the same time.

During Surratt's trial in 1867, the Government produced a number of witnesses who testified that they had seen Surratt in Washington on the day of the assassination. The defense brought forth an equally impressive collection of people who swore that he had been in Elmira, New York. This trial, unlike that of the conspirators who had been brought before a military tribunal, was held in a civil court where a jury found itself unable to reach a verdict in the face of these diametrically opposed statements. Four of the jurymen were Northern born, and eight were Southern born. The vote, by what may, of course, have been a remarkable coincidence, stood at four for conviction and eight for acquittal. The case was nolle prossed, and Surratt was finally allowed to go free.

# Afterword

A careful review of the testimony printed in the two volumes of the Surratt trial leaves the impression that the Government's case was at least as good as the defense's, and we do know that someone traveled on Grant's train in order to try to assassinate him. Some people have believed that Michael O'Laughlin was the man who followed Grant, but O'Laughlin's alibi was certainly an infinitely better one than Surratt's.

Whoever it was that rode on General Grant's train was destined to disappointment. The door to the car in which Grant and his wife were traveling was locked, and the would-be assassin had no opportunity to strike.

Surratt's adventures after the assassination were strange enough to form the basis of a picaresque novel. He reached Montreal on April 18, and immediately left the city to stay in a house forty miles out in the country. He remained there all during the Conspirators' Trial—and during his mother's execution. In September, he sailed for England in disguise, was betrayed by a surgeon on the boat, but was able to proceed to Rome because the United States Government was inexplicably slow in expressing any interest in apprehending this one conspirator after the case had presumably been settled.

In Rome, Surratt enlisted in the Papal Zouaves under the name of Watson. By a freakish coincidence there was another American in his company who immediately recognized him, for they had met three years previously in Maryland. This man promptly denounced Surratt to the United States Government in the hope of getting the $25,000 reward which he believed was still standing. (Actually it had been withdrawn by this time.) Surratt was arrested, but

# Afterword

while he was being taken to prison he escaped from his guards, jumped into a ravine, was miraculously unhurt, and managed to make his way to Naples and then to Alexandria, Egypt. He was again arrested there, and was finally brought back in an American warship to Washington to face a charge of murder.

After Surratt's case had been nolle prossed, the much-pursued conspirator went to Baltimore and entered into business in that city. He died there in 1916, after maintaining a discreet silence on his part in the conspiracy, which was broken only once when he delivered what was to be the first of a series of lectures. In his maiden speech Surratt admitted nothing of importance that had not already been brought out during his trial. The public lost all interest and the speaking tour was canceled.

Surratt was lucky, but the four surviving conspirators, who were certainly no more guilty than he, did not share his good fortune. Arnold and O'Laughlin, together with Spangler, the unlucky stagehand who was guilty chiefly of friendship with Booth, and Dr. Mudd, who had given medical aid to him, were sent to Fort Jefferson, a moated prison on one of the Dry Tortugas. Yellow fever struck the island in 1868, carrying off Michael O'Laughlin as one of its many victims.

When all the doctors on the island had died from the epidemic, the prison authorities permitted Mudd to take charge of the medical work during the emergency. He was pardoned by President Johnson in 1869 in recognition of his services. Spangler was released in 1871. He sought refuge in Mudd's house, where he was permitted to stay for the rest of his life. He died in 1879. Mudd outlived him only a short while and died in 1882. Arnold, the most obscure and unimportant of all the conspirators, lived on into the twentieth century. He wrote an article entitled "The Lincoln Plot," which was published in *The Baltimore American* in 1902, and he died almost as obscurely as he had lived, in Johns Hopkins Hospital in Baltimore in 1906.

Yet these men who had been connected in some way, however slight, with a plot to abduct the person of Abraham Lincoln, if not to kill him, got off easily compared with the innocent people who had been in the state box at Ford's Theater on the night of the assassination. They were all touched with disaster. Lincoln died the next morning. Mrs. Lincoln later became insane and was confined in an asylum for a while. She died in Springfield in 1882, in the same house in which she had been married forty years before to Abraham Lincoln, then an unknown country lawyer. Even more terrible than her fate was the destiny in store for the young couple who had been invited to the theater by the Lincolns. Some years after his marriage to the young lady he had accompanied to the theater that night, Major Rathbone went violently insane. He murdered his wife during one of his maniacal spells and then killed himself.

Bessie Hale, Booth's unfortunate fiancée, managed to avoid any serious scandal. She went to Spain with her father, and eventually married and settled down in West Point, New York. She was the only one near to Booth who did not have to pay a public penalty for having been associated with him.

Booth's act brought suffering and ruin to almost everyone he had touched in his mad orbit, and it had, of course, a sudden and devastating effect on the fortunes of his own

# Afterword

family. The news of what his brother had done did not reach Edwin Booth until the morning of April 15. The manager of the Boston Theater, in which Edwin had just begun a successful engagement, at once decided to close the house until further notice, in order to avoid any possible trouble. Edwin was in complete accord with this decision and immediately addressed this letter to him:

HENRY C. JARRETT, ESQ.

MY DEAR SIR: With deepest sorrow and great agitation I thank you for relieving me of my engagement with yourself and the public. The news of the morning has made me wretched, indeed, not only because of a brother's crime, but because a most justly honored and patriotic ruler has fallen, in an hour of national joy, by the hand of an assassin. The memory of the thousands who have fallen in the field, in our country's defense, during this struggle, cannot be forgotten by me, even in this, the most distressing day of my life. And I most sincerely pray that the victories we have already won may stay the brand of war and the tide of loyal blood. While mourning, in common with all other loyal hearts, the death of the President, I am oppressed by a private woe not to be expressed in words. But whatever calamity may befall me and mine, my country, one and indivisible, has my warmest devotion.

EDWIN BOOTH

Edwin retired from the stage, convinced that his career was hopelessly damaged. He tried to avoid all public contact during the long months of unhappy notoriety for the Booth family. In January, 1866, persuaded by his friends to return to the theater, he reluctantly agreed to appear at the Winter Garden in New York in his familiar role of

# Afterword

Hamlet. He was greeted with tremendous cheers by an audience that rose to honor him as soon as he walked out upon the stage.

Edwin Booth was always unwilling to speak about John Wilkes. In 1881, in answer to a friend's inquiry, he made the following reply, which is the only recorded comment made by him about his brother:

To NAHUM CAPEN

Windsor Hotel, July 28th, 1881

DEAR SIR:

I can give you very little information regarding my brother John. I seldom saw him since his early boyhood in Baltimore. He was a rattle-pated fellow, filled with Quixotic notions. While at the farm in Maryland he would charge on horseback through the woods, "shouting" heroic speeches with a lance in his hand, a relic of the Mexican war, given to father by some soldier who had served under Taylor. We regarded him as a good-hearted, harmless, though wild-brained boy, and used to laugh at his patriotic froth whenever secession was discussed. That he was insane on that one point, no one who knew him well can doubt. When I told him that I had voted for Lincoln's re-election he expressed deep regret, and declared his belief that Lincoln would be made king of America; and this, I believe, drove him beyond the limits of reason. I asked him once why he did not join the Confederate army. To which he replied: "I promised mother I would keep out of the quarrel, if possible, and I am sorry that I said so." Knowing my sentiments, he avoided me, rarely visiting my house, except to see his mother, when political topics were not touched upon, at least in my presence. He was of a gentle, loving disposition, very boyish and full of fun,—his mother's darling,—and his deed and death crushed her spirit. He possessed rare dramatic talent, and would have made a brilliant mark in the theatrical world. This is positively all that I know about him, having left him a mere schoolboy when I went with my father to California in 1852. On my return in '56, we were separated by professional engagements, which kept him mostly in the South. while I was employed in the Eastern and Northern States.

I do not believe any of the wild, romantic stories published in the papers concerning him, but of course he may have been engaged in political matters of which I know nothing. All his theatrical friends speak of him as a poor, crazy boy, and such his family think of him.

I am sorry I can afford you no further light on the subject.

*Very truly yours,*
EDWIN BOOTH

Nevertheless, Edwin never forgot his brother, never forgot that he had been a Booth and that they had played together as children on their father's farm in Belair. In the brownstone building on Gramercy Square, New York, which Edwin Booth left as a meeting place for people in the theater and the arts, the bedroom of its former owner is carefully preserved as it was on the day he died in it. On the dresser, near the bed, is a photograph of John Wilkes Booth.

The other members of the Booth family also had the normal course of their lives violently interrupted by the act of their kinsman. Junius Brutus Booth, Jr., who was playing in Cincinnati at the time, was sought by an angry mob which came to his hotel to lynch him. It was nearly a week before he was able to leave the building, and then he had to be smuggled out. Soon afterwards he was arrested and sent to the Old Capitol Prison in Washington.

# Afterword

The home of Asia Booth Clarke in Philadelphia was searched; her husband was arrested and sent to the prison in which Junius Brutus was temporarily being held. Even Joseph Brutus, the youngest member of the family, who had been away for three years in Australia, was arrested at the pier as soon as his ship touched shore.

The blow, of course, fell most heavily of all on Booth's mother. A few hours after the terrible news had been broken to her, a letter was delivered to Edwin's house in New York where she was staying. It was a message from her son, John Wilkes, written before the assassination and delayed in its delivery by the wartime mails. She received word of his death while she was on her way to Philadelphia, where she had been summoned by her daughter Asia, who was alone, ill and about to give birth to her fourth child. Newspapers were brought to the train, and in the midst of the excited comment from strangers who were discussing the capture of the President's assassin, Mary Holmes Booth learned that her son had died a shameful death in a burning barn somewhere in Virginia.

No one in Booth's family was permitted to see the body of the man who had died at Garrett's farm. The corpse was immediately sewed up in a saddle blanket, loaded on a Negro's market wagon, and driven to Belle Plain, where it was placed on board a steamer and shipped to Washington. There it was laid out on the deck of the monitor *Montauk*, in the hold of which Herold and the other conspirators were confined.

The next morning (April 27) means were taken to establish formal identification of the corpse. Various persons who had known Booth more or less intimately were brought on board the *Montauk* to view his body. One of these was Charles Dawson, chief clerk of the National Hotel, where Booth had been accustomed to stay. Dawson not only identified the body by recognition of the dead man's features, but also pointed out the initials, J. W. B., tattooed on the right hand of the corpse. The body was then still further identified by a Washington dentist who had recently done work on Booth's teeth.

An even more important witness was Dr. J. F. May, who had removed a small tumor from the left side of Booth's neck a few years before. The doctor's own statement is of interest in this connection:

The body was on deck, completely concealed by a tarpaulin. The cover was removed, and to my great astonishment, revealed a body in whose lineaments there was to me no resemblance to the man I had known in life! My surprise was so great that I at once said to General Barnes, "There is no resemblance in that corpse to Booth, nor can I believe it to be that of him."

After looking at it for a few moments, I asked, "Is there a scar upon the back of its neck?" He replied, "There is." I then said, "If that *is* the body of Booth, let me describe the scar before it is seen by me;" and did so as to its position, its size and its general appearance, so accurately as to cause him to say, "You have described the scar as well as if you were looking at it; and it looks, as you have described it, more like the cicatrix of a burn than that made by a surgical operation."

The body being turned, the back of the neck was examined and my *mark* was unmistakably found by me upon it. And it being afterwards, by my request, placed in a sitting position, standing, and looking down upon it, I was finally enabled to imperfectly recognize the features of Booth. But never in a human being had a greater change taken place, from the man whom I had seen in the vigor of life and health, than in that of the haggard corpse which was before me, with its yellow and discolored skin, its unkempt and matted hair, and its whole facial expression sunken and sharpened by the exposure and starvation it had undergone.

Shortly afterwards the body, wrapped in a gunny sack, was removed to the Arsenal grounds, where it was secretly buried at night under the stone floor of one of the cells in the prison there. It was in these same grounds that the conspirators were to be hanged and buried less than three months later.

In 1867, the Arsenal Prison was torn down. Booth's body and those of his four fellow conspirators were exhumed and stored for two years in a warehouse on the grounds. In 1869, permission was at last given to the Booth family to claim the body. It was taken to an undertaker's establishment on F Street, around the corner from Ford's Theater. In fact, the furniture wagon carrying the remains of John Wilkes Booth was driven into the alley at the rear of the theater, bringing Booth back to the very place from which he had begun his long journey.

The corpse was examined on the undertaker's premises and satisfactorily identified by the Booth family. It was then removed to the Booth family plot in Greenmount Cemetery, Baltimore, where it was finally buried in an unmarked grave.

Although the corpse on the *Montauk* had been legally identified with as much care as could be given in establishing the identity of any dead body in the days before finger printing and other scientific methods were known, rumors

# Afterword

soon began to spring up that the body was not that of John Wilkes Booth at all.

As time went on, many people began to believe that Booth had not only gotten away free, but that his escape had been made possible by the connivance of high officials in Washington. During the impeachment trial of Andrew Johnson, it was said openly in Congress that Johnson had stood to benefit by Lincoln's death, and that he might very well in some way have been connected with it. It was known, of course, that Booth had called on Johnson during the afternoon preceding the assassination, and that he had left his card for him.

In 1907, Finis L. Bates published a book in which he flatly accused Johnson of complicity in the crime. Bates said that in 1872, in Texas, he had met a man by the name of John St. Helen who told him that he was really John Wilkes Booth and that Johnson had helped him to escape. In 1903, Bates received word that a man living under the name of David E. George in Enid, Oklahoma, had committed suicide there, and before his.death had announced that he was John Wilkes Booth. Bates went to Oklahoma and was convinced that the body he saw there was that of his old friend, John St. Helen. The body was mummified and removed to Memphis, Tennessee, where Bates lived. After Bates' death, the mummy was purchased from his widow and has been serving as a carnival attraction ever since.

The case made out by Bates for Booth's survival is a very flimsy one, vitiated by internal contradictions and by misstatements by Bates, who had neither the training nor the respect for accuracy needed by a historian.

# Afterword

A more recent publication which attempts to prove that Booth did not die at Garrett's farm is *This One Mad Act* by Izola Forrester. The author tries to show not only that Booth lived for many years after the assassination, but also that he was her grandfather by a secret marriage which had taken place in 1859. Her case for Booth's survival is hardly more logical or better documented than Bates' opus.

Both these books imply that Booth had had an opportunity to escape from the barn before the soldiers closed in around the place. The authors assert that some other person was killed in his stead, and that the Government, realizing that a mistake had been made, tried to hush up the matter by keeping the official identification and the disposal of the body a close secret. Under the circumstances, however, the Government had good reason for secrecy in handling the corpse of John Wilkes Booth. It was simply afraid that some of the Confederate die-hards might use the body of the famous assassin as a symbol around which they could rally their forces.

The question of whether or not the man who died at Garrett's farm was John Wilkes Booth is one that doubtless will never be settled. Historians refuse to take seriously the possibility of Booth's survival, but the legend of the great assassin living on to realize the enormity of his crime and later expiate it by suicide has become firmly embedded in American folklore.

The Government was, however, remiss in permitting one simple matter to remain in doubt—a matter which could easily have been settled definitely at the time. This was the exact manner in which Booth met his death. It was never positively established whether Booth was killed by his own

# Afterword

hand or by the shot that Boston Corbett claimed to have fired. A careful weighing of the evidence would seem to indicate a more probable verdict of suicide. Conger, who had been watching Booth through one of the openings in the barn, took it for granted that Booth had killed himself, until Corbett came forward to announce that he had shot him. M. B. Ruggles, one of the three Confederate soldiers who had guided Booth to Garrett's farm, not only said that Booth had committed suicide, but that one of the chambers in the revolver held in his hand was empty. The issue was carefully avoided at the Conspirators' Trial. Corbett was never censured for having disobeyed orders and was given a large part of the cash reward for Booth's capture. Yet Corbett was a man whose word was hardly to be trusted. He was a religious monomaniac who had castrated himself in 1858 after having been approached by a prostitute. In 1887, while serving as a guard in the Kansas State Legislature, he went violently insane and tried to shoot the members of the assembly. He promptly disappeared, but was afterwards traced to the same Enid, Oklahoma, that provided the famous Booth mummy.

However, such matters as the possibility of Booth's survival, or the exact manner of his death, are unimportant in comparison with some of the still-unsolved mysteries surrounding Lincoln's death. One of these concerns the diary which had been taken from Booth's body and sent to Washington, where it was placed in Stanton's hands. This exceedingly important bit of evidence was not even mentioned during the Conspirators' Trial—its very existence, in fact, was not suspected then. In 1867, Lafayette Baker let it be known that there had been such a document. The diary was impounded as evidence at the Surratt Trial. When it was produced in court, only two pages covered with writing were left in it. Eighteen pages had been cut out and were missing. Whether these had been removed by Booth himself, or by someone after his death, there was no way of telling, but everyone knew that the diary had been in Stanton's possession, and there was much speculation as to how the missing pages had disappeared. There was at least one sentence still in the diary which created a stir. This was contained in the entry for Friday, April 21, when Booth wrote: "To-night I will once more try the river, with the intention to cross; though I have a greater desire and almost a mind to return to Washington, and in a measure clear my name, which I feel I can do." How could this self-confessed assassin "clear his name" unless he knew something that would implicate people who were so important that the sensational nature of his disclosures would dwarf even the enormity of his own crime?

That Booth had other unknown and secret accomplices has long been suspected. Herold, after his capture, made a rambling forty-page affidavit regarding his own part in the case. Most of what he said was already known from other sources or obviously manufactured in an effort to save his own skin. But Herold did say, quite unequivocally, that Booth had told him that thirty-five men in Washington were involved in the plot.

One other important fact lends support to the belief that Booth was assisted by a number of men. It has long been known that the commercial telegraph wires leading from Washington were mysteriously put out of commission on the night of the assassination. Service was cut off for two hours until it was found that wires in the main batteries had been crossed. Another curious fact is that Booth was not only allowed to pass easily across the guarded Anacostia Bridge, but that no one was even sent in that direction during the night of the assassination to check up on this most obvious of all southern exits from the city.

It is impossible to tell just how closely any outside force worked with Booth and his little band of conspirators. It may very well be that Booth himself did not know exactly who these men were, or what self-interest they had in wishing to see Lincoln killed. It is for this reason that I have used John Surratt as an intermediary to bring the two conspiracies together. It is interesting to note that Surratt admitted in his one and only lecture that another group of conspirators had been working simultaneously to strike a blow at Lincoln.

The identity of the men who worked with Booth on that terrible night has never been established. It is not even known whether they were some of the many Confederate sympathizers who were secretly attempting to undermine the Government in Washington, or, as has often been darkly hinted, whether they had some connection with the Government officials who were opposed to Lincoln's policies of conciliation for the conquered South.

One thing is sure—they have preserved their secrecy well. Not one of them has ever spoken. The terrific outburst of condemnation from North and South alike froze them into terrified silence. They are probably all dead now— almost everyone even remotely connected with the case has died. Now that there are no longer any personal reasons for secrecy, some hidden record—if any was made—may be brought to light. The next few years should be fruitful ones for the publication of long-suppressed Civil War material. It is not too much to hope that even the murder case of Abraham Lincoln will eventually be solved.

An indication of the sort of information the future may bring forth can be seen in an incident quoted by Emanuel Hertz in the preface to his book, *The Hidden Lincoln*.

A few years before Mr. [Robert] Lincoln's death, Mr. Young went as usual to visit him at Mr. Lincoln's home in Manchester, Vermont. On arriving at the house he found Mr. Lincoln in a room surrounded by a number of large boxes and with many papers scattered about the floor, and with the ashes of many burnt papers visible in the fireplace. Mr. Young asked Mr. Lincoln what he was doing, and Mr. Lincoln replied that he was destroying some of the private papers and letters of his father, Abraham Lincoln. Mr. Young at once remonstrated with Mr. Lincoln and said that no one had any right to destroy such papers, Mr. Lincoln least of all. Mr. Lincoln replied that he did not intend to continue his destruction—but the papers he was destroying contained the documentary evidence of the treason of a member of Lincoln's Cabinet, and he thought it was best for all that such evidence be destroyed. Mr. Young immediately visited Dr. [Nicholas Murray] Butler, who was in town, and told him what Robert T. Lincoln was doing. Dr. Butler promptly called on Robert T. Lincoln and argued and pleaded with him and finally prevailed upon him to desist— and place the papers where they would be safe in order that they might be preserved for posterity.

The material in question was deposited in the Library of Congress with the reservation that it was not to be consulted until 1947. In that year, when these secret papers will be

# Bibliography

made public, we shall find out who it was that sat at the Cabinet table betraying the President and the people he served. Perhaps we shall even be able to trace some connection to the men who shared with John Wilkes Booth the responsibility for the murder of Abraham Lincoln.

## A Selected Bibliography

ANON. *Assassination and History of the Conspiracy.* Cincinnati, 1865.

BAKER, L. C. *History of the United States Secret Service.* Philadelphia, 1867.

BAKER, R. S. "The Capture, Death and Burial of John Wilkes Booth." McClure's Magazine, May, 1897.

BATES, FINIS L. *The Escape and Suicide of John Wilkes Booth.* Memphis, n.d.

BROOKS, NOAH. *Washington in Lincoln's Time.* New York, 1896.

BUCKINGHAM, J. E. *Reminiscences and Souvenirs of the Assassination of Abraham Lincoln.* Washington, 1894.

CAMPBELL, W. P. *The Escape and Wanderings of John Wilkes Booth until Ending of the Trail by Suicide in Oklahoma.* Oklahoma City, 1922.

CLARKE, ASIA BOOTH. *The Elder and the Younger Booth.* Boston, 1882.

————. *The Unlocked Book; a Memoir of John Wilkes Booth.* New York, 1938.

COGGESHALL, E. W. *The Assassination of Lincoln.* Chicago, 1920.

DEWITT, D. M. *The Assassination of Abraham Lincoln and Its Expiation.* New York, 1909.

————. *The Impeachment and Trial of Andrew Johnson.* New York, 1903.

————. *Judicial Murder of Mary E. Surratt.* Baltimore, 1895.

EISENSCHIML, OTTO. *Why Was Lincoln Murdered?* Boston, 1937.

FERGUSON, W. J. *I Saw Booth Shoot Lincoln.* Boston, 1930.

FORRESTER, IZOLA. *This One Mad Act.* Boston, 1937.

GARRETT, WILLIAM. "The True Story of the Capture of John Wilkes Booth." Confederate Veteran Magazine, April, 1921.

GOBRIGHT, L. A. *Recollections of Men and Things at Washington During Half a Century.* Philadelphia, 1869.

# Bibliography

GRAY, JOHN A. "The Fate of the Lincoln Conspirators." McClure's Magazine, October, 1911.

HARRIS, T. M. *Assassination of Lincoln.* Boston, 1892.

HOWARD, H. G. *Civil-War Echoes.* Washington, 1907.

JONES, THOMAS A. *John Wilkes Booth.* Chicago, 1893.

LAUGHLIN, CLARA E. *The Death of Lincoln.* New York, 1909.

LEWIS, LLOYD. *Myths After Lincoln.* New York, 1929.

LINCOLN MEMORIAL, THE. *A Record of the Life, Assassination and Obsequies of the Martyred President.* New York, 1865.

LOCKRIDGE, RICHARD. *Darling of Misfortune.* New York, 1932.

MAHONEY, ELLA V. *Sketches of Tudor Hall and the Booth Family.* Belair, 1925.

MASON, V. L. "Four Lincoln Conspiracies." Century Magazine, April, 1896.

MUDD, NETTIE. *The Life of Dr. Samuel A. Mudd.* New York, 1906.

OFFICIAL RECORDS OF THE WAR OF THE REBELLION. Series I, Vol. 46, pt. 3; Vol. 47; Series II, Vol. 8.

OLDROYD, O. H. *Assassination of Abraham Lincoln.* Washington, 1901.

PITMAN, BENN (Editor). *Assassination of the President and the Trial of the Conspirators.* New York, 1865.

RUGGLES, M. B., BAINBRIDGE, A. R. and DOHERTY, E. P. "Pursuit and Death of John Wilkes Booth." Century Magazine, January, 1890.

SHEPHERD, W. G. "Shattering the Myth of John Wilkes Booth's Escape." Harper's Magazine, November, 1924.

STARR, JOHN W., JR. *Lincoln's Last Day.* New York, 1922.

TINDAL, W. "Booth's Escape from Washington." Columbia Historical Society Records. Vol. 28, 1915.

TOWNSEND, G. A. *Katy of Catoctin.* New York, 1886.

————. "How Wilkes Booth Crossed the Potomac." Century Magazine, April, 1884.

————. *The Life, Crime and Capture of John Wilkes Booth.* New York, 1865.

TRIAL OF JOHN SURRATT. Washington, 1867.

UNITED STATES SENATE. *Report of the Committee of the Judiciary on the Assassination of President Lincoln.* Washington, 1866.

WILSON, FRANCIS. *John Wilkes Booth.* Boston, 1929. (Contains Miss Holloway's account of Booth's capture at Garrett's farm.)

WINTER, WILLIAM. *Life and Art of Edwin Booth.* New York, 1894.